THE TEACH YOURSELF BOOKS

STATISTICS

TEACH YOURSELF

STATISTICS

By

RICHARD GOODMAN

M.A., B.Sc.

Formerly Head of Department of Computing, Cybernetics and Management, Brighton College of Technology

THE ENGLISH UNIVERSITIES PRESS LTD

ST. PAUL'S HOUSE WARWICK LANE

LONDON E.C.4

For
HETTY *and* ROBIN
with love

First printed 1957
This impression 1968

S.B.N. 340 05727 0

Printed in Great Britain for the English Universities Press, Ltd., by Richard Clay (The Chaucer Press), Ltd., Bungay, Suffolk

PREFACE TO SECOND IMPRESSION

> "It is all very well to say that the world of reality should be kept separate and distinct from the world of mathematics. In the trivial operations of daily life, you may be able to keep clear of the concepts of mathematics, but once you begin to touch science, the dangerous contact is established."
>
> Professor John L. Synge (*Science—Sense and Nonsense*)

OF recent years, many people, often with little mathematical training, have had to teach themselves some Statistics. Few, probably, have found it easy, for, at least from one point of view, Statistics is a branch of applied mathematics, and, so, some mathematics is essential, even in an elementary treatment of the subject.

One can, of course, try to learn some of the basic routines and tests as rules of thumb, hoping that whatever situation may arise will be a text-book one to which the appropriate text-book test will obligingly apply. The trouble is, however, that such situations are rare, and very soon one begins to wish that one had learned a little about the actual nature of the fundamental tests.

It is the aim of this book to help those who have to teach themselves some Statistics to an understanding of some of the fundamental ideas and mathematics involved. Once that has been acquired, problems of application are the more readily and successfully tackled. For this reason, and for reasons of space, the concentration has been on fundamentals. But Statistics is a dynamic, developing science. New techniques, new methods of analysis are constantly arising and influencing even the foundations. The reader is urged to bear this fact in mind all the time and, particularly, when reading Chapters VI and IX.

The standard of mathematics assumed is not high. Occasionally the algebra may appear to be a little tedious, but it is not difficult. Whenever possible, references to Mr. Abbott's books in this series, especially *Teach Yourself Calculus*, have been given, and the reader is strongly advised to follow them up. Where this has not been possible and new ground has been broken, a note has been added at the end of the appropriate chapter. Continuous bivariate distributions, including the normal bivariate distribution, which involve double integrals, have been treated in an appendix. In case notation should present difficulties, a list of a few mathematical symbols and their meanings follows that appendix. A set of Exercises concludes each chapter, except the first, but the student is urged also to tackle those provided in some of the books listed on page 239. Specially important as, perhaps, the most useful collection of exercises at present available is that provided by the two parts of *Elementary Statistical Exercises* issued, and obtainable from, the Department of Statistics, University College, London. To be adequately equipped to tackle such exercises the student is recommended to have by him:

(1) *Chambers's Shorter Six-Figure Mathematical Tables* by the late Dr. L. J. Comrie (W. and R. Chambers); and
(2) *Lanchester Short Statistical Tables* by G. R. Braithwaite and C. O. D. Titmus (English Universities Press).

A desk calculator is not essential, but if the student can possibly obtain one he should certainly do so. Of the hand-operated models, the Madas 10R is recommended.

Lastly, to the staff of the English Universities Press and to the printers I wish to express my appreciation of the care they have bestowed upon this book; to my sister, Miss Nancy Goodman, to Messrs. F. T. Chaffer, Alec Bishop, and Leonard Cutts, and to the late Dr. J. Wishart, my thanks are due for their encouragement and suggestions; while to all those who have drawn my attention to mistakes and errors, especially Dr. P. G. Moore, the Rev. Liam Grimley and Dr. van de Geer, I express my gratitude; wherever possible the necessary corrections have been made.

R. G.

BRIGHTON,
1960.

PREFACE TO 1965 IMPRESSION

In this impression a determined effort has been made to eliminate residual mistakes and misprints. In this I have had the encouragement and invaluable assistance of Mr. C. V. Durrell, to whom I am immensely grateful.

R. G.

ACKNOWLEDGEMENTS

The Author wishes to express his thanks to the following for so kindly and readily allowing him to use quotations, examples and tables :

Sir R. A. Fisher, Professor A. C. Aitken and Messrs. Oliver and Boyd; Professor M. G. Kendall and Messrs. Charles Griffin; Professor C. E. Weatherburn and the Cambridge University Press; Messrs. Brookes and Dick and Messrs. Heinemann; Mr. P. R. Rider and Messrs. John Wiley and Sons; Messrs. Paradine and Rivett and the English Universities Press; Professor G. W. Snedecor and the Collegiate Press, Inc., Ames, Iowa; Professor J. L. Synge and Messrs. Jonathan Cape; Mr. S. Rosenbaum, the Directorate of Army Health and the Editors of the *Journal of the Royal Statistical Society*; the Royal Statistical Society, the Association of Incorporated Statisticians, the Institute of Actuaries, and the American Statistical Association; the Rand Corporation, California, and the Free Press, Glencoe, Illinois; and the Senate of the University of London.

Detailed acknowledgements are given in the text.

CONTENTS

CHAPTER ONE

INTRODUCTORY : A FIRST LOOK AROUND

1.1. Statistics and Statistics. Most of us have some idea of what the word *statistics* means. We should probably say that it has something to do with tables of figures, diagrams and graphs in economic and scientific publications, with the cost of living, with public-opinion polls, life insurance, football pools, cricket averages, population-census returns, "intelligence" tests, with production planning and quality control in industry and with a host of other seemingly unrelated matters of concern or unconcern. We might even point out that there seem to be at least two uses of the word :

the *plural use*, when the word denotes some systematic collection of numerical data about some topic or topics ;
the *singular use*, when the word denotes a somewhat specialised human activity concerned with the collection, ordering, analysis and interpretation of such data, and with the general principles involved in this activity.

Our answer would be on the right lines. Nor should we be unduly upset if, to start with, we seem a little vague. Statisticians themselves disagree about the definition of the word : over a hundred definitions have been listed (W. F. Willcox, *Revue de l'Institut International de Statistique*, vol. 3, p. 288, 1935), and there are many others. One of the greatest of British statisticians, M. G. Kendall, has given his definition as follows :

> " Statistics is the branch of scientific method which deals with the data obtained by counting or measuring the properties of populations of natural phenomena. In this definition ' natural phenomena ' includes all the happenings of the external world, whether human or not " (*Advanced Theory of Statistics*, vol. 1, p. 2).

Statistics, as a science, is, however, not merely descriptive ; like all sciences, it is concerned with action. In his 1952 Presidential Address to the American Statistical Association, A. J. Wickens remarked :

> " Statistics of a sort can, of course, be traced back to ancient times, but they have flowered since the industrial

revolution. Beginning in the 19th century, statistical records were developed to describe the society of that era, and to throw light on its economic and social problems. No doubt they influenced the course of men's thinking then, and even, in some instances, may have led to new policies and new laws; but primarily their uses were descriptive. Increasingly, in the 20th century, and especially since World War I, statistics have been used to settle problems, and to determine courses of action. In private enterprise, quality control tests now change the production lines of industrial enterprises. New products are developed and tested by statistical means. Scientific experiments turn upon statistics. . . ." (" Statistics and the Public Interest," *Journal of the American Statistical Association*, vol. 48, No. 261, March 1953, pp. 1–2).

Two other U.S. writers, F. C. Mills and C. D. Long, have stressed :

" In high degree the emphasis in the work of the statistician has shifted from this backward-looking process to current affairs and to proposed future operations and their consequences. Experiments are designed, samples selected, statistics collected and analysed with reference to decisions that must be made, controls that must be exercised, judgments that entail action " (" Statistical Agencies of the Federal Government, 1948 ", quoted by S. S. Wilks in " Undergraduate Statistical Education ", *Journal of the American Statistical Association*, vol. 46, No, 253, March 1951).

Let us suppose that you, the reader, have been appointed to be one of the M.C.C. Selectors responsible for picking an English cricket team to tour Australia. Clearly, it would be necessary to start by collecting information about the play of a group of " possibles ". (For the moment, we shall not consider how we have chosen these.) We might begin by noting down each man's score in successive innings and by collecting bowling figures. Ultimately, our collection of figures would tell us quite a lot, though by no means everything, about the batsmen and bowlers, as batsmen and bowlers, on our list. The sequence of numbers set down against each batsman's name would tell us something about his run-scoring *ability*. It would not, however, tell us much, if anything, about his *style*—that, for instance, on one occasion, he scored a boundary with a superlative cover-drive, while, on another, although he scored a boundary, his stroke was certainly not superlative. The list of number-pairs (5 wickets, 63 runs, for example) against a bowler's name would, likewise, tell us something about his bowling over a certain period. Such lists of classified numbers are the raw stuff of statistics.

Let x be the number of runs scored by a particular batsman in a given innings of a given season. Then x is a *variable* which can take any positive integral value, including zero. More precisely, x is a *discrete* or *discontinuous variable*, because the smallest, non-zero, difference between any two possible values of x is a finite amount (1 in this case). Not all variables are, however, of this kind. Let, now, x denote the average number of runs scored off a particular bowler per wicket taken by him on a given occasion his side fielded in a specified season. Then x may take on values like 12·6, 27·897, 3·333333 . . . , etc. Theoretically x can range over the entire set of positive rational numbers,[1] not merely the positive integers, from zero to infinity (0 wickets, 41 runs). Again, let x denote the number of yards run by a particular fielder on a given occasion in the field; now x can take on any positive real number [2] as value, not merely any positive rational (for instance, if a fielder walks round a circle of radius 1 yard, he traverses 2π yards, and π, while being a real number, is not rational). Thus the variable can vary continuously in value and is called a *continuous variable*.

Any aspect of whatever it may be we are interested in that is countable or measurable can be expressed numerically, and, so, may be represented by a variable taking on values from a *range* of values. It may be, however, that we are primarily interested in a batsman's style rather than his score. Assume, then, that, together with our fellow Selectors, we have agreed upon some standard enabling us to label any particular stroke *first-class* and *not-first-class*. Although, in the common-sense use of *measure*, such a difference is not measurable, we can, nevertheless, assign the number 1 to a first-class stroke and the number 0 to one that is not. Any particular innings of a given batsman would then be described, from this point of view, by a sequence of 0's and 1's, like 00010011101111010111110000000. This, too, would constitute a set of statistical observations.

[1] A RATIONAL NUMBER is any number that can be expressed in the form r/s, where r and s are integers and s is positive.

[2] A REAL NUMBER is any number that can be expressed as a terminating or unterminating decimal. Thus any rational number is a real number, but not all real numbers are rational. See T. Dantzig, *Number, the Language of Science*, or G. H. Hardy, *A Course of Pure Mathematics*.

When we have gathered together a large collection of numerical data about our players, we must begin to " sort them out ".

Our *statistics* (in the plural), the numerical data collected in our field of interest, requires *statistical* (in the singular) treatment (ordering, tabulating, summarising, etc.). Indeed, in the very process of collecting we have already behaved statistically (in the singular), for we shall have been forced to develop some *system* to avoid utter chaos.

Thus the systematic collection of numerical data about a set of objects, *for a particular purpose*, the systematic collection of statistics (plural) is the first phase of Statistics (singular).

(WARNING: Thus far, we have been using the term *statistics* (plural) in the sense in which it is often used in everyday conversation. Actually, among statisticians themselves, this use, to denote a set of quantitatively measured data, is almost obsolete. The plural use of *statistics* is confined to the plural of the word *statistic*, a rather technical word we shall explain later.)

1.2. Descriptive Statistics. How do we go about sorting out our data?

First, we *display* them so that the salient features of the collection are quickly discernible. This involves *tabulating* them according to certain convenient and well-established principles, and, maybe, simultaneously presenting them in some simple, unambiguous *diagrammatic or graphical* form.

Secondly, we *summarise* the information contained in the data, so ordered and displayed, by a single number or, more usually, a set of numbers (e.g., for a batsman, number of innings, times not out, total number of runs scored, highest score, average number of runs scored per completed innings).

Which of these " summarising numbers " we use depends upon the question we are trying to answer about the subject to which the data relate. We might want to compare the average (arithmetic mean score) of each one of our " possible " batsmen with the overall average of all the batsmen in the group. In an attempt to assess consistency, we might try to arrive at some figure, in addition to the mean score, which would tell us how a batsman's scores in different innings are spread about his mean. In doing such things we should be engaged in *descriptive statistics*—ordering and summarising a given set of numerical data, without *direct* reference to any inferences that may be drawn therefrom.

1.3. Samples and Populations. The data we have collected, ordered, displayed and summarised will tell us much that we want to know about our group of possible Test players, and may help us to pick the touring party. Indirectly, they will also tell us something about the state of first-class cricket in England as a whole. But because the group of " possibles " we have been studying is a *special* group selected from the entire *population*, as we call it, of first-class cricketers, the picture we obtain from our group, or *sample*, will not be truly representative of that population. To obtain a more nearly representative picture, we should have picked a sample, or, better still, a number of samples, at *random* from the population of all first-class players. In this way we meet with one of the central ideas of the science of statistics—that of *sampling a population*.

Ideally, of course, to obtain a really reliable picture we should need all the scores, bowling averages, etc., of every player in every first-class county. But this would be, if not theoretically impossible, certainly impracticable. So we are forced back to the idea of *drawing conclusions about the population from the information presented in samples*—a procedure known as *statistical inference*.

To fix our ideas, let us set down some definitions:

POPULATION (or UNIVERSE): the total set of items (actual or possible) defined by some characteristic of those items, e.g., the population of all *first-class cricketers in the year* 1956; the population of all actual and possible *measurements of the length of a given rod*; the population of all *possible selections of three cards from a pack of* 52. A population, note, need not be a population of what, in everyday language, we call individuals. Statistically, we speak of a population of scores or of lengths. Such a population may have a *finite* number of elements, or may be so large that the number of its elements will always exceed any number, no matter how large, we may choose; in this latter case, we call the population *infinite*.

SAMPLE: Any finite set of items drawn from a population. In the case of a finite population, the whole population may be a sample of itself, but in the case of an infinite population this is impossible.

RANDOM SAMPLE: A sample from a given population, each element of which has an "equal chance" of being drawn. Let us say at once that this definition is opened to serious objection, for when we think about what exactly we mean by " equal chance ", we begin to suspect that it, in its turn, may involve the very idea of randomness we are trying to define.

There are various methods by which we may obtain a random sample from a given population. The common method of drawing names from a hat occurs to us at once. This suffices to emphasise the very important point that—

> **the adjective *random* actually qualifies the *method* of selecting the sample items from the population, rather than designating some property of the aggregate of elements of the sample discovered after the sample has been drawn.**

That section of Statistics concerned with methods of drawing samples from populations for statistical inference is called *Sampling Statistics*.

Switching to a new field, assume that from all National Servicemen born in a certain year, 1933, we draw a random sample or a number of samples, of 200. What can we infer about the distribution of height in the population from that in the sample? And how accurate will any such inference be?

We repeat that unless we examine *all* the elements of a population we cannot be *certain* that any conclusion about the population, based on the sample-data, will be 100% accurate. We need not worry about this. The great mass of our knowledge is *probability-knowledge*. We are " absolutely certain " that a statement is " 100% true " only in the case of statements of a rather restricted kind, like : *I was born after my father was born, a black cat is black, one plus one equals two*. Such statements, called *tautologies* by logicians, are sometimes of considerable interest because, like the third example given, they are in fact disguised *definitions* ; but none is a statement *about the world*, although at first sight it may appear to be so. We may be " pretty confident " that any statement saying something remotely significant about the world is a probability-statement. It is for this reason, among others, that Statistics is important :

> " The characteristic which distinguishes the present-day professional statistician, is his interest and skill in the measurement of the fallibility of conclusions " (G. W. Snedecor, " On a Unique Feature of Statistics ", Presidential Address to the American Statistical Association, December 1948, *Journal of the American Statistical Association*, vol. 44, No. 245, March 1949).

Central, therefore, in this problem of inference from sample to population, *statistical inference*, is the concept of *probability*. Indeed, *probability theory is the foundation of all statistical theory that is not purely descriptive*. Unfortunately it is not possible to give a simple, universally acceptable definition of *probability*. In the next chapter we shall try to clarify our ideas a little. For the moment, we assume that we know roughly what the word means.

In a sample of 200 of all National Servicemen born in 1933, we shall find that there are so many with heights of 59 *in. and under*, so many with heights exceeding 59 in. but not exceeding 60 in. and so on. Our variable here is *height in inches of National Servicemen born in* 1933. It is distributed over the 200-strong sample in a definite manner, the number of values of the variable falling within a specified interval being called the *frequency* of the variable in that interval. We may thus set up a table giving the frequency of the variable in each interval for all the intervals into which the entire range of the variable is divided. We thereby obtain the *frequency-distribution* of the variable in the sample.

We now define :

VARIATE: A variable possessing a frequency distribution is usually called a *variate* by statisticians (more precise definition is given in 2.13).

SAMPLE STATISTIC: A number characterising some aspect of the sample distribution of a variate, e.g., sample mean, sample range.

POPULATION PARAMETER: A number characterising some aspect of the distribution of a variate in a population, e.g., population mean, population range.

Using these new terms, we may now formulate the question raised above in this way :

How can we obtain estimates of population parameters from sample statistics, and how accurate will such estimates be?

1.4. Statistical Models, Statistical Distributions. When we examine actual populations we find that the variate tends to be approximately distributed over the population in a relatively small number of ways. Corresponding to each of these ways, we set up an ideal distribution which will serve as a model for the type. These are our *standard distributions* (just as the equation $ax^2 + bx + c = 0$ is the standard quadratic equation, to which we refer in the course of solving actual quadratic equations). Each is defined by means of a mathematical function called a *frequency-function* (or, in the case of a distribution of a continuous variate, a *probability-density-function*) in which the population parameters appear as parameters, i.e., as controllable constants in the function, which, when varied, serve to distinguish the various specific cases of the general functional form. (In the function $f(x, a, b, c) \equiv ax^2 + bx + c$, the constants a, b, c are parameters: when we give them different values, we obtain different cases of the same functional form.)

Once we have defined a standard distribution, we can sample theoretically the corresponding ideal population. It is then frequently possible to work out the manner in which any specific statistic will vary, as a result of the random-sampling process, with the size of the sample drawn. In other words, we obtain a *new distribution* which tells us the manner in which the statistic in question varies over the set of all possible samples from the parent population. Such distributions we call *Sampling Distributions*. Thus, *providing our model is appropriate*, we are able to decide how best to estimate a parameter from the sample data and how to assess the accuracy of such an estimate. For example, we shall find that the mean value of the mean values of all possible samples from a population is itself the mean value of the variate in the population, and that the mean of a particular sample has only a specific probability of differing by more than a stated amount from that value.

In this way, we are led to the idea of statistics or functions of statistics as *estimators* of population parameters, and to the closely related idea of *confidence limits*—limits, established from the sample data with the help of our knowledge of some model distribution, outside which a particular parameter will lie with a probability of only " one in so many ".

1.5. Tests of Significance. Very often we are not primarily concerned with the values of population parameters as such. Instead, we may want to decide whether or not a certain assumption about a population is likely to be untenable in the light of the evidence provided by a sample or set of samples from that population. This is a very common type of problem occurring in very many different forms:

> Is it reasonable to assume, on the basis of the data provided by certain samples, that a certain modification to a process of manufacturing electric-light bulbs will effectively reduce the percentage of defectives by 10%?
>
> Samples of the eggs of the common tern are taken from two widely separated nesting sites: is it reasonable to assume, on the evidence of these samples, that there is no difference between the mean lengths of the eggs laid by birds in the two localities?

Consider the light-bulb problem. Previous sampling may have led us to suspect that the number of defective light bulbs in a given unit of output, 10,000 bulbs, say, is too high for the good name of the firm. Technical experts have suggested a certain modification to the production process. This modification has been agreed upon, introduced and production has been resumed. Has the modification been successful?

The assumption that the modification has reduced the number of defectives by 10% is a *hypothesis* about the distribution of defectives in the population of bulbs. If the hypothesis is true, we may conclude, from our knowledge of the appropriate model distribution, that, if we draw from each 10,000 bulbs produced, a random sample of, say, 100 bulbs, the probability of obtaining 5 or more defectives in such a sample will be 1 in 20, i.e., we should expect not more than 1 sample in every 20 to contain 5 or more defectives : if, then, we find that 3 samples, say, in 20 contain 5 or more defectives, an event *improbable at the level of probability chosen* (in this case $\frac{1}{20}$ or 0·05) has occurred. We shall have reason, therefore, to suspect our hypothesis—that the modification has reduced the number of defectives by 10%.

Now *the level of probability chosen is essentially arbitrary*. We might well have made the test more exacting and asked of our model what number of defectives in a sample of the size specified is likely to be attained or exceeded with a probability of 0·01. In other words, if our hypothesis is true, what is the value of m such that we should expect only 1 sample in 100 to contain m or more defectives? Had we chosen this, 0·01, level and found that more than 1 in 100 samples contained this number of defectives or more, a very improbable event would have occurred. We should then be justified in *very strongly suspecting* the hypothesis.

Such tests are TESTS OF SIGNIFICANCE. The hypothesis to be tested is a—

NULL HYPOTHESIS, because it is to be nullified if the evidence of random sampling from the population specified by the hypothesis is " unfavourable " to that hypothesis.

We decide what shall be considered " unfavourable " or " not unfavourable " by choosing a *level of significance* (level of probability). It is up to us to fix the dividing line between " unfavourable " and " not unfavourable ". In practice, the levels chosen are frequently the 0·05 and 0·01 levels. But any level may be chosen.

In all this, however, there is need to remember that it is

always dangerous to rely too much on the evidence of a single experiment, test or sample. For, as we shall see, although each test in a series of tests may yield a non-significant result, it is quite possible that, when we pool the data of each test, and subject this pooled data to the test, the result may actually be significant at the level selected. Again, although a significant result is evidence for suspecting the hypothesis under test, a *non-significant result is no evidence of its truth* : the alternative is not one between " Guilty " and " Not guilty ", " False " or " True ", but, rather, between " Guilty " and " Not proven ", " False " and " Not disproved ".

Problems such as these we have rapidly reviewed are, then, a few of the many with which statistics is concerned. Statistics is a tool, a very powerful tool, in the hands of the scientist, technologist, economist and all who are confronted with the job of taking decisions on the basis of probability statements. But any tool is limited in its uses, and all tools may be misused. The more we know about a tool, of the principles underlying its operation, the better equipped we are both to employ it effectively and to detect occasions of its misuse and abuse. Here we attempt to make a small start on the job of understanding.

CHAPTER TWO

FREQUENCIES AND PROBABILITIES

2.1. Frequency Tables, Histograms and Frequency Polygons. I take six pennies, drop them into a bag, shake them well and empty the bag so that the pennies fall on to the table. I note the number of heads shown, and repeat the experiment. When I have carried out the routine 200 times, I make out the following table showing upon how many occasions out of the 200 all the pennies showed tails (no heads), one out of the six pennies showed a head, two pennies showed heads and so on :

Number of Heads (H) .	0	1	2	3	4	5	6	Total
Frequency (f) . .	2	19	46	62	47	20	4	200

Such a table summarises the result of the experiment, and is called a *Frequency Table*. It tells at a glance the number of times (frequency) a variable quantity, called a *variate* (in this case H, the number of heads shown in a single emptying of the bag), takes a specified value in a given total number of occasions (the *total frequency* ; here, 200). In this case the variate is *discontinuous* or *discrete*, being capable of taking certain values only in the *range* of its variation. But not all variates are of this kind. Consider the following frequency table showing the distribution of length of 200 metal bars :

Length (L) .	30	31	32	33	34	35	36	37	38	39	Total
Frequency (f) .	4	8	23	35	62	44	18	4	1	1	200

Here the lengths have been measured correct to the nearest inch, and all bars having lengths in the range 34·5000 . . . to 35·4999 . . . are included in the 35-in. class. In other words, the variate (L) here could have taken any value between say 29·50000 . . . and 39·4999 . . . inches. The variate is, in other words, a *continuous* variate, but for convenience and because no measurement is ever " exact ", the frequencies have been *grouped* into classes corresponding to equal subranges of the variate and labelled with the value of the mid-point of the class interval. But although the variate, L, could have taken any value in its range, in practice a distribution of observed frequencies only covers a finite number of values of the variate, although this may at times be very large. Thus in a sense, this

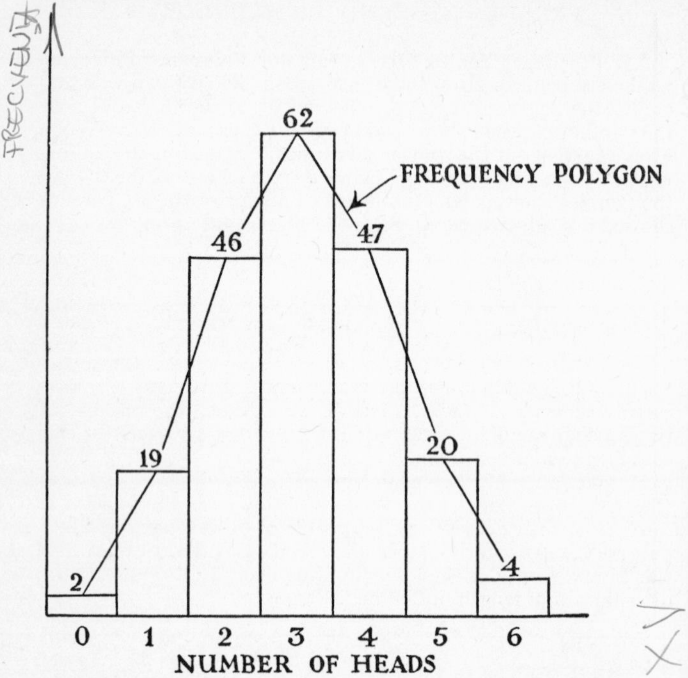

FIG. 2.1.1 (*a*).—Frequency Diagram.

second distribution may also be regarded as a discrete distribution, especially as the frequencies have been grouped.

How do we display such distributions diagrammatically?

(a) *The Histogram.* On a horizontal axis mark out a number of intervals, usually of equal length, corresponding to the values taken by the variate. The mid-point of each such interval is labelled with the value of the variate to which it corresponds. Then, upon each interval as base, erect a rectangle *the area of which is proportional to the frequency of occurrence of that particular value of the variate.* In this way we obtain a diagram built up of cells, called, from the Greek for cell, a *histogram*.

The *area of each cell, we emphasise, measures the frequency of occurrence of the variate in the interval upon which it is based.*

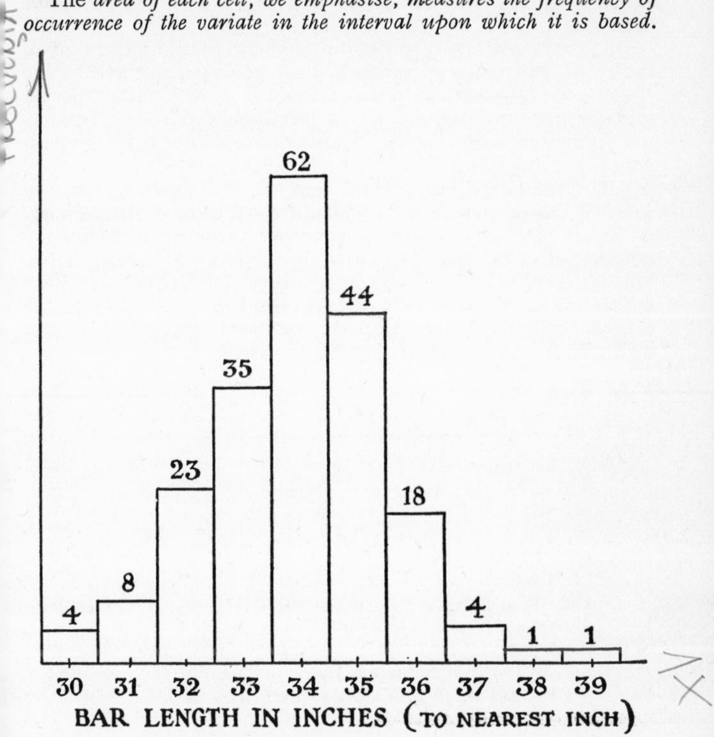

FIG. 2.1.1 (*b*).—Histogram.

Of course, if, as is often the case, all the intervals are of equal length, the height of each cell serves as a measure of the corresponding frequency; but this is, as it were, only accidental.

The area of all the cells taken together measures the total frequency.

Figs. 2.1.1 (*a*) and (*b*) show the histograms for our two distributions. It should be noted that, whereas in the case of the first distribution, when the variate was really discrete, each class-interval represents a single value, in the case of the second distribution, each class value represents in fact a range of values, the mid-point of which is used to denote the interval.

(b) *Frequency Polygon.* Alternatively, at the mid-point of each interval, erect an ordinate proportional in length to the frequency of the variate in that interval. Now join together by straight-line segments the upper terminal points of neighbouring ordinates. The figure so obtained is a *frequency polygon* (see Fig. 2.1.1 (*a*)).

2.2. Cumulative Frequency Diagrams. We may be interested more in the frequency with which a variate takes values *equal to or less than some stated value* rather than in the frequency with which it takes individual values. Thus, for example, we may want to show diagrammatically the frequencies with which our six pennies showed three heads or less or five heads or less. To do this we set up a *cumulative frequency diagram* in either of the two following ways :

(*a*) On each interval corresponding to the different values of the variate, set up rectangles in area proportional to the combined frequency of the variate in that interval and in all those corresponding to lower values of the variate. Thus, in our pennies example, on the "0" interval, set up a rectangle of area 2, on the "1" interval, a rectangle of area $2 + 19 = 21$, on the interval "2" a rectangle of area $2 + 19 + 46 = 67$ and so on. The area of the rectangle set up on the last interval will measure the total frequency of the distribution. The diagram shown in Fig. 2.2.1 results.

(*b*) Alternatively, at the mid-point of each interval, erect an ordinate measuring the "accumulated" frequency up to and including that value of the variate. Join the upper end-points of neighbouring ordinates. The resulting figure is a *cumulative frequency polygon* (see Fig. 2.2.1).

Exercise : *Draw a cumulative frequency histogram and polygon for the data given in the second table in* 2.1.

2.3. Samples and Statistics. Theoretically, the experiment with the six pennies could have been continued indefinitely. Consequently the actual results obtained may be regarded as those of but one *sample* of 200 throws from an indefinitely large *population* of samples of that size. Had we performed the experiment again, emptying the bag another 200 times, we should have obtained a somewhat different frequency distribution, that of another sample of 200 throws. Had we made 350

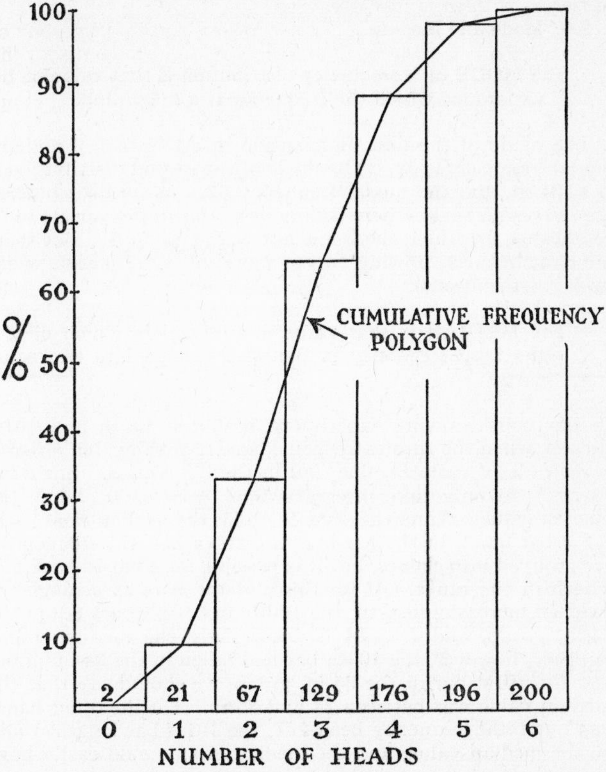

FIG. 2.2.1.—Cumulative Frequency Diagram.

throws, we should have obtained yet another distribution, this time of a sample of 350.

We therefore require some method of describing frequency distributions in a concentrated fashion, some method of summarising their salient features by, say, a set of " descriptive numbers ". As we said in Chapter One we call these " descriptive numbers " *statistics* when they describe the frequency distribution exhibited by a sample, and *parameters* when they describe that of a *population*. For the present, we concern ourselves with samples only.

2.4. Mode and Median.

The MODE of a frequency distribution is that value of the variate for which the frequency is a maximum.

The mode of the first distribution in 2.1 is $H = 3$ and the modal frequency is 62. The mode of the second distribution is $L = 34$ in. and the modal frequency 62. Many distributions are *unimodal*, that is there is only one value of the variate in its total range for which the frequency is a maximum. But there are distributions showing two or more modes (*dimodal*, *multimodal* distributions).

The MEDIAN is that value of the variate which divides the total frequency in the whole range into two equal parts.

In our coin-throwing experiment both the 100th and 101st throws, when the throws are considered as arranged in order of magnitude of variate-value, fall in the " 3 " class. Since the variate can only take integral values between 0 and 6, the median value is 3 and the class $H = 3$ is the median class. On the other hand, in the bar-length distribution the frequencies are grouped into classes, but it is possible for a bar to have any length in the range. If we think of the bars as arranged in order of increasing length, the 100th and 101st bars fall in the 34-in. group, and $L = 34$ is accordingly the median value. Suppose, however, the 100th bar had fallen in the 34-in. group and the 101st bar in the 35-in. group, we should say that the median value was between 34 and 35 in. On the other hand, had our total frequency been 201, the 101st bar length would be the median value, and the median group could easily have been found.

To find an approximation to the median length, suppose that the median group is the 34-in. group (33·5–34·5 in.), that the cumulative frequency up to and including the 33-in. group is 98, and that the frequency of the 34-in. group is 14. Let the median value be L_m. Then the difference between the median value and that of the lower endpoint of the 34-in. interval will be $L_m - 33{\cdot}5$. The median cumulative frequency is 100; the difference between this and the cumulative frequency at the lower end-point is 100 − 98, while the frequency in the 34-in. class is 14. Consequently it is reasonable to write

$$\frac{L_m - 33 \cdot 5}{34 \cdot 5 - 33 \cdot 5} = \frac{100 - 98}{14}$$

or $L_m = 33 \cdot 5 + 0 \cdot 143 = \underline{33 \cdot 6}$, correct to 1 d.p.

Alternatively, the median value may be estimated *graphically* by using the cumulative frequency polygon for the distribution. The last ordinate in such a diagram measures the total frequency of the distribution. Divide this ordinate into 100 equal parts and label them accordingly. Through the 50th division draw a horizontal line to meet the polygon; then through this point of intersection draw a vertical line to cut the axis of variate values. The point where it cuts this axis gives an approximation to the median value.

Exercise : *Find the median value for the distribution whose frequency polygon was drawn as an exercise in* 2.2.

2.5. The Mean. More important than either of the two preceding statistics is the *arithmetic mean*, or briefly, the *mean* of the distribution.

If the variate x takes the values x_i with frequencies f_i respectively ($i = 1, 2, 3 \ldots k$), where $\sum_{i=1}^{k} f_i = N$, the total frequency, the mean, $\bar{x}$, is defined by

$$N\bar{x} = \sum_{i=1}^{k} f_i x_i \quad . \quad . \quad . \quad . \quad (2.5.1)$$

Thus the mean number of heads shown in our penny-distribution is given by

$$200\bar{H} = 2 \times 0 + 19 \times 1 + 46 \times 2 + 62 \times 3 + 47 \times 4 + 20 \times 5 + 4 \times 6 = 609$$

or $\bar{H} = \underline{3 \cdot 045}$

Frequently much arithmetic may be avoided by using a *working mean*. We use this method to calculate the mean of our second distribution in 2.1.

Examining the frequency table, we see that the mean will lie somewhere in the region of 34 in. Consequently, let $x = L - 34$. Then $\Sigma f_i L_i = \Sigma f_i (x_i + 34) = \Sigma f_i x_i + 34 \Sigma f_i$ or, dividing by $\Sigma f_i = 200$, $\bar{L} = \bar{x} + 34$. We therefore set up the following table :

L.	f.	$x = L - 34$.	fx.
30	4	-4	-16
31	8	-3	-24
32	23	-2	-46
33	35	-1	-35
34	62	0	-121
35	44	1	44
36	18	2	36
37	4	3	12
38	1	4	4
39	1	5	5
	200		101

$$\therefore \quad \Sigma fx = -20 ; \quad \bar{x} = -20/200 = -0{\cdot}1$$

$$\text{or} \quad L = \bar{x} + 34 = \underline{33{\cdot}9}$$

The reader will notice that, since in the histogram of a distribution, the frequency f_i in the x_i class is represented by the area of the corresponding rectangular cell, $N\bar{x} = \sum_i f_i x_i$ is *the first moment of the area of the histogram about* $x = 0$. Consequently, the mean of a distribution, $\bar{x}$, is the abscissa, or x-co-ordinate, of the centroid of the area of the histogram (see Abbott, *Teach Yourself Calculus*, Chapter XVII).

2.6. Measures of Spread. Two distributions may have the same mean value, same mode and same median, but differ from each other according as the values of the variate cluster closely around the mean or are spread widely on either side. In addition, therefore, to statistics of position or of central tendency—mean, mode and median—we require additional statistics to measure the degree to which the sample values of the variate cluster about their mean or spread from it. The RANGE, the difference between the greatest and least values taken by the variate, is, of course, such a statistic, but two distributions having the same mean and range may yet differ radically in their " spread ".

If we refer back to the method of finding the median graphically from a cumulative frequency polygon, we see that this method can also be used to find the value of the variate below which any given percentage of the distribution lies. Such values are called PERCENTILES. The p-percentile being that value of the variate which divides the total frequency in the ratio $p : 100\text{-}p$. Thus the median is the 50th percentile. Together, the 25th percentile, the median and the 75th percentile quarter the distribution. They are, therefore, known as QUARTILES. The difference between the 75th and 25th percentile is the *inter-quartile range*. This and the *semi-inter-quartile range* are often useful as practical measures of spread, for the smaller the inter-quartile range the more closely the distribution clusters about the median.

More important theoretically as a measure of spread, is a statistic called the VARIANCE. Using the notation in which we defined the mean, the variance, s^2, is given by

$$Ns^2 = \sum_{i=1}^{k} f_i(x_i - \bar{x})^2 \quad . \quad . \quad . \quad (2.6.1)$$

In words, it is the mean squared deviation from the mean of the sample values of the variate. If we think in terms of moments of area of the histogram of the distribution, Ns^2 is the second moment of area about the vertical axis through the centroid of the histogram. Thus s, commonly called the *standard deviation* of the distribution (it is the root mean square deviation), corresponds to the radius of gyration of the histogram about this axis (see Abbott, *Teach Yourself Calculus*, Chapter XVII).

Expanding the right-hand side of (2.6.1).

$$Ns^2 = \sum_{i=1}^{k} f_i(x_i^2 - 2\bar{x}x_i + \bar{x}^2) = \sum_{i=1}^{k} f_i x_i^2 - 2\bar{x} \sum_{i=1}^{k} f_i x_i + N\bar{x}^2.$$

But $N\bar{x} = \sum_{i=1}^{k} f_i x_i$ and, therefore,

$$s^2 = \left(\sum_{i=1}^{k} f_i x_i^2/N\right) - \bar{x}^2 \quad . \quad . \quad . \quad (2.6.2)$$

When a desk calculator is used, this is better formulated as:

$$s^2 = \left[N \sum_{i=1}^{k} f_i x_i^2 - \left(\sum_{i=1}^{k} f_i x_i\right)^2\right]/N^2 \quad . \quad (2.6.3)$$

Now let m be any value of the variate. We have

$$Ns^2 = \sum_{i=1}^{k} f_i(x_i - \bar{x})^2 = \sum_{i=1}^{k} f_i(x_i - m - (\bar{x} - m))^2$$

$$= \sum_{i=1}^{k} f_i(x_i - m)^2 - 2(\bar{x} - m) \sum_{i=1}^{k} f_i(x_i - m) + N(\bar{x} - m)^2$$

$$= \sum_{i=1}^{k} f_i(x_i - m)^2 - N(\bar{x} - m)^2$$

or

$$\sum_{i=1}^{k} f_i(x_i - m)^2 = Ns^2 + N(\bar{x} - m)^2 \qquad (2.6.2(a))$$

This equation shows how we may calculate the variance using a working mean, m. It also shows that the sum of the squared deviations from the true mean is always less than that of the squared deviations from any other value. It is, in fact, the analogue of the so-called Parallel Axis Theorem for Moments of Inertia (see Abbott, *Teach Yourself Calculus*, p. 313).

We now calculate the variance of the distribution of bar-lengths, the mean of which we have already found. We extend the table set out in 2·5 as follows:

Distribution of bar-lengths in 200 *bars*

(Working mean = 34 in.)

L.	f.	x = L–34.	x^2.	fx.	fx^2.
30	4	−4	16	−16	64
31	8	−3	9	−24	72
32	23	−2	4	−46	92
33	35	−1	1	−35	35
34	62	0	0	−121	0
35	44	1	1	44	44
36	18	2	4	36	72
37	4	3	9	12	36
38	1	4	16	4	16
39	1	5	25	5	25
—	200 = N	—	—	101	$\Sigma fx^2 = 456$
				−121	
				$\Sigma fx = -20$	

From 2.6.2(*a*) $s^2 = \Sigma f(\text{L} - 34)^2/N - (\bar{\text{L}} - 34)^2$
$$= \tfrac{456}{200} - (0{\cdot}1)^2 = 2{\cdot}27$$
and $s = \underline{1{\cdot}51}$

We shall see later (2.15) that in the case of grouped distributions of a continuous variate (as here), a small correction to the variance is necessary to compensate for the fact that the frequencies are grouped. The variance of the present distribution, so corrected, is $\underline{2{\cdot}20}$ correct to 2 d.p.

2.7. Moments of a Frequency Distribution. The quantity Ns^2 is the second moment of the distribution about its mean. We shall find it useful to extend this idea and define the *higher moments* of such distributions.

For the present we shall assume that we are dealing with finite sample distributions of a discrete variate.

The *r*th moment of a distribution about its mean, or the r*th mean-moment*, m_r is defined by

$$Nm_r \equiv \sum_{i=1}^{k} f_i(x_i - \bar{x})^r \quad . \quad . \quad . \quad (2.7.1)$$

where the variate x takes the k values x_i, $(i = 1, 2 \ldots k)$, with frequency f_i, $(i = 1, 2 \ldots k)$, $\sum_{i=1}^{k} f_i = N$, the sample size or total frequency, and $\bar{x}$ is the sample mean. The *r*th moment about $x = 0$, m_r', is, likewise, defined to be

$$Nm_r' \equiv \sum_{i=1}^{k} f_i x_i^r \quad . \quad . \quad . \quad . \quad (2.7.2)$$

Expanding the right-hand side of (2.7.1) by the binomial theorem, we have

$$m_r = m_r' - \binom{r}{1} m_1' m_{r-1}' + \binom{r}{2} (m_1')^2 m_{r-2}' - \ldots$$
$$+ (-1)^s \binom{r}{s} (m_1')^s m_{r-s}' + \ldots + (-1)^{r-1} \binom{r}{r-1} (m_1')^{r-1} m_1'$$
$$+ (-1)^r (m_1')^r \quad (2.7.3)$$

where $\binom{r}{s}$ is the binomial coefficient, $r(r-1)(r-2) \ldots (r-s+1)/s!$ or $r!/s!(r-s)!$. In particular, since we may always combine the last two terms,

$$m_1 = 0;\ m_2 = m_2' - (m_1')^2;\ m_3 = m_3' - 3m_1'm_2' + 2(m_1')^3;$$
and $$m_4 = m_4' - 4m_1'm_3' + 6(m_1')^2 m_2' - 3(m'_1)^4 \quad (2.7.4)$$

2.8. Relative Frequency Distributions. When we have a large sample of observations, some at least of the class-frequencies will also be great. In this situation it is often convenient to reduce the frequency distribution to a *relative-frequency distribution.* If the variate x takes the value x_i, f_i times and the total frequency $\sum_{i=1}^{k} f_i = N$, the relative frequency of the value x_i is f_i/N. Clearly, the total area of the cells in a relative-frequency histogram is unity, and it follows at once that, if we write $F_i \equiv f_i/N$ and, so $\sum_{i=1}^{k} F_i = 1$,

$$\bar{x} = \sum_{i=1}^{k} F_i x_i$$

and
$$s^2 = \sum_{i=1}^{k} F_i(x_i - \bar{x})^2 = \left(\sum_{i=1}^{k} F_i x_i^2\right) - \bar{x}^2$$

Thus, when we are dealing with *relative frequencies*, the mean is simply the first moment of the distribution about $x = 0$ and the variance is simply the second moment about the mean.

2.9. Relative Frequencies and Probabilities. Directly we begin to speak of " relative frequencies " we are on the threshold of probability theory, the foundation of statistical analysis.

Suppose that, having witnessed the measurement of the length of each of the two hundred metal bars we have been talking about, we are asked to predict the length of the 201st bar. If we take into account the information provided by the first 200 bars, we shall probably argue something like this : we notice that, of the 200 bars already measured, 62 were in the 34-in. class, 44 were in the 35-in. class, 35 were in the 33-in. class. The next two hundred bars are not likely to reproduce this distribution exactly, but if the 200 bars already measured are anything like a representative sample of the total batch of bars, it is reasonable to assume that the distribution of length of the next 200 will not be radically different from that of the first 200. Of all the lengths the three occurring most frequently in the sample are 33, 34 and 35 in. If, then, we have to plump for any one length, we shall choose the 34-in. class, the class with the highest relative frequency.

Suppose now that we are asked to *estimate* the *probability* that the 201st bar will have a length falling in the 34-in. class. In reply we should probably say that if a numerical measure of that probability has to be given, the best we can do is to give the fraction $\frac{62}{200}$, for this is the relative frequency of the 34-in.

class in the available sample of 200; and if the drawing of each sample of 200 bars is indeed random, we have no reason to expect that the relative frequency of this class in the next sample will be greatly different.

Assume now that the next sample of 200 has been drawn and that the relative frequency of the 34-in. class in this sample is $\frac{66}{200}$. The relative frequency of this class in the combined distribution of 400 bars will be $\frac{128}{400}$ or $\frac{64}{200}$. In assessing the probability that the 401st rod will fall in the 34-in. class, we should, presumably, use this latest figure. In so doing we are actually implying that, as sampling is continued, the relative frequency of an occurrence tends to some unique limit which is "the probability" of the occurrence we are trying to estimate.

There can be little doubt that it was somewhat in this way that the concept of "the probability of an event E given conditions C" arose. But there are difficulties in the way of developing a "relative-frequency" definition of that probability.

In the first place, have we any grounds for assuming that in two different sampling sequences, made under exactly similar conditions, the relative frequency of the 34-in. class would lead to exactly the same limit?

Secondly, we made the explicit assumption that the sampling was random, that each sample was really *representative* of the population of all the bars available. But, as we saw in the first chapter, the generally accepted definition of a random selection from a population is that it is one made from a population all the items of which have an equal probability of being selected. So our definition of the probability of a particular event E, given a set of conditions C, itself depends on knowing what you mean by the probability of another event E', given another set of conditions C'!

What is the chance that when you toss a penny it will "show heads"? More precisely, what is the probability of a head in a single toss of a penny? In trying to answer this question, we might argue as follows:

> There are only two possible outcomes (assuming that the penny does not land standing on its edge!): one is that it will land showing a head, the other that it will show a tail. If the coin is perfectly symmetrical and there is no significant change in the method of tossing, a head or a tail is equally likely. There is then one chance in two that a head will show. The required measure of the probability of a head in a single throw of the penny is then 1 in 2 or $\frac{1}{2}$.

But even this " geometrical " line of argument is open to criticism. Once again that haunting " equally likely " has cropped up,[1] but, apart from the suspicion of circularity, how do we know that the coin is " perfectly symmetrical ", is, in fact, unbiased? Surely the only way to test whether it is or not is to make a sequence of tosses to find out whether the relative frequency of a head ultimately tends to equality with the relative frequency of a tail. So we are back again at the relative frequency position! But, assuming that the coin is asymmetrical, is biased, how are we to estimate the probability of a head in a single throw without recourse to some relative frequency experiment? A battered coin can have a very complicated geometry! On the other hand, the " perfectly symmetrical " coin and the " completely unbiased " die do not exist except as conceptual models which we set up for the purposes of exploration and analysis. And the very process of setting up such models entails assigning precise probability-measures: in saying that a coin is " perfectly symmetrical " we are in fact assigning the value $\frac{1}{2}$ to the probability of a head and to that of a tail in a single throw, while the very term " completely unbiased " six-faced die is only another way of saying that the probabilities of throwing a 1, 2, 3, 4, 5, or 6, in a single throw are each equal to 1/6.

The matter is too complicated for full discussion here, but sufficient has been said for us to adopt the following definitions:—

Definition 1: If the single occurrence of a set of circumstances, C, can give rise to m mutually exclusive events E_i ($i = 1, 2, \ldots m$), and if a reasonably large number, n, of actual occurrences of C are observed to give rise to f_1 occurrences of E_1, f_2 occurrences of E_2, and so on (where necessarily $\Sigma_i f_i/n = 1$), then the probability of E_i, $p(E_i|C)$, is in this situation measured, with a margin of error, by the relative frequency f_i/n ($0 \leqslant f_i/n \leqslant 1$), it being assumed that, as n increases, each empirical frequency tends to stabilise. Correspondingly, in any *mathematical model* we set up we assign certain probability numbers, p_i, to each E_i, such that, for all i, $0 \leqslant p_i \leqslant 1$ and $\Sigma_i p_i = 1$, i.e., we automatically postulate a probability distribution for the E_i's in setting up the model.

[1] Professor Aitken has said:

" Every definition which is not pure abstraction must appeal somewhere to intuition or experience by using some such verbal counter as ' point ', ' straight line ' or ' equally likely ', under stigma of seeming to commit a circle in definition " (*Statistical Mathematics*, p. 11).

Definition 2: An event E_2 is said to be dependent on an event E_1, if the occurrence of E_1 affects the probability of the occurrence of E_2. If, however, the occurrence of E_1 does not affect the probability of E_2, the latter is *independent* of E_1. If E_2 is independent of E_1 and E_1 is independent of E_2, the events E_1 and E_2 are said to be *independent*. On the other hand, if the occurrence of E_1 precludes the occurrence of E_2 and the occurrence of E_2 precludes the occurrence of E_1, the two events are said to be *mutually exclusive*.

(In a single throw of a coin, the event " Heads " and the event " Tails " are mutually exclusive. On the other hand, the occurrence of a head in the first throw does not influence the outcome of a second throw, and thus the two events are independent. In contrast, the second of two successive shots at shove-halfpenny is usually dependent on the first.)

2.10. Elementary Probability Mathematics. It follows from the postulated correspondence between probabilities and relative frequencies that

If the two events E_1 and E_2 are mutually exclusive and $p(E_1|C) = p_1$ and $p(E_2|C) = p_2$, then we assert that the probability of the event " either E_1 or E_2 ", which we write $p(E_1 + E_2|C)$, is

$$p_1 + p_2 \quad . \quad . \quad . \quad (2.10.1)$$

For suppose in a large number of occurrences of C, n, say, the event E_1 is observed to occur f_1 times and E_2 is observed to occur f_2 times, then the event " either E_1 or E_2 " will have occurred $f_1 + f_2$ times, i.e., with a relative frequency $(f_1 + f_2)/n = f_1/n + f_2/n$. 2.10.1 is the *law of addition of probabilities* for mutually exclusive events.

It follows that the probability of the non-occurrence of any E, $\bar{E}$, is given by

$$p(\bar{E}|C) = 1 - p(E|C) \quad . \quad . \quad (2.10.2)$$

$\bar{E}$ is often called the event *complementary* to E. If $p(E|C)$ is p and $p(\bar{E}|C)$ is q, then, in the case of complementary events

$$p + q = 1 \quad . \quad . \quad . \quad (2.10.3)$$

2.10.1 also gives immediately, if we have n mutually exclusive events E_i with probabilities p_i $(i = 1, 2, \ldots n)$, the probability of " either E_1 or E_2 or E_3 or . . . or E_k " as

$$p(E_1 + E_2 + E_3 + \ldots + E_k)$$
$$= p_1 + p_2 + p_3 + \ldots + p_k = \sum_{=1}^{k} p_i.$$

Multiplication Law: Group some of the events E_i ($i = 1$ to n) together in a set S_1, group some of the remaining events into a set S_2 and continue in this way until all the E_i's are exhausted. Each S_i may be considered as a new event. Then the events S_i are mutually exclusive and together exhaust the set of original E_i's. Let the probability of the event S_i, $p(S_i) = p_{i.}$. Now, using the same method, group the E_i's into a different set of events T_j and let $p(T_j) = p_{.j}$. In general, any S_i and any T_j will have some of the E_i's in common. Denote the E_i's common to S_i and T_j by $S_i \,.\, T_j$. We now have another set of mutually exclusive events, the $S_i \,.\, T_j$'s, taken over all values of i and j, also exhausting the E_i's. Let $p(S_i \,.\, T_j) = p_{ij}$. If we consider the events $S_i \,.\, T_j$ for which i is fixed but j varies, it is clear that $\Sigma_j S_i \,.\, T_j = S_i$. Likewise, $\Sigma_i S_i \,.\, T_j = T_j$. Consequently, $p_{i.} = \Sigma_j p_{ij}$ and $p_{.j} = \Sigma_i p_{ij}$. Also $\Sigma_j (p_{ij}/p_{i.}) = 1 = \Sigma_i (p_{ij}/p_{.j})$ and

$$0 \leqslant p_{ij}/p_{i.} \leqslant 1.$$

(Every $p_{ij}/p_{i.}$ is essentially positive). Hence it would appear that the quantities $p_{ij}/p_{i.}$ are also *probability-numbers.*

To see that this is in fact the case consider the identity

$$p_{ij} = p_{i.}(p_{ij}/p_{i.}) \quad . \quad . \quad . \quad (2.10.4)$$

The corresponding frequency identity is $f_{ij} = f_{i.}(f_{ij}/f_{i.})$, but $f_{ij}/f_{i.}$ is the relative frequency with which the event $S_i \,.\, T_j$ occurs in all the occurrences of the event S_i, i.e., it is the relative frequency with which the event T_j occurs on those occasions in which S_i occurs. Consequently $p_{ij}/p_{i.}$ is the *conditional probability of T_j given S_i*, i.e.,

$$\boldsymbol{p(S_i \,.\, T_j) = p(S_i) \,.\, p(T_j|S_i)} \quad . \quad (2.10.5)$$

This is the *probability multiplication law.*

Referring to *Definition* 2, if T_j and S_i are *independent*

$$p(T_j|S_i) = p(T_j) = p_{.j} \text{ and } p(S_i|T_j) = p(S_i) = p_{i.}.$$

Hence

$$p_{ij} = p_{i.} \cdot p_{.j} \quad . \quad . \quad . \quad (2.10.5a)$$

Consequently

If k independent events E_i have probabilities $p(E_i|C_i) = p_i$, the probability that they all *occur in a context situation C, in which all the C_i's occur once only, is*

$$p(E_1 \,.\, E_2 \,.\,.\,.\, E_k|C) = p_1 \cdot p_2 \,.\,.\,.\, p_k = \prod_{i=1}^{k} p(E_i|C_i) \qquad (2.10.5b)$$

Example : *What is the probability of throwing exactly 9 with two true dice ?*

To score 9 we must throw 6 and 3, 5 and 4, 4 and 5, or 3 and 6. If we throw any one of these we cannot throw any of the rest. The events are, therefore, mutually exclusive. The number of possible outcomes is $6 \,.\, 6 = 36$. Therefore the required probability is $\frac{4}{36}$ or $\frac{1}{9}$.

Example : *A bag contains 5 white balls and 4 black balls. One ball is drawn at a time. What is the probability that the balls drawn will be alternately white and black ?*

The probability of drawing a white ball at the first draw is $\frac{5}{9}$, since there are 5 white balls in the 9 to be drawn from; the probability of then drawing a black ball is $\frac{4}{8}$, since there are now 8 balls to draw from, of which 4 are black; the probability that the third ball drawn will be white is, consequently, $\frac{4}{7}$ and so on. The required probability is, then,

$$\frac{5}{9} \cdot \frac{4}{8} \cdot \frac{4}{7} \cdot \frac{3}{6} \cdot \frac{3}{5} \cdot \frac{2}{4} \cdot \frac{2}{3} \cdot \frac{1}{2} \cdot 1 = \frac{1}{126}$$

Example : *If the events E_1 and E_2 are neither independent nor mutually exclusive, what is the probability that at least one of E_1 and E_2 occurs ?*

Let $p(E_1) = p_1$, $p(E_2) = p_2$ and $p(E_1 \,.\, E_2) = p_{12}$. The required probability is the probability of one of three mutually exclusive events—either both occur, or E_1 occurs and E_2 does not, or E_2 occurs and E_1 does not.

Now the probability that E_1 occurs **is** the sum of the probabilities that both E_1 and E_2 occur and that E_1 occurs and E_2 does not. Consequently $p(E_1 \,.\, \bar{E}_2) = p(E_1) - p(E_1 \,.\, E_2) = p_1 - p_{12}$. Likewise, $p(\bar{E}_1, E_2) = p_2 - p_{12}$. Therefore, the required probability that at least one of the two events occurs, being the sum of the probabilities $p(E_1 \,.\, \bar{E}_2)$, $p(\bar{E}_1 \,.\, E_2)$ and $p(E_1 \,.\, E_2)$, is given by

$$p(E_1 + E_2) = (p_1 - p_{12}) + (p_2 - p_{12}) + p_{12} = p_1 + p_2 - p_{12}$$

Problem : *If from n unlike objects, r objects are selected, in how many ways can these r objects be ordered or arranged ?*

Imagine r places set out in a row. We may fill the first place in any one of n ways. Having filled the first place, there are $n - 1$ objects left, and there are therefore $n - 1$ ways of filling the second place. Arguing on these lines, there will be $(n - r + 1)$ ways of filling the last place. The total number of ways in which the r objects may be ordered is, then, $n(n - 1)(n - 2) \ldots (n - r + 1)$. We may write this

$${}^nP_r \equiv n!/(n - r)!$$

Problem : *In how many ways may r objects be picked from n objects regardless of order ?*

Let this number be x. Now x times the number of ways in which r objects can be ordered among themselves will be the number of arrangements of r objects selected from n objects. The number of ways r objects may be arranged among themselves is clearly $r!$ (by the previous problem). Hence

$$x = n!/r!(n - r)!$$

This number is usually denoted by the symbol ${}^nC_r$ or by $\binom{n}{r}$.

Example : *In how many different orders can a row of coins be placed using 1 shilling, 1 sixpence, 1 penny and 6 halfpennies ?*

If we treat the halfpennies as all different the number of arrangements is 9 ! But it is possible to arrange the halfpennies in 6 ! different ways, all of which we now consider to be equivalent. Consequently the required number of different orders is $9!/6! = 504$.

Problem : *In how many ways can n objects be divided into one group of n_1 objects, a second group of n_2 objects and so on, there being k groups in all ?*

We have $n_1 + n_2 + n_3 + \ldots + n_k = n$. Now the first group may be chosen in $n!/n_1!(n - n_1)!$ ways, the second in $(n - n_1)!/n_2!(n - n_1 - n_2)!$ ways and so on.

The total number of ways is, then, the product of all these terms :

$$\frac{n!}{n_1!(n - n_1)!} \cdot \frac{(n - n_1)!}{n_2!(n - n_1 - n_2)!} \cdots \frac{(n - n_1 - n_2 - \ldots - n_{k-1})!}{n_k!\ (n - n_1 - n_2 - \ldots - u_k)!}$$

Since $\sum_{i=1}^{k} n_i = n$, the term on the right of the last denominator is, apparently, 0! Has this symbol a meaning? We have $(n - 1)! = n!/n$. Putting $n = 1$, we find $0! \equiv 1$, which must be taken as the definition of the symbol 0! Consequently, the required number of ways is

$$\frac{n!}{n_1!\,n_2!\ldots n_k!} \quad \text{or} \quad n!/\prod_{i=1}^{k}(n_i!)$$

Example : *In how many ways can all the letters of the word* CALCULUS *be arranged ?*

If all the letters were unlike there would be 8! ways. But there are 2 C's, 2 L's and 2 U's, consequently the number of ways is

$$8!/2!\,2!\,2! = 7!,$$

since the indistinguishable C's may be arranged in 2! ways and so also the L's and U's.

2.11. Continuous Distributions. Let us return to the bars of metal we were measuring and, imagining now the supply to be inexhaustible, continue measuring bar after bar. If, simultaneously, we greatly increase the accuracy with which we measure, we shall be able progressively to reduce the range of our class-intervals. Since length is a continuous variable, if we go on measuring indefinitely, none of our class intervals, no matter how small their range, will be vacant. On the contrary, the frequency of each interval will increase indefinitely. If, then, Δf_i is the relative frequency of the variate in the interval $x_i \pm \frac{1}{2}\Delta x_i$, centred at $x = x_i$, the height of the relative-frequency histogram cell based on this interval, y_i say, will be given by $y_i = \Delta f_i/\Delta x_i$. And, *in the limit*, we shall have a continuous relative frequency curve, $y = \phi(x)$, such that the relative frequency with which the variate x lies within an interval $x \pm \frac{1}{2}dx$ will be given by $ydx = \phi(x)dx$; but this, on the relative-frequency method of estimating probability, is the probability, $dp(x)$ that x will lie between $x \pm \frac{1}{2}dx$. Thus, in the limit, our simple, relative frequency diagram for grouped frequencies of a continuous variate is transformed into the population probability curve of that continuous variate. It follows that the probability that x lies within an interval $a < x \leqslant b$ is given by

$$P(a < x \leqslant b) = \int_a^b \phi(x)dx$$

and, defining $\phi(x)$ to be zero at any point outside the range of the variate x, $\int_{-\infty}^{+\infty} \phi(x)dx = 1$, since x must lie somewhere within its range.

In the case of a continuous variate, it is meaningless to speak of the probability that this variate, x, say, shall take a specified value x_i, for instance. For the number of possible values, in any finite range of the variate, that can be taken is infinite; and, therefore, theoretically, the probability that $x = x_i$ would appear to be zero. Yet, clearly, it is not impossible that $x = x_i$. We therefore confine ourselves to speaking of the probability $dp(x)$ that x lies in an interval $x \pm \frac{1}{2}dx$. In this way we have

$$dp(x) = \phi(x)dx,$$

where $\phi(x)$ is called the *probability density* and defines the particular distribution of x; it is measured by the ordinate at x of the *probability curve* $y = \phi(x)$.

2.12. Moments of a Continuous Probability Distribution. Just as we described a sample-frequency distribution by means of moments of the distribution about some specified value of the variate, so too we describe continuous probability distributions. Thus, the *mean of the distribution is the first moment about* $x = 0$. Following the convention that *Greek letters* *denote population parameters while the corresponding Roman letters denote the corresponding sample statistics*, we write the first moment about $x = 0$,

$$\mu_1' = \int_{-\infty}^{+\infty} x\phi(x)dx \quad (2.12.1)$$

[1]

and for the rth moment about $x = 0$, μ'_r, and the rth moment about the mean, μ_r,

$$\mu_r' = \int_{-\infty}^{+\infty} x^r\phi(x)dx; \text{ and } \mu_r = \int_{-\infty}^{+\infty} (x - \mu_1')^r\phi(x)dx \quad (2.12.2)$$

In particular the *second moment about the mean is the population variance*, and we write

$$\sigma^2 \equiv \mu_2 = \int_{-\infty}^{+\infty} (x - \mu_1')^2\phi(x)dx = \int_{-\infty}^{+\infty} x^2\phi(x)dx - (\mu_1')^2 \quad (2.12.3)$$

or

$$\sigma^2 \equiv \mu_2 = \mu_2' - (\mu_1')^2 \quad . \quad . \quad (2.12.3(a))$$

The probability curve $y = \phi(x)$ may be *symmetrical* about its central ordinate, or it may be " skew ". If it is uni-modal and the mode lies to the right of the mean, there will be a long tail on the negative side, and the curve is accordingly called *negatively skew*; if, however, the mode lies to the left of the mean, the curve is called *positively skew*. It may happen that a mode, given in the case of a continuous curve by $dy/dx = 0$, $d^2y/dx^2 < 0$ (see Abbott, *Teach Yourself Calculus*, p. 88), does not exist. The curve is then often J-*shaped*, positively J-shaped if dy/dx is everywhere negative, and negatively J-shaped if dy/dx is everywhere positive (the " tail " of the distribution being towards the positive or negative side respectively). A U-*shaped* curve occurs if d^2y/dx^2 is everywhere positive and $dy/dx = 0$ at some interior point of the range (see Fig. 2.12).

In order *to compare the skewness of two distributions*, it is necessary to have some measure of skewness which will not depend upon the particular units used.

One such measure (Karl Pearson's) is given by: **(Mean — Mode)/(Standard Deviation).**

It is more in keeping with the use of the moments of a distribution to describe that distribution that we should use the *third moment about the mean*, μ_3. $\mu_3 = \int_{-\infty}^{+\infty} (x - \mu'_1)^3\phi(x)\,dx$,

and, if the curve $y = \phi(x)$ is symmetrical about $x = \mu_1'$, $\mu_3 = 0$.

[1] If the range of x is finite, from $x = a$ to $x = b$, for instance, we define $\phi(x)$ to be zero for all values of x outside this range.

This is easily shown by transferring to the mean as origin, i.e., by making the transformation $X = x - \mu_1'$, then $\mu_3 = \int_{-\infty}^{+\infty} X^3\phi(X)dX$. If the curve is symmetrical about $X = 0$, $\phi(-X) = \phi(X)$, but $(-X)^3\phi(-X) = -X^3\phi(X)$, and, consequently, $\int_{-\infty}^{+\infty} X^3\phi(X)dX = 0$, in this case. If, now, the curve is positively skew, the cubes of the positive values of x together

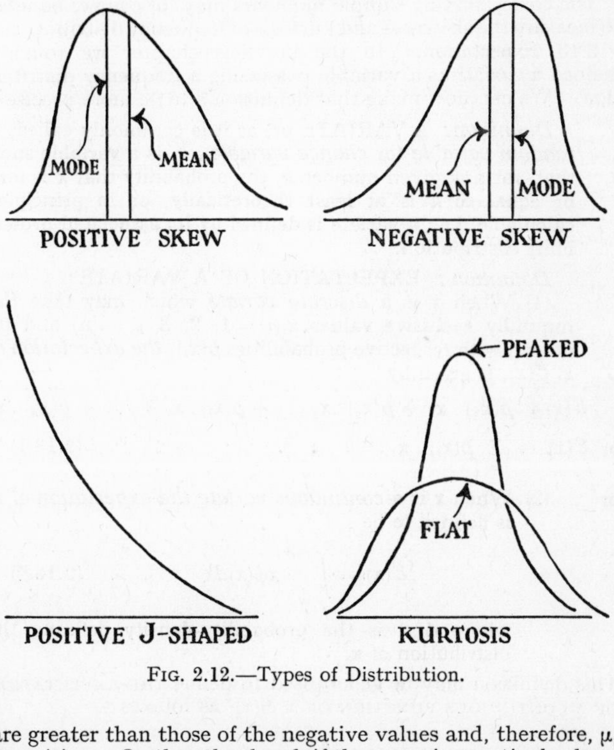

FIG. 2.12.—Types of Distribution.

are greater than those of the negative values and, therefore, μ_3 is positive. On the other hand, if the curve is negatively skew, the cubes of the negative values are greater than those of the positive values, and μ_3 is negative. To ensure independence of units employed, it is necessary to divide by σ^3.

> **The square of this quantity, denoted by β_1, is the conventional measure of skewness. Thus $\beta_1 = \mu_3{}^2/\mu_2{}^3$.**

We use the *fourth mean-moment* to measure the degree to which a given distribution is flattened at its centre (*kurtosis*). This measure, denoted by β_2, is given by $\mu_4/\mu_2{}^2$. In the case of the normal distribution, $\beta_2 = 3$; if, then, this distribution is used as a standard, the quantity $\beta_2 - 3$ measures what is called *excess of kurtosis*.

The corresponding sample moments may, of course, be used to measure the skewness and kurtosis of frequency distributions.

2.13. Expectation. In the previous chapter we roughly defined a *variate* as a variable possessing a frequency distribution. We can now make that definition a little more precise.

> ***Definition:*** **A VARIATE or, as it is commonly called, a *random variable* (or *chance variable*), x, is a variable such that, for any given number k, the probability that x is less or equal to k is at least theoretically, or in principle, calculable, i.e., a variate is defined by its associated probability distribution.**

> ***Definition :*** **EXPECTATION OF A VARIATE:**
>
> **(1) When x is a *discrete variate* which may take the mutually exclusive values x_i(i = 1, 2, 3, . . . n) and no others, with respective probabilities $p(x_i)$, *the expectation of* x, $\mathcal{E}(x)$, is given by**

$$\mathcal{E}(x) \equiv p(x_1) \cdot x_1 + p(x_2) \cdot x_2 \ldots + p(x_i) \cdot x_i + \ldots + p(x_n) \cdot x_n$$

$$\text{or } \mathcal{E}(x) \equiv \sum_{i=1}^{n} p(x_i) \cdot x_i \quad . \quad . \quad . \quad . \quad . \quad . \quad . \quad . \quad . \quad . \quad (2.13.1)$$

or **(2) When x is a *continuous variate the expectation of* x, is defined to be**

$$\mathcal{E}(x) \equiv \int_{-\infty}^{+\infty} x\phi(x)dx \quad . \quad . \quad . \quad (2.13.2)$$

where $\phi(x)$ is the probability-density defining the distribution of x.

This definition may be generalised to define THE EXPECTATION OF A CONTINUOUS FUNCTION OF x, $\theta(x)$, as follows:

$$\mathcal{E}(\theta(x)) \equiv \int_{-\infty}^{+\infty} \theta(x) \cdot \phi(x)dx \quad . \quad . \quad (2.13.3)$$

providing the integral has a finite value (see Abbott, *Teach Yourself Calculus*, pp. 227–232).

The concept of *expectation* arose from gambling. Suppose that your chance of winning a sum of money £x_1 is p_1, that of winning £x_2 is p_2 and so on until, finally, your chance of winning £x_n is p_n; then, if these are the only amounts you have a chance of winning, your expectation is

$$£\left(\sum_{i=1}^{n} p_i x_i\right)$$

This is, in fact, the limit of the average sum won if you were to go on gambling indefinitely. For suppose that in N " goes " you win £x_1 on n_1 occasions, £x_2 on n_2 occasions and so on, and, finally, £x_k on n_k occasions, the mean amount won (and, remember, some or all of the x's may be *negative*, i.e., losses!) is $\sum_{i=1}^{k} n_i x_i/N = \sum_{i=1}^{k} (n_i/N)x_i$. But when N tends to infinity, n_i/N tends to p_i, the *probability* of winning £x_i. Thus $\mathcal{E}(x) = \lim_{N\to\infty}\left[\sum_{i=1}^{n} n_i x_i/N\right]$.

Example : *Show that the expectation of the number of failures preceding the first success in an indefinite series of independent trials, with constant probability of success, is q/p, where $q = 1 - p$.*

The probability of 1 failure and then the success is qp;
" " 2 failures " " $qqp = q^2p$;
" " k failures " " q^kp.

Therefore the required expectation is

$$1 \cdot qp + 2 \cdot q^2p + 3 \cdot q^3p + \ldots + k \cdot q^kp + \ldots$$
$$= qp(1 + 2q + 3q^2 \ldots + kq^{k-1} + \ldots) = qp/(1-q)^2$$
$$= qp/p^2 = q/p.$$

Example : *A point P is taken at random in a line AB, of length $2a$, all positions of the point being equally likely. Show that the expected value of the area of the rectangle $AP \cdot PB$ is $2a^2/3$ (C. E. Weatherburn,* A First Course in Mathematical Statistics).

Let pdx, where p is constant, be the probability that the point P is taken at a distance $x \pm \frac{1}{2}dx$ from A. Then, since P is somewhere in AB, we have

$$\int_0^{2a} pdx = 1 \text{ or } p = 1/2a$$

The area of the rectangle $AP \cdot PB$ is $x(2a - x)$. Therefore the expected value of the area is

$$\mathcal{E}(x(2a-x)) = \int_0^{2a} x(2a-x) \cdot \frac{1}{2a} \cdot dx = (4a^3 - 8a^3/3)/2a = 2a^2/3$$

2.14. Probability Generating Functions. Suppose that x is a discrete variate taking the values x_i, $(i = 1, 2, \ldots k)$, with respective probabilities p_i, $(i = 1, 2, \ldots k)$. It follows from our definition of the expectation of a function of x that the expectation of the function t^x of x is:

$$\mathcal{E}(t^x) = p_1 t^{x_1} + p_2 t^{x_2} + \ldots + p_i t^{x_i} + \ldots + p_k t^{x_k} \quad (2.14.1)$$

The coefficient of t^{x_i} on the right-hand side is precisely the probability that x takes the value x_i.

Let us now assume that it is possible to sum the series on the right-hand side of this equation, obtaining a function of t, $G(t)$, say. Now if we can keep this function by us, so to speak, whenever the situation supposed occurs, we have only to bring out $G(t)$, expand it in a series of powers of t and read off the coefficient of t^{x_i}, say, to find the probability that, in this situation, x takes the value x_i. Such a function would, in fact, *generate* the probabilities p_i with which x takes the values x_i. We, therefore, call it the *Probability Generating Function for* x in that situation.

The corresponding expression when x is a continuous variate with probability density $\phi(x)$ is

$$G(t) \equiv \mathcal{E}(t^x) = \int_{-\infty}^{+\infty} t^x \phi(x) dx \quad . \quad . \quad . \quad (2.14.2)$$

which is clearly a function of t.

> ***Definition:*** **Whether x be a discrete or continuous variate, the function, $G(t)$, defined by**
>
> $$G(t) \equiv \mathcal{E}(t^x) \quad . \quad . \quad . \quad . \quad (2.14.3)$$
>
> **is the *Probability Generating Function for* x (p.g.f. for x).**

The most important property of generating functions lies in the fact that:

> When x and y are independent, discrete variates, and, often, when they are continuous variates, the product of the generating function for x and that for y is the generating function for the new variate $(x + y)$.

Let us take three coins, a shilling, a sixpence and a penny, so worn that they are unsymmetrical. Let the probability of throwing a head with the shilling in a single throw be p_1 and that of a tail, q_1. Let the corresponding probabilities for the other coins be p_2, q_2 and p_3, q_3, respectively. When a head is thrown let the variate x take the value 1 and when a tail is thrown the value 0. The p.g.f. for the shilling is $q_1t^0 + p_1t^1$; that for the sixpence, $q_2t^0 + p_2t^1$, and that for the penny $q_3t^0 + p_3t^1$. Consider the product of these p.g.f.'s :

$$(q_1t^0 + p_1t^1)(q_2t^0 + p_2t^1)(q_3t^0 + p_3t^1);$$

this may be written

$$(q_1 + p_1t)(q_2 + p_2t)(q_3 + p_3t) = q_1q_2q_3 + (p_1q_2q_3 + q_1p_2q_3 + q_1q_2p_3)t + (p_1p_2q_3 + p_1q_2p_3 + q_1p_2p_3)t^2 + p_1p_2p_3t^3.$$

We recognise immediately that the coefficient of t^3 ($x = 3$ indicates 3 heads when the coins are thrown together) is the probability of exactly 3 heads, that of t^2 is the probability of 2 heads and 1 tail ($t^2 = t^{2(1)+1(0)}$), that of t, the probability of 1 head and 2 tails ($t = t^{1(1)+2(0)}$) and that of t^0 ($t = t^{0(1)+3(0)}$), the probability of all 3 coins showing tails.

If now we select any one of the coins, the shilling, say, and toss it n times, the p.g.f. for x, the number of heads shown in the n throws, is $(q_1 + p_1t)^n$. If, however, we score in such a way that each time a head is thrown we gain 5 points and each time a tail turns up we lose 3, the generating function is $(q_1t^{-3} + p_1t^5)^n$, for, in a single throw, if our variate x is now the points scored, the probability of scoring 5 is p_1 and that of scoring -3 is p_2.

In the last case, let the coin be symmetrical, so that $p = \frac{1}{2} = q$. Suppose it is tossed thrice. The p.g.f. for the score will be

$$(\tfrac{1}{2}t^{-3} + \tfrac{1}{2}t^5)^3 = (\tfrac{1}{2})^3t^{-9}(1 + t^8)^3 = \tfrac{1}{8}t^{-9}(1 + 3t^8 + 3t^{16} + t^{24})$$
$$= \tfrac{1}{8}t^{-9} + \tfrac{3}{8}t^{-1} + \tfrac{3}{8}t^7 + \tfrac{1}{8}t^{15}$$

This shows, as the reader should confirm by other methods, that the only possible scores are -9, -1, 7 and 15, with respective probabilities $\frac{1}{8}$, $\frac{3}{8}$, $\frac{3}{8}$, $\frac{1}{8}$.

It is reasonable to say, therefore, that :

If $G_i(t)$ is the p.g.f. for x in the situation S_i, and the situations S_i are all independent, then the p.g.f. for x in the compound situation $S_1S_2S_3 \ldots$ is $G(t) = G_1(t) \,.\, G_2(t) \,.\, G_3(t) \ldots$

2.15. Corrections for Groupings. When we group all the values of a *continuous* variate x lying between $x_i \pm \frac{1}{2}h$ into a single class and treat them as all being exactly x_i, we distort the true distribution of x. Consequently, if we calculate the moments of the distribution from the distorted, or grouped, distribution, the values we obtain will in general be inaccurate, and so corrections must be applied to counteract the distortion due to grouping. These corrections are known as Sheppard's corrections, and may be applied only under certain conditions. Even then they do not counteract the distortion completely, nor do they, in any particular case, *necessarily* improve matters, although they tend to do so on the average. If, then, the terminal frequencies for the range are small (i.e., the distribution is not, for example, J-shaped) the calculated first moment need not be corrected, but the *calculated variance should be reduced by an amount equal to* $h^2/12$, *where* h *is the length of each class-interval.* If, however, h is less than one-third of the calculated standard deviation, this adjustment makes a difference of less than $\frac{1}{2}\%$ in the estimate of the standard deviation. If the variate is essentially discrete, Sheppard's correction should not be applied (see Aitken, *Statistical Mathematics*, pp. 44–47).

Note to Chapter Two

When a desk calculator is used to compute the moments of a grouped distribution, it is often convenient to take as *working mean* the lowest of the variate values occurring and to rescale using the (constant) interval length as unit. Let the given variate values be $x_1, x_2, \ldots\ldots, x_i, \ldots, x_n$, where $x_2 - x_1 = x_3 - x_2 = \ldots = x_n - x_{n-1} = d$, say. Using the transformation $X_i = (x_i - x_1)/d$, so that $X_1 = 0$, $X_2 = 1$, $X_3 = 2, \ldots X_i = (i - 1), \ldots X_n = (n - 1)$,

$$\sum_{i=1}^{n} f_i X_i = 0.f_1 + 1.f_2 + 2.f_3 + \ldots + (n-1)f_n \text{ and}$$

$$\sum_{i=1}^{n} f_i X_i^2 = 0.f_1 + 1^2.f_2 + 2^2.f_3 \ldots\ldots + (n-1)^2.f_n.$$

These quantities are easily evaluated, often simultaneously, in one continuous machine operation, the latter being accumulated in the product register, the former in the counting register, for example. This transformation also enables higher moments to be computed by a simple method of repeated summation (see Aitken, *Statistical Mathematics*, pp 40–41).

EXERCISES ON CHAPTER TWO

1. Measurements are made to the nearest inch of the heights of 100 children. Draw the frequency diagram of the following distribution:

Height . .	60	61	62	63	64	65	66	67	68
Frequency . .	2	0	15	29	25	12	10	4	3

Calculate the mean and the standard deviation. (L.U.)

2. Draw a cumulative frequency polygon for the data of Question 1, and from it estimate both the median value and the standard deviation.

3. Construct a cumulative frequency diagram from:

Average Earnings of Women (18 *and Over*) *in* 56 *Principal Manufacturing Trades, Great Britain, April* 1947

s. d. per week.							
66/10	73/5	69/10	52/7	65/2	62/3	61/6	65/1
60/7	73/1	71/–	59/4	63/11	67/6	58/4	67/–
63/–	79/9	68/5	56/–	68/9	56/9	64/7	69/1
68/6	71/8	71/–	65/7	63/6	64/2	65/6	64/2
78/7	67/8	65/1	64/11	74/1	63/5	71/–	74/9
64/3	71/–	71/11	62/5	64/2	62/–	64/7	74/8
72/4	70/7	69/7	60/1	61/11	66/9	64/9	66/5

(Source: *Ministry of Labour Gazette*, October 1947.)

Estimate the median and quartile earnings and give a measure of dispersion of the distribution. (L.U.)

4. Find the mean of each of the distributions:

Wife's age (at last birthday)	% Distribution of Wives with Husbands aged: 25–29	45–49
15–19	0·8	—
20–24	27·1	0·1
25–29	57·8	0·7
30–34	12·5	3·0
35–39	1·5	9·7
40–44	0·2	29·9
45–49	0·1	44·3
50–54	—	10·3
55–	—	2·0
TOTAL	100·0	100·0

(L.U.)

5. In the manufacture of a certain scientific instrument great importance is attached to the life of a particular critical component. This component is obtained in bulk from two sources, A and B, and in the course of inspection the lives of 1,000 of the components from each source are determined. The following frequency tables are obtained:

Source A.		Source B.	
Life (hours).	No. of components.	Life (hours).	No. of components.
1,000–1,020	40	1,030–1,040	339
1,020–1,040	96	1,040–1,050	136
1,040–1,060	364	1,050–1,060	25
1,060–1,080	372	1,060–1,070	20
1,080–1,100	85	1,070–1,080	130
1,100–1,120	43	1,080–1,090	350

Examine the effectiveness of the measures of dispersion with which you are familiar for comparing the dispersions of the two distributions. (R.S.S.)

6. In a room containing 7 chairs, 5 men are sitting each on a chair. What is the probability that 2 particular chairs are not occupied? (L.U.)

7. In how many different ways can 3 letters out of 25 different letters be arranged if any letter may be used once, twice or three times? If two and not more than two different letters are used? (L.U.)

8. Using the symbols given in the table below, derive expressions for the probabilities that, of four men aged exactly 75, 80, 85 and 90 respectively (i) all will attain age 95; (ii) all will die before attaining age 95; (iii) at least one will survive 10 years; (iv) none will die between ages 90 and 95.

Exact age	75	80	85	90	95
Probability of surviving 5 years	p_0	p_1	p_2	p_3	p_4

(I.A.)

9. From a bag containing 6 red balls, 6 white balls and 6 blue balls, 12 balls are simultaneously drawn at random. Calculate the probability that the number of white balls drawn will exceed the number of red balls by at least two. (I.A.)

10. A property E_1 is known to be independent of a property E_2, of a property $(E_2 + E_3)$ and of a property (E_2E_3). Show that it is also independent of the property E_3. (L.U.)

11. A probability curve, $y = \phi(x)$, has a range from 0 to ∞. If $\phi(x) \equiv e^{-x}$, sketch the curve and find the mean and variance. Find also the third moment about the mean.

12. Prove that if x and y are discrete variates, $\mathcal{E}(x + y) = \mathcal{E}(x) + \mathcal{E}(y)$, and that, if x and y are independent, $\mathcal{E}(xy) = \mathcal{E}(x) \cdot \mathcal{E}(y)$.

Solutions

1. 63·89″; 1·6″. 2. Median value, 63·2″.

3. Median : 65/6; semi-interquartile range $\simeq$ 3/2.

4. 26·89; 45·14.

5. *Range*: (A) 120; (B) 60. *Interquartile Range*: (A) 27; (B) 46. *Standard deviation*: (A) 21; (B) 22.

6. 1/21. 7. 25^3; $25 \times 24 \times 3$.

8. (i) $p_0p_1^2p_2^3p_3^4$; (ii) $[1-p_0p_1p_2p_3][1-p_1p_2p_3][1-p_2p_3][1-p_3]$; (iii) $p_0p_1 + p_1p_2 + p_2p_3 + p_3p_4$; $[1 - p_0p_1^2p_2^3(1 - p_3)^4]$.

9. $\frac{9}{28}$.

10. *Full solution*: Let E_1 occur n_1 times out of n; E_2 n_2 times; E_3 n_3 times; E_1E_2 n_{12} times; E_{23} n_{23} times; E_3E_1 n_{31} times; $E_1E_2E_3$ n_{123} times; and none of E_1, E_2 or E_3 n_0 times. Then the conditions of independence are: $p(E_1) = p(E_1; E_2) = p(E_1; E_2 + E_3) = p(E_1; E_2E_3)$, i.e.,

$$\frac{n_1}{n} = \frac{n_{12} + n_{123}}{n_2 + n_{12} + n_{23} + n_{123}} = \frac{n_{12} + n_{13} + n_{123}}{n_2 + n_3 + n_{12} + n_{13} + n_{23} + n_{123}}$$
$$= \frac{n_{123}}{n_{23} + n_{123}}$$

Now if $a/b = c/d = e/f = \lambda$, say, $\lambda = (c - a + e)/(d - b + f)$. Accordingly

$$p(E_1) = n_1/n = \frac{n_{13} + n_{123}}{n_3 + n_{13} + n_{23} + n_{123}} = P(E_1;\ E_3).$$

11. Mean, 1; Variance, 1; $\mu_3 = 2$.

12. *Full solution*: Let x take the values x_i with probabilities p_i, $(i = 1, 2, \ldots n)$ and let y take the values y_j with probabilities P_j, $(j = 1, 2, \ldots m)$. Also let π_{ij} be the probability that $x + y$ takes the values $x_i + y_j$. Clearly $x + y$ may take nm values. We have then

$$\mathcal{E}(x + y) = \sum_i\sum_j \pi_{ij}\,(x_i + y_j) = \sum_i\sum_j \pi_{ij}x_i + \sum_i\sum_j \pi_{ij}y_j.$$

But
$$\sum_j \pi_{ij} = \pi_{i1} + \pi_{i2} + \ldots + \pi_{im},$$

the sum of the probabilities that x takes the value x_i when y takes any one of the possible values y_j, and this is p_i. Likewise

$$\sum_j \pi_{ij} = P_j.$$

Hence
$$\mathcal{E}(x + y) = \sum_i p_ix_i + \sum_j P_jy_j = \mathcal{E}(x) + \mathcal{E}(y).$$

If now x and y are independent, the probability that xy takes the value x_iy_j is p_iP_j. Therefore

$$\mathcal{E}(xy) = \sum_i\sum_j p_iP_jx_iy_j = \sum_i\sum_j (p_ix_i)\,.\,(P_jy_j).$$

Summing first over j,

$$\mathcal{E}(xy) = \sum_i [p_ix_i\mathcal{E}(y)] = \mathcal{E}(y) \sum_i p_ix_i = \mathcal{E}(y)\,.\,\mathcal{E}(x) = \mathcal{E}(x)\,.\,\mathcal{E}(y).$$

The reader should now prove these two theorems for the case when both x and y are continuous variates.

CHAPTER THREE

STATISTICAL MODELS
I: THE BINOMIAL DISTRIBUTION

3.1. Tossing a Penny. Let $C(E, \bar{E})$ denote an event the outcome of which is either the occurrence of a certain event E or its non-occurrence, denoted by $\bar{E}$. Now suppose that the probability of E happening, given C, is p, and that of $\bar{E}$ is q. We ask what is the probability that in n occurrences of C there will be exactly x occurrences of E?

Once again we toss a penny, and assume that the constant probability of obtaining a head in each throw is equal to that of obtaining a tail. Hence, $p = q = \frac{1}{2}$. The outcome of a single toss is either a head (H) or a tail (T). We toss again, and the outcome of this second toss is again either H or T, and is *independent* of the outcome of the first toss. Consequently the outcome of two tosses will be

either HH or HT or TH or TT

The outcome of 3 tosses may be written down as

either HHH or HHT or HTH or THH
or HTT or THT or TTH or TTT

If now we *disregard the order in which H and T occur*, we may rewrite the outcome of 2 tosses as

1 HH or 2HT or 1 TT

and that of 3 tosses as

1 HHH or 3HHT or 3 HTT or 1 TTT

Writing HHH as H^3, HHT as H^2T^1, etc., we have

outcome of 2 tosses : either $1H^2$ or $2H^1T^1$ or $1T^2$
,, ,, 3 ,, either $1H^3$ or $3H^2T^1$ or $3H^1T^2$ or $1T^3$

By analogy, in 4 tosses we shall have :

either $1H^4$ or $4H^3T^1$ or $6H^2T^2$ or $4H^1T^3$ or $1T^4$

In 4 tosses then there are $1 + 4 + 6 + 4 + 1 = 16 = 2^4$ possible outcomes, and the respective frequencies of 4 heads, 3 heads, 2 heads, and 0 heads will be 1, 4, 6, 4, 1 and the corresponding *relative frequencies*, $\frac{1}{16}$, $\frac{4}{16}$, $\frac{6}{16}$, $\frac{4}{16}$, and $\frac{1}{16}$.

We may arrive at these figures by a different route. We have $p = q = \frac{1}{2}$. Since each toss is independent of every other toss, the probability of four heads, H^4, in four tosses is $(\frac{1}{2})(\frac{1}{2})(\frac{1}{2})(\frac{1}{2}) = (\frac{1}{2})^4 = \frac{1}{16}$. Next, the probability of throwing 2 heads and 2 tails, say, *in some* specified order (HHTT, for instance) is $(\frac{1}{2})(\frac{1}{2})(1 - \frac{1}{2})(1 - \frac{1}{2}) = \frac{1}{16}$; but we may arrange 2H and 2T in a group of 4 in 6 different ways (HHTT HTTH TTHH THHT THTH HTHT); therefore the probability of obtaining H^2T^2, *irrespective of order*, is $6 \times \frac{1}{16} = \frac{3}{8}$, the relative frequency we obtained before.

Suppose now we require to know the probability of exactly 47 heads and 53 tails in 100 tosses. Is there some comparatively simple way of obtaining this probability without, for instance, setting out all the possible arrangements of 47 heads and 53 tails in 100 tosses?

3.2. Generating Function of Binomial Probabilities. Looking once more at the possible outcomes of 4 tosses, we recall that there are sixteen possible results—either H^4 or 4 different arrangements of H^3T^1 or 6 different arrangements of H^2T^2 or 4 different arrangements of H^1T^3 or T^4. And we notice that

$$H^4,\ 4H^3T^1,\ 6H^2T^2,\ 4H^1T^3,\ T^4$$

are the successive terms in the expansion of

$$(H + T)(H + T)(H + T)(H + T), \text{ i.e., of } (H + T)^4$$

Now, in the general case, where p is the constant probability of the event E and q is that of $\bar{E}$, and $p + q = 1$, the probability of E occurring exactly x times in n occurrences of $C(E, \bar{E})$ in *some specified order* is $p^x q^{n-x}$. And since the number of different order-arrangements of x E's and $(n - x)$ $\bar{E}$'s is $n!/x!(n - x)!$ or $\binom{n}{x}$, the probability of exactly x E's is

$$\binom{n}{x} p^x q^{n-x} \quad . \quad . \quad . \quad . \quad . \qquad (3.2.1)$$

Now the expansion of $(q + pt)^n$ is, by the Binomial Theorem,

$$(q + pt)^n = q^n + \binom{n}{1} q^{n-1} pt + \binom{n}{2} q^{n-2} p^2 t^2 + \ldots + \binom{n}{x} q^{n-x} p^x t^x + \ldots + p^n t^n \quad . \qquad (3.2.2)$$

Hence, denoting the probability of exactly x E's in n occurrences of the context-event $C(E, \bar{E})$ by $p_n(x)$,

$$(q + pt)^n = p_n(0) + p_n(1)t + p_n(2)t^2 + \ldots + p_n(x)t^x + \ldots + p_n(n)t^n \quad . \qquad (3.2.3)$$

If now we put $t = 1$, we have

$$1 = p_n(0) + p_n(1) + p_n(2) + \ldots + p_n(x) + \ldots + p_n(n)$$

and this is only to be expected, for the right-hand side is the probability of either 0 or 1 or 2 or . . . or n E's in n occurrences of C, which is clearly 1.

We may say, then,

> **If the probability, p, of an event E is constant for all occurrences of its context event C, the outcome of which is either E or $\bar{E}$, then the probability of exactly x E's in n occurrences of C is given by the coefficient of t^x in the expansion of $(q + pt)^n$.**

Thus $(q + pt)^n$ is the *Probability Generating Function*, p.g.f., for this particular distribution, which because of its method of generation, is called the BINOMIAL DISTRIBUTION.

3.3. Binomial Recursion Formula. Replacing x by $x + 1$ in (3.2.1), we have

$$p_n(x + 1) = \binom{n}{x + 1} q^{n - x - 1} p^{x + 1}$$

Hence

$$p_n(x + 1) = \frac{n - x}{x + 1} \cdot \frac{p}{q} \cdot p_n(x) \quad . \quad . \quad (3.3.1)$$

Now $p_n\,(0) = q^n$, which for a given q and n is quickly calculated. Then $p_n(1) = \frac{n}{1} \cdot \frac{p}{q} \cdot p_n(0)$; $p_n(2) = \frac{n - 1}{2} \cdot \frac{p}{q} \cdot p_n(1)$, etc.

3.4. Some Properties of the Binomial Distribution. Let us calculate the binomial probabilities for $p = \frac{1}{10}$, $n = 5$.

By (3.3.1)

$$p_5(x + 1) = \frac{5 - x}{x + 1} \cdot \frac{1}{9} \cdot p_5(x).$$

Since

$$p_5(0) = (0{\cdot}9)^5 = 0{\cdot}59049,$$

$$p_5(1) = \frac{5}{1} \cdot \frac{1}{9} \cdot 0{\cdot}59049 = 0{\cdot}32805$$

$$p_5(2) = \frac{4}{2} \cdot \frac{1}{9} \cdot 0{\cdot}32805 = 0{\cdot}07290$$

$$p_5(3) = \frac{3}{3} \cdot \frac{1}{9} \cdot 0{\cdot}07290 = 0{\cdot}00810$$

$$p_5(4) = \frac{2}{4} \cdot \frac{1}{9} \cdot 0{\cdot}0081 = 0{\cdot}00045$$

$$p_5(5) = \frac{1}{5} \cdot \frac{1}{9} \cdot 0{\cdot}00045 = 0{\cdot}00001 = (0{\cdot}1)^5,$$

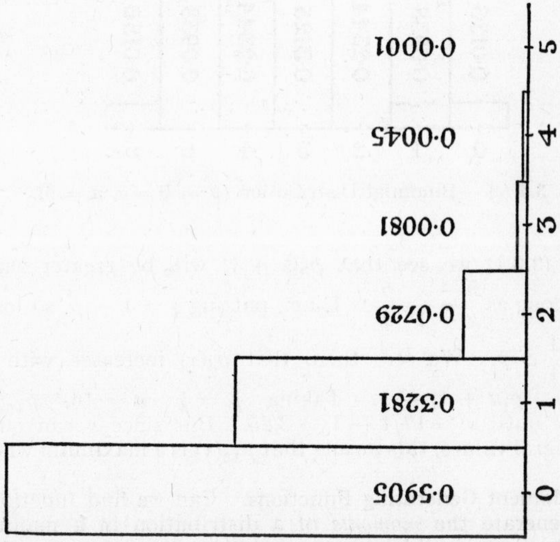

FIG. 3.4 (a).—Binomial Distribution ($p = \frac{1}{10}$, $n = 5$).

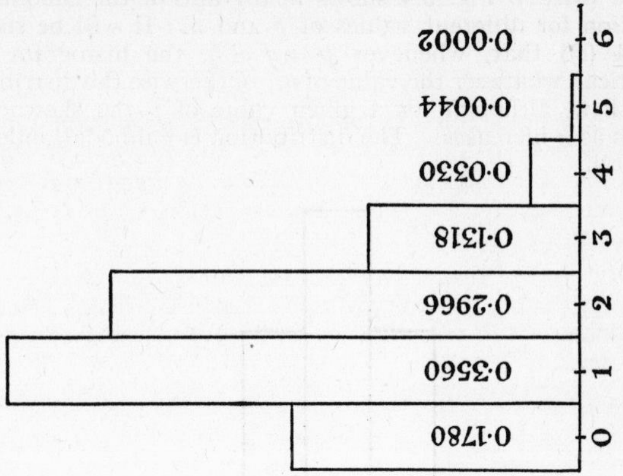

FIG. 3.4 (b).—Binomial Distribution ($p = \frac{1}{4}$, $n = 6$).

of course (why?). Fig. 3.4 shows histograms of the Binomial distribution for different values of p and n. It will be seen (Fig. 3.4 (c)) that, whenever $p = q = \frac{1}{2}$, the histogram is symmetrical, whatever the value of n. Otherwise the distribution is skew, although for a given value of p the skewness decreases as n increases. The distribution is unimodal, unless pn is small.

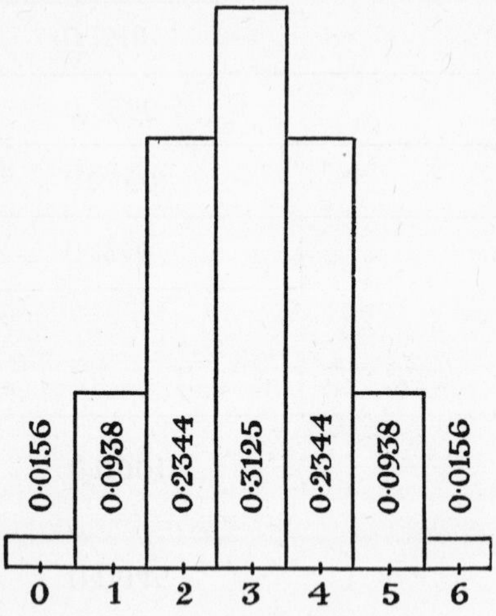

FIG. 3.4 (c).—Binomial Distribution ($p = \frac{1}{2} = q$, $n = 6$).

From (3.3.1) we see that $p_n(x + 1)$ will be greater than $p_n(x)$ so long as $\frac{n - x}{x + 1} \cdot \frac{p}{q} > 1$, i.e., putting $q = 1 - p$, so long as $\frac{x + 1}{n + 1} > p$. We see, then, that $p_n(x)$ increases with x until $x > p(n + 1) - 1$. Taking $p = \frac{1}{4}$, $n = 16$, $p_{16}(x)$ increases until $x > 17/4 - 1 = 3{\cdot}25$. But since x can only take integral values, this means that $p_{16}(x)$ is a maximum when $x = 4$.

3.5. Moment Generating Functions. Can we find functions which generate the *moments* of a distribution in a manner similar to that in which the probability generating function generates the probabilities of a variate in a certain set of circumstances? Let us replace the t in the p.g.f., $G(t)$, of a distribution by e^t and call the function of t so formed $M(t)$. Then

$$M(t) = G(e^t) = \mathscr{E}(e^{xt}) = \sum_{i=1} p(x_i)e^{x_it}, \ (i = 1, 2, 3, \ldots n)$$

$$= \sum_{i=1}^{n} (p(x_i)(1 + x_it + x_i^2t^2/2! + \ldots + x_i^rt^r/r! + \ldots))$$

$$= \sum_{i=1}^{n} p(x_i) + \left[\sum_{i=1}^{n} p(x_i)x_i\right] t + \left[\sum_{i=1}^{n} p(x_i)x_i^2\right] t^2/2!$$

$$+ \ldots + \left[\sum_{i=1}^{n} p(x_i)x_i^r\right] t^r/r! + \ldots$$

$$= 1 + \mu_1' t/1! + \mu_2' t^2/2! + \ldots + \mu_r' t^r/r! + \ldots \quad (3.5.1)$$

The rth moment about $x = 0$, μ_r', is consequently the coefficient of $t^r/r!$ in the expansion of $M(t)$, and $M(t)$ is the *Moment-generating Function* required. We see then that, providing the sum $\sum_{i=1}^{n} p(x_i)e^{x_it}$ exists—which it will always do when n is finite—the *Moment-generating Function*, $M(t)$, for a given distribution is obtained by replacing t in the probability-generating function, $G(t)$, of that distribution, by e^t.

Assuming now that we may differentiate both sides of (3.5.1),

$$\frac{dM(t)}{dt} = \mu_1' + \mu_2' t/1! + \ldots + \mu_r' \frac{t^{r-1}}{(r-1)!} + \ldots$$

and putting $t = 0$,

$$\mu_1' = \left[\frac{dM(t)}{dt}\right]_{t=0} = M'(0), \quad \text{say,}$$

and, in general,

$$\mu_r' = \left[\frac{d^rM(t)}{dt^r}\right]_{t=0} = M^{(r)}(0) \quad . \quad . \quad (3.5.2)$$

For a continuous variate with probability-density $\phi(x)$,

$$M(t) = \mathscr{E}(e^{xt}) = \int_{+\infty}^{+\infty} e^{xt}\phi(x)dx \quad . \quad . \quad (3.5.2a)$$

Compare with 2.14.2.

In the particular case of the *Binomial Distribution*, $G(t) \equiv (q + pt)^n$. Hence $M(t) \equiv (q + pe^t)^n$. Consequently, the mean μ_1', is given by

$$\mu_1' = M'(0) = \left[\frac{d}{dt}\{(q + pe^t)^n\}\right]_{t=0}$$

$$= [npe^t(q + pe^t)^{n-1}]_{t=0}, \text{ which, since } (q + p) = 1, \text{ gives}$$

$$\underline{\mu_1' = np} \quad . \quad . \quad . \quad . \quad . \quad . \quad . \quad . \quad . \quad . \quad . \quad . \quad . \quad (3.5.3)$$

Likewise,

$$\mu_2' = M''(0) = \left[\frac{d^2}{dt}(q + pe^t)^n\right]_{t=0} = \left[\frac{d}{dt}[npe^t(q + pe^t)^{n-1}]\right]_{t=0}$$

$$= [npe^t(q + pe^t)^{n-1} + n(n-1)p^2e^{2t}(q + pe^t)^{n-2}]_{t=0}$$

$$= np + n(n-1)p^2 = \mu_1' + n(n-1)p^2$$

Therefore, the *second moment about the mean*, the variance of the distribution, μ_2, is given by

$$\underline{\mu_2} = \mu_2' - (\mu_1')^2 = np + n(n-1)p^2 - n^2p^2 = np(1-p) = \underline{npq} \quad . \quad (3.5.4)$$

The mean of the Binomial distribution is *np* and the variance is *npq*.

Exercise : *Show that* $\mu_3' = np[(n-1)(n-2)p^2 + 3(n-1)p + 1]$.

Generally, however, we are more interested in the *mean-moments* (moments about the mean of a distribution) than in those about $x = 0$. If now we assume that $\mu_1' = M'(0) = m$, say, and transfer the origin to $x = m$, then, measuring the variate from this new origin and calling the new variate so formed, X, we have $x = X + m$. Consequently,

$$\mathscr{E}(e^{xt}) = \mathscr{E}(e^{Xt + mt}) = e^{mt}\mathscr{E}(e^{Xt}),$$

or, if $M_m(t)$ denotes *the mean-moment generating function*,

$$M(t) = e^{mt}M_m(t), \text{ and } M_m(t) = e^{-mt}M(t) \quad . \quad (3.5.5)$$

It follows that the generating function for moments about any line $x = a$ is obtained by multiplying $M(t)$ by e^{-at}, while the rth mean-moment of the distribution, μ_r, is given by

$$\mu_r = \left[\frac{d^r}{dt^r}M_m(t)\right]_{t=0} \equiv M_m^{(r)}(0) . \quad . \quad (3.5.6)$$

Exercise : *Show by direct differentiation that for the binomial distribution :*

$$(i)\ \mu_1 = M_m'(0) \equiv \left[\frac{d}{dt}\{e^{-mt}(q+pe^t)^n\}\right]_{t=0} = 0$$

$$(ii)\ \mu_2 = M_m''(0) \equiv \left[\frac{d^2}{dt}\{e^{-mt}(q+pe^t)^n\}\right]_{t=0} = npq$$

3.6. Fitting a Binomial Distribution. So far we have considered Binomial distributions for which the probability of E in n occurrences of C has been known in advance. In practice this rarely happens. Consider the following example :

Worked Example : *The distribution of headless matches per box of* 50 *in a total of* 100 *boxes is given in the following table* :

No. of headless matches per box.	0	1	2	3	4	5	6	7	Total
No. of boxes .	12	27	29	19	8	4	1	0	100

Let us assume that the distribution of headless matches per box over 100 boxes is binomial. We have $n = 50$, but we have no *a priori* value for p. We remember, however, that the mean is np. If, then, we find the mean of the observed distribution, we can *estimate* p. Thus

$$np = 50p = \frac{0.12 + 1.27 + 2.29 + 3.19 + 4.8 + 5.4 + 6.1}{100}$$

which gives $p = 0{\cdot}04$ and the mean $= 2$. With this value of p, the binomial distribution of frequencies of headless matches per box over 100 boxes is given by

$$100(0{\cdot}96 + 0{\cdot}04t)^{50}.$$

Using the method of **3.4**, the reader should verify that the *estimated* frequencies are those given in the following table :

No. of headless matches per box	0	1	2	3	4	5	6	7
Observed No. of boxes . .	12	27	29	19	8	4	1	0
Estimated No. of boxes . .	12·97	26·99	27·50	18·30	8·95	3·43	1·07	0·28
Estimated No. of boxes (nearest integer) . .	13	27	28	18	9	3	1	0

The "fit" is seen to be quite good. If now we compare the variance of the observed distribution with that of the theoretical, estimated, distribution, we find that, the mean being 2,

(a) *variance of observed distribution*

$$= \frac{12 . (-2)^2 + 27 . (-1)^2 + 19 \cdot 1^2 + 8 \cdot 2^2 + 4 \cdot 3^2 + 1 \cdot 4^2}{100}$$

$$= 1 \cdot 78$$

(b) *variance of theoretical, estimated distribution*

$$= npq = 50 \times 0 \cdot 04 \times 0 \cdot 96 = 1 \cdot 92$$

3.7. "So Many or More". Usually we are more interested in the probability of *at least* so many occurrences of an event, E, in n occasions of $C(E, \bar{E})$ rather than in the probability of exactly so many occurrences of E. Thus our match-manufacturer would, probably, not worry unduly about how many boxes in a batch of 100 contained exactly 4 headless matchsticks, but he might well be concerned to estimate the probable number of boxes containing 4 *or more* headless sticks.

Let $P_n(x \geqslant k)$ denote the probability of k or more occurrences of E in n $C(E, \bar{E})$, and let $P_n(x < k)$ denote the probability of less than k such occurrences. Then the probability of four or more headless matchsticks per box of 50 is denoted by $P_{50}(x \geqslant 4)$. Now

$$P_{50}(x \geqslant 4) = p_{50}(4) + p_{50}(5) + \ldots + p_{50}(50) \equiv \sum_{x=4}^{50} p_{50}(x)$$

Since, however,

$$\sum_{x=0}^{50} p_{50}(x) = 1, P_{50}(x \geqslant 4) = 1 - \sum_{x=0}^{3} p_{50}(x) = 1 - P_{50}(x < 4)$$

Generally,

$$P_n(x \geqslant k) = 1 - P_n(x < k) \quad . \quad . \quad (3.7.1)$$

When k is small and n not too large, this formula is useful, for the calculation of $P_n(x < k)$ is then not too tedious and the successive values $p_n(0), p_n(1), \ldots p_n(k - 1)$ may be evaluated directly using the formula (3.3.1). When n is large and k is large, however, the evaluation of a single binomial probability is tiresome enough, let alone that of the sum of several such probabilities. We may overcome this difficulty by using the facts that:

> when n is large and p is small, the binomial distribution approximates to the Poisson distribution (see next chapter); while

when n is large but p is not small, it approximates to the normal distribution (see Chapter Five).

In such situations we use the properties of these distributions to approximate $P_n(x \geqslant k)$. Alternatively, for $k \leqslant 50$, $n \leqslant 99$ we may use what is known as the *Incomplete Beta Function Ratio*,[1] usually denoted by $I_p(k, n - k + 1)$, which gives the value of $P_n(x \geqslant k)$, for probability, p, of E,

$$P_n(x \geqslant k) = I_p(k, n - k + 1) \quad . \quad . \quad (3.7.2)$$

Tables of the Incomplete B-Function Ratio, edited by Karl Pearson, are published by the Biometrika Office, University College, London.

Mathematical Note to Chapter Three

A. The Gamma Function. If n is positive the infinite integral[2] $\int_0^\infty x^{n-1} \exp(-x)dx$ has a finite value. It is clearly a function of n and is called the *Gamma Function*; we write

$$\Gamma(n) \equiv \int_0^\infty x^{n-1} \exp(-x)dx \quad . \quad . \quad (3.A.1)$$

We have immediately

$$\Gamma(1) \equiv \int_0^\infty \exp(-x)dx = 1 \quad . \quad . \quad (3.A.2)$$

If in (3.A.1) we put $x = X^2$, we have an alternative definition of $\Gamma(n)$, for, writing $dx = 2XdX$, we have

$$\Gamma(n) \equiv 2\int_0^\infty X^{2n-1} \exp(-X^2)dX \quad . \quad (3.A.3)$$

Returning to (3.A.1) and integrating by parts,[3] we have, if $n > 1$,

$$\Gamma(n) = \Big[-x^{n-1} \exp(-x)\Big]_0^\infty + (n-1)\int_0^\infty x^{n-2} \exp(-x)dx$$
$$= (n-1)\Gamma(n-1) \quad (3.A.4)$$

[1] See Note at end of this chapter.
[2] See P. Abbott, *Teach Yourself Calculus*, pp. 227 *et seq.*
[3] Abbott, *op. cit.*, pp. 188 *et seq.*

Applying this formula to the case *where* n *is a positive integer*, we have

$$\Gamma(n) = (n-1)(n-2) \ldots 2.1\Gamma(1) \equiv (n-1)! \quad . \quad . \quad . \quad (3.A.5)$$

B. The Beta Function. Next consider the integral $\int_0^1 x^{m-1}(1-x)^{n-1}dx$. If m and n are positive, this integral is finite and is a function of m and n. We call this function the *Beta Function* and write

$$B(m, n) \equiv \int_0^1 x^{m-1}(1-x)^{n-1}dx \quad . \quad (3.B.1)$$

Clearly, $B(1, 1) = 1 \quad . \quad . \quad . \quad . \quad . \quad . \quad (3.B.2)$

Now put $z = 1 - x$, then $dz = -dx$

and

$$B(m, n) = -\int_1^0 (1-z)^{m-1}z^{n-1}dz = \int_0^1 z^{n-1}(1-z)^{m-1}dz[1] = B(n, m) \quad (3.B.3)$$

Thus we see that the Beta Function is symmetrical in m and n. Now make another substitution, $x = \sin^2\phi$, $dx = 2\sin\phi\cos\phi d\phi$. When $x = 0$, $\phi = 0$ and when $x = 1$, $\phi = \pi/2$. Thus

$$B(m, n) = 2\int_0^{\pi/2} \sin^{2m-1}\phi \cos^{2n-1}\phi d\phi \quad . \quad (3.B.4)$$

a useful alternative form. It follows at once that

$$B(\tfrac{1}{2}, \tfrac{1}{2}) = 2\int_0^{\pi/2} d\phi = \pi \quad . \quad . \quad (3.B.5)$$

C. Relation between Gamma and Beta Functions. It can be shown that $B(m, n)$ and $\Gamma(m)$ and $\Gamma(n)$ are related by the formula

$$B(m, n) = \frac{\Gamma(m) \, . \, \Gamma(n)}{\Gamma(m+n)} \quad . \quad . \quad . \quad (3.C.1)$$

which immediately displays the symmetry of the B-function in m and n. It follows that, since $B(\tfrac{1}{2}, \tfrac{1}{2}) = \pi$ and $\Gamma(1) = 1$

$$B(\tfrac{1}{2}, \tfrac{1}{2}) = (\Gamma(\tfrac{1}{2}))^2 \text{ or } \Gamma(\tfrac{1}{2}) = \sqrt{\pi} \quad . \quad (3.C.2)$$

[1] Abbott, *op. cit.*, p. 225.

But, using (3.A.3), we have

$$\Gamma(\tfrac{1}{2}) = 2\int_0^\infty \exp\,(-x^2)dx.$$

Consequently

$$\int_0^\infty \exp\,(-x^2)dx = \tfrac{1}{2}\sqrt{\pi} \quad . \quad . \quad . \quad (3.C.3)$$

a result we shall need later.

D. The Incomplete B-function Ratio. We have seen that if the function $x^{m-1}(1-x)^{n-1}$ is integrated over the range (0, 1) the result is a function of m and n. Suppose now that we integrate over only a portion of the range, from 0 to t, say, then $B_t(m, n) \equiv \int_0^t x^{m-1}(1-x)^{n-1}dx$ is a function of t, m and n and is called the *Incomplete B-Function*. Dividing this incomplete B-function by the complete B-function gives us another function of t, m and n, called the *Incomplete B-Function Ratio,* to which we referred in 3.7. We denote it by $I_t(m, n)$ and write

$$I_t(m, n) \equiv B_t(m, n)/B(m, n) = \frac{\Gamma(m+n)}{\Gamma(m)\,.\,\Gamma(n)}\int_0^t x^{m-1}(1-x)^{n-1}dx$$

If, moreover, m and n are integers,

$$I_t(m, n) = \frac{(m+n-1)!}{(m-1)!\,(n-1)!}\int_0^t x^{m-1}(1-x)^{n-1}\,dx \quad (3.D.1)$$

Now put $t = p$, $m = k$, and $n = n - k + 1$. Then

$$I_p(k, n-k+1) = \frac{n!}{(k-1)!\,(n-k)!}\int_0^p x^{k-1}(1-x)^{n-k}dx \quad (3.D.2)$$

Integrating by parts and putting $q = 1 - p$,

$$\int_0^p x^{k-1}(1-x)^{n-k}dx = \frac{p^k q^{n-k}}{k} + \frac{(n-k)p^{k+1}}{k(k+1)}q^{n-k-1} + \ldots + \frac{(n-k)!}{k(k+1)\ldots(n-1)n}p^n$$

Consequently,

$$I_p(k, n-k+1) = \binom{n}{k} p^k q^{n-k} + \binom{n}{k+1} p^{k+1} q^{n-k-1} + \ldots + p^n$$
$$= p_n(k) + p_n(k+1) + \ldots + p_n(n)$$
$$= P_n(x \geqslant k) \quad . \quad . \quad . \quad . \quad . \quad . \quad . \quad (3.7.2)$$

The Tables of the Incomplete B-function Ratio referred to in 3.7 give the values of $I_t(m, n)$ for $0 \leqslant n \leqslant 50$ and $n \leqslant m \leqslant 50$. The values of t are given in steps of 0·01. Thus if $n > m$ we cannot use the tables directly to evaluate $I_t(m, n)$. However, we can make use of the simple relation

$$I_t(m, n) = 1 - I_{1-t}(n, m) \quad . \quad . \quad (3.D.3)$$

which is easily proved as follows. Writing $x = 1 - X$ in (3.D.1), we have

$$I_t(m, n) = -\frac{(m+n-1)!}{(m-1)!\,(n-1)!}\int_1^{1-t}(1-X)^{m-1}X^{n-1}dX$$

$$= \frac{(m+n-1)!}{(m-1)!\,(n-1)!}\int_{1-t}^1 X^{n-1}(1-X)^{m-1}dX$$

$$= \frac{(m+n-1)!}{(m-1!\,(n-1)!}\left[\int_0^1 X^{n-1}(1-X)^{m-1}dX - \int_0^{1-t} X^{n-1}(1-X)^{m-1}dx\right]$$

$$= 1 - I_{1-t}(n, m)$$

EXERCISES ON CHAPTER III

1. Calculate, correct to the four decimal places, the binomial probabilities for $p = \frac{1}{4}$, $n = 8$. Calculate the mean and variance.

2. If on the average rain falls on twelve days in every thirty, find the probability (i) that the first three days of a given week will be fine, and the remainder wet; (ii) that rain will fall on just three days of a given week. (L.U.)

3. In a book of values of a certain function there is one error on the average in m entries. Prove that when r values are turned up at random (with the possibility that any value may be selected more than once), the chance of all being accurate is $(m-1)/r$ times as great as that of having only one error included in the selection. Find r/m in terms of m in order that there may be a nine to one chance that the selection is free from any errors. In

this case prove that as a very large set of tabulated values approaches perfection in accuracy, r increases to a limiting value of nearly 10·5% of the size of m. (L.U.)

4. Show that a measure of the skewness of the binomial distribution is given by $(q - p)/(npq)^{\frac{1}{2}}$ and its kurtosis is

$$3 + (1 - 6pq)/npq.$$

5. Calculate the value of p if the ratio of the probability of an event happening exactly r times in n trials to the probability of the event happening exactly $n - r$ times in n trials is independent of n. $(0 < p < 1)$. (I.A.)

6. Table 7.1, page 136, gives 500 random digits grouped in 100 groups of 5 digits. Let the digits 0, 1, 2, 3 be each taken as indicating a success, S, in a certain trial and the digits 4, 5, 6, 7, 8, 9 a failure. Working along the rows of the table, count the number of S in each 5-digit group. Form a frequency table giving the number of groups with 0, 1, 2, etc., S's. The theoretical distribution will be given by $100\left(\frac{6}{10} + \frac{4t}{10}\right)^5$. Calculate the theoretical frequencies and compare these with those actually obtained. Repeat using the columns of Table 7.1, i.e., the first five random digits will be 28986. Repeat taking 0, 1, 2 as indicating an S and 3, 4, 5, 6, 7, 8, 9 as indicating failure.

Solutions

1. 0, 0·000; 1, 0·0004; 2, 0·0038; 3, 0·0231; 4, 0·0865; 5, 0·2076; 6. 0·3115; 7, 0·2675; 8, 0·1001.

2. (i) 0·00829; (ii) 0·2903.

3. $r/m = (1/m) \log 0{\cdot}9/\log [(m - 1)/m]$.

5. $p = \frac{1}{2}$.

CHAPTER FOUR

STATISTICAL MODELS. II: THE POISSON DISTRIBUTION: STATISTICAL RARITY

4.1. On Printer's Errors. I am correcting the page-proofs of a book. After having corrected some 50 pages, I find that, on the average, there are 2 errors per 5 pages. How do I set about estimating the percentage of pages in the whole book with 0, 1, 2, 3 . . . errors?

To use the Binomial distribution, we need to know not merely the number of times an event E, whose probability we wish to estimate, has occurred, but also the number of times *it could have occurred but did not*, i.e., we want to know n, the total number of occasions upon which the event both did and did not occur. But in our present problem, it is clearly ridiculous to ask how many times an error could have been made on one page but was not.

Here is a similar problem:

A small mass of a radioactive substance is so placed that each emission of a particle causes a flash on a specially prepared screen. The number of flashes in a given time-interval is recorded, and the mean number of flashes over a specified number of such intervals is found. On the assumption that the disintegration of any particular atom is purely fortuitous, what is the chance of observing some specified number of flashes in one time-interval?

Both these problems arise from situations in which the number, n_i, of occasions upon which an event, E, could or could not have occurred in a fixed interval of time or space is, to all intents and purposes, infinite, although over the N intervals sampled, E in fact is found to have occurred only a finite number of times, Nm, say.

We can use the Binomial distribution as a model only when we can assign values to p and to n. But in such cases as we are now discussing this is not possible: $n = Nn_i$ is indefinitely large because, although N is finite, n_i is indefinitely large. Moreover, although we know the number of times, Nm, E has occurred in the N equal intervals, the ratio Nm/Nn_i, which we could have used, in the event of n_i being known and finite, as an estimate of p, is now meaningless.

4.2. The Poisson Model. We are therefore faced with the

task of so modifying our old model that we can circumvent difficulties of this kind. Our clue is this: if the number, Nm, of occurrences of E is finite in N fixed intervals (of time, length, area, volume) and the n of the Binomial expansion ($= Nn_i$ here) is very, very large, $p(= Nm/Nn_i = m/n_i)$ must be very small. We ask, then, what happens to the Binomial distribution under the conditions that (1) n tends to infinity, but (2) np remains finite, and thus p is extremely small (i.e., the event is relatively rare)?

The probability-generating function of the Binomial distribution is $(q + pt)^n$. Put $np = m$ and, in accord with this, $q = 1 - m/n$. Then the p.g.f. becomes $(1 + m(t - 1)/n)^n$ and this (see Abbott, *Teach Yourself Calculus*, p. 127) tends to the limit $e^{m(t-1)}$ as n tends to infinity. Thus under the conditions set down, *the probability-generating function of the new, limit-distribution, is* $e^{m(t-1)}$. This new distribution is called the *Poisson Distribution*. We have

$$e^{m(t-1)} = e^{-m} . e^{mt} = e^{-m}(1 + mt/1! + m^2t^2/2! + \ldots + m^rt^r/r! + \ldots)$$

The probability of exactly x occurrences of a statistically rare event in an interval of a stated length will then be the coefficient of t^x in this series, thus

$$p(x, m) = e^{-m}m^x/x! \quad . \quad . \quad . \quad (4.2.1)$$

We note at once:

(i) that it is theoretically possible for any number of events to occur in an interval; and
(ii) that the probability of *either* 0 *or* 1 *or* 2 *or* . . . occurrences of the event in the interval is

$$e^{-m}(1 + m/1! + m^2/2! + \ldots + m^r/r! + \ldots) = e^{-m} . e^m = 1,$$ as we should expect.

4.3. Some Properties of the Poisson Distribution. (*a*) What exactly does the m in (4.2.1) signify? Since we have derived the Poisson distribution from the Binomial by putting $p = m/n$ and letting n tend to infinity, we shall obtain the Poisson Mean and the Poisson variance by operating in the same way on the Binomial mean, np, and the Binomial variance, npq. Thus we have

Poisson Mean

$$= \underset{n\to\infty}{\text{Limit}}\ np = \underset{n\to\infty}{\text{Limit}}\ n . m/n = m \quad . \quad . \quad . \quad . \quad (4.3.1)$$

Poisson Variance

$$= \underset{n \to \infty}{\text{Limit}}\ npq = \underset{n \to \infty}{\text{Limit}}\ n \,.\, m/n \,.\, (1 - m/n) = m \,. \qquad (4.3.2)$$

Thus we see that the m in (4.2.1) is the value of both the mean and the variance of the new distribution.

(*b*) *Higher moments of the distribution* may be worked out by using 3.5.2. Since $G(t) = e^{m(t-1)}$, it follows that the moment-generating function is given by

$$M(t) = \exp\,[m(e^t - 1)] \quad . \quad . \quad . \quad (4.3.3)$$

and the mean-moment generating function by

$$M_m(t) = e^{-mt} \,.\, \exp\,[m(e^t - 1)] \quad . \quad . \quad (4.3.4)$$

We have, for example,

$$\mu_2' = M''(0) = \left[\frac{d^2}{dt^2} \exp\,(m(e^t - 1))\right]_{t=0}$$

$$= \left[\frac{d}{dt}\{M(t)me^t\}\right]_{t=0} = [M(t)me^t + me^tM'(t)]_{t=0}$$

$$= mM(0) + mM'(0) = m(m + 1).$$

(*c*) To ease the work of calculating Poisson probabilities, we note that :

$$p(x + 1, m) = e^{-m} \,.\, m^{x+1}/(x + 1)\,! = \frac{m}{x + 1} \cdot p(x, m) \quad (4.3.5)$$

where $p(0) = e^{-m}$. For convenience we give the following table :

TABLE 4.3. *Values of* e^{-m}

m.	e^{-m}.	m.	e^{-m}.	m.	e^{-m}.
0·01	0·9900	0·1	0·9048	1·0	0·3679
0·02	0·9802	0·2	0·8187	2·0	0·1353
0·03	0·9704	0·3	0·7408	3·0	0·0498
0·04	0·9608	0·4	0·6703	4·0	0·0183
0·05	0·9512	0·5	0·6065	5·0	0·0067
0·06	0·9418	0·6	0·5488	6·0	0·0025
0·07	0·9324	0·7	0·4966	7·0	0·0009
0·08	0·9231	0·8	0·4493	8·0	0·0003
0·09	0·9139	0·9	0·4066	9·0	0·0001

NOTE : Since $e^{-(x+y+z)} = e^{-x} \,.\, e^{-y} \,.\, e^{-z}$, we see that, if we *have* to use this table, $e^{-5\cdot 23}$, for example, $= 0\cdot 0067 \times 0\cdot 8187 \times 0\cdot 9704 = 0\cdot 0053$.

(*d*) Fig. 4.3. shows probability polygons for $m = 0{\cdot}1$ and $m = 3{\cdot}0$. It will be seen that when $m < 1$, the polygon is *positively* J-*shaped*, but, when $m > 1$, it becomes *positively skew*, tending towards symmetry as m assumes larger and

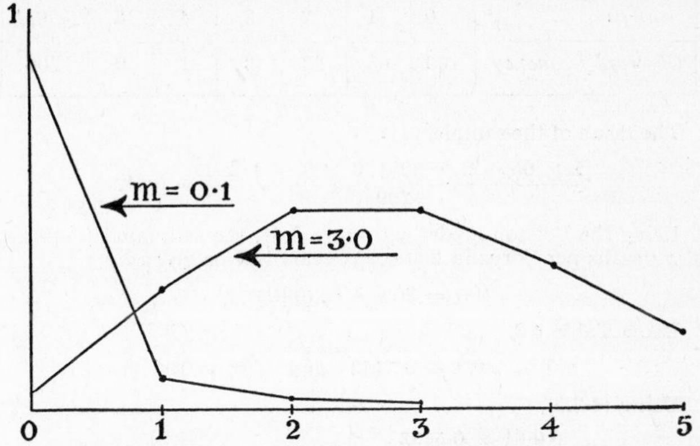

FIG. 4.3.—Poisson Probability Polygons.

larger values. From (4.3.5), it follows that $p(x)$ increases with x, for $m > 1$, while $x < m - 1$ and, thereafter, decreases.

4.4. Worked Examples

1. *Consider the proof-correcting problem discussed at the beginning of this chapter. m, the mean, is here* 0·4. *Consequently using Table* 4.3 *and formula* (4.3.5), *the probabilities of* 0, 1, 2, 3 . . . *errors per page based on the* 50 *pages sampled are* :

x . .	0	1	2	3	4
$p(x)$.	0·6703	0·2681	0·0536	0·0071	0·0007

Thus, in 100 pages, we should expect 67 pages with 0 errors, 27 pages with 1 error, 5 pages with 2 errors and 1 page with 3 errors.

2. *This is a classical example, but sufficiently entertaining to bear repetition.*

Bortkewitsch collected data on the number of deaths from kicks from a horse in 10 *Prussian Army Corps over a period of* 20 *years. It is assumed that relevant conditions remained sufficiently stable over this period for the probability of being kicked to death to remain constant.*

His figures are :

Actual deaths per corps . .	0	1	2	3	4	5	*Total*
Observed frequency	109	65	22	3	1	0	200

The mean of the sample, m is

$$\frac{1 \times 65 + 2 \times 22 + 3 \times 3 + 4 \times 1}{200} = 0{\cdot}61.$$

Using the Poisson model with $m = 0{\cdot}61$, the estimated frequency of x deaths per Corps in 200 corps-years will be given by

$$f(x) = 200e^{-0{\cdot}61} \,.\, (0{\cdot}61)^x/x!$$

Using Table 4.3,

$$p(0) = e^{-0{\cdot}61} = 0{\cdot}5433 \quad \text{and} \quad f(0) = 108{\cdot}66$$

Using (4·3.5),

$$p(1) = \frac{0{\cdot}61 \times 0{\cdot}5433}{1} = 0{\cdot}3314 \quad \text{and} \quad f(1) = 66{\cdot}28$$

$$p(2) = \frac{0{\cdot}61 \times 0{\cdot}3314}{2} = 0{\cdot}1011 \quad \text{and} \quad f(2) = 20{\cdot}22$$

$$p(3) = \frac{0{\cdot}61 \times 0{\cdot}1011}{3} = 0{\cdot}0206 \quad \text{and} \quad f(3) = 4{\cdot}12$$

$$p(4) = \frac{0{\cdot}61 \times 0{\cdot}0206}{4} = 0{\cdot}0031 \quad \text{and} \quad f(4) = 0{\cdot}62$$

$$p(5) = \frac{0{\cdot}61 \times 0{\cdot}0031}{5} = 0{\cdot}0004 \quad \text{and} \quad f(5) = 0{\cdot}008$$

The " fit " is good.

4.5. Approximation to Binomial Distribution. Being the limit of the Binomial distribution, when p becomes very small (the event is rare) and n tends to infinity, the Poisson distribution may be expected to provide a useful approximation to such a Binomial distribution. Moreover, it is much easier to calculate $e^{-m}m^x/x!$ than it is to calculate $\binom{n}{x} p^x q^{n-x}$.

Suppose we have a consignment of 1,000 cartons, each carton containing 100 electric light bulbs. Sampling reveals an average of 1 bulb per 100 defective.

If we use the Binomial model, with $p = \frac{1}{100}$, $q = \frac{99}{100}$ and $n = 100$, probability of x defectives in 100 bulbs will be given by

$$p_{100}(x) = \binom{100}{x}(1/100)^x(99/100)^{100-x}$$

and $$p_{100}(x+1) = \frac{100-x}{99(x+1)} \cdot p_{100}(x)$$

Since the occurrence of a defective bulb is a rare event, we may use the Poisson model. In this case $m = np = 1$ and so

$$p(x, 1) = e^{-1}/x! \quad \text{while} \quad p(x+1)/p(x) = 1/(x+1).$$

The following table results :

No. defectives per 100 . .	0	1	2	3	4	5	6
Binomial model .	36·64	37·01	18·51	6·11	1·49	0·29	0·05
Poisson model .	36·79	36·79	18·40	6·13	1·53	0·31	0·05

The reader should check these figures as an exercise.

4.6. The Poisson Probability Chart. As we saw when discussing Binomial probabilities, we frequently require to know the probability of so many or more occurrences of an event. It follows from (4.2.1) that the probability of k or more events in any interval, when the mean number of occurrences in a sample set of such intervals is m, will be given by

$$P(x \geqslant k, m) = \sum_{x=k}^{\infty} e^{-m}m^x/x! \quad . \quad . \quad (4.6.1)$$

To avoid having to calculate successive terms of this series, we use the Poisson Probability Chart of Fig. 4.6. On the horizontal axis are values of m; across the chart are a series of curves corresponding to values of $k = 1, 2, 3, \ldots$; while along the vertical axis are values of $P(x \geqslant k, m)$.

In the case considered in 4.5, $m = 1$. If we want to find the probability that a given batch of 100 bulbs shall contain 2 or more defectives, we run our eye up the line $m = 1$ until it intersects the curve $k = 2$; then, moving horizontally to the left, we find the required probability marked on the vertical

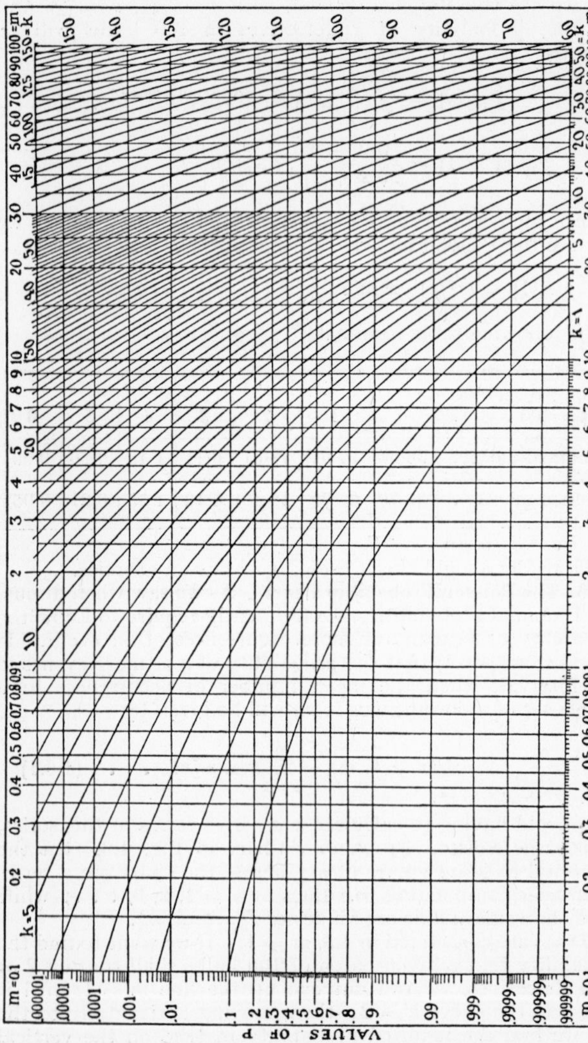
VALUES OF P
m = 0.1
100 = m
k = 1
k = 5
150 = k
50 = k
.000001
.00001
.0001
.001
.01
.1
.2
.3
.4
.5
.6
.7
.8
.9
.99
.999
.9999
.99999
.999999

FIG. 4.6.

axis—in this case 0·26. This means that of the 1,000 batches of 100 bulbs about 260 will contain 2 or more defectives.

We could have arrived at this result by recalling that the probability of 2 or more defectives is

$$\begin{aligned} P(x \geqslant 2, 1) &= 1 - (p(0) + p(1)) \\ &= 1 - (0{\cdot}3679 + 0{\cdot}3679) \\ &= 0{\cdot}2642. \end{aligned}$$

We may also use the chart to find approximately the probability of an exact number of defectives, 2, say. We have already used the chart to find $P(x \geqslant 2, 1) = 0{\cdot}26$. In a similar way we find that $P(x \geqslant 3, 1) = 0{\cdot}08$, approximately. Therefore, $p(2) = 0{\cdot}26 - 0{\cdot}08 = 0{\cdot}18$, approximately. The calculated value is, as we have seen, 0·1840.

4.7. The Negative Binomial Distribution. We have derived the Poisson distribution from the Binomial, and a necessary condition for the Binomial distribution to hold is that the probability, p, of an event E shall remain constant for all occurrences of its context-event C. Thus this condition must also hold for the Poisson distribution. But it does not follow that, if a set of observed frequencies is fairly closely approximated by some Poisson series, p is in fact constant, although, in certain circumstances, this may be a not unreasonable inference. If, however, it is known that p is not constant in its context C, another distribution, known as the Negative Binomial distribution, may provide an even closer " fit ".

Suppose we have a Binomial distribution for which the variance, npq, is greater than the mean, np. Then q must be greater than 1, and since $p = 1 - q$, p must be negative. But np being positive, n must be negative also. Writing $n = -N$ and $p = -P$, the p.g.f. for such a distribution will be

$$G(t) \equiv (q - Pt)^{-N}$$

The trouble about this type of distribution lies in the interpretation, for we have defined probability in such a way that its measure must always be a number lying between 0 and 1 and, so, essentially positive. Again, since n is the number of context-events, how can it possibly be negative?

Any detailed discussion of this problem is beyond our scope, but the following points may be noted :

(1) It is often found that observed frequency distributions are represented by negative binomials and in some cases that this should be the case can be theoretically justified

(G. U. Yule, *Journal of the Royal Statistical Society*, vol. 73, pp. 26 *et seq.*).

(2) In many cases, if two or more Poisson series are combined term by term, a negative binomial results.

(3) Frequency distributions with variance greater than the mean often arise when the probability p does not remain constant.

We conclude this section with an example of a kind fairly common in bacteriology, where, although a Poisson distribution might reasonably be expected to hold, a negative binomial gives a better fit.

The following table gives the number of yeast cells in 400 squares of a hæmacytometer :

Number of cells	0	1	2	3	4	5	Total
Frequency .	213	128	37	18	3	1	400

The mean is 0·68 and the variance 0·81, both correct to two decimal places. Putting $np = 0{\cdot}68$ and $npq = 0{\cdot}81$, we have $q = 1{\cdot}19$ and, so, $p = -0{\cdot}19$ and $n = -3{\cdot}59$. The p.g.f. is thus $(1{\cdot}19 - 0{\cdot}19t)^{-3{\cdot}59}$. Hence

$$p(x+1) = \frac{3{\cdot}59 + x}{x+1} \cdot \frac{0{\cdot}19}{1{\cdot}19} \cdot p(x)$$

Calculating these probabilities and comparing them with those obtained from a Poisson model with $m = 0{\cdot}68$, we have

No. of cells . .	0	1	2	3	4	5
Observed frequency .	213	128	37	18	3	1
Negative binomial .	214	123	45	13	4	1
Poisson	203	138	47	11	2	0

EXERCISES ON CHAPTER FOUR

1. Rutherford and Geiger counted the number of alpha-particles emitted from a disc in 2,608 periods of 7·5 seconds duration. The frequencies are given below :

Number per period.	Frequency.	Number per period.	Frequency.
0	57	8	45
1	203	9	27
2	383	10	10
3	525	11	4
4	532	12	2
5	408	13	0
6	273	14	0
7	139		

Show that the mean of the distribution is 3·870 and compare the relative frequencies with the corresponding probabilities of the "fitted" Poisson distribution.

2. If on the average m particles are emitted from a piece of radioactive material in 1 second, what is the probability that there will be a lapse of t seconds between 2 consecutive emissions?

3. A car-hire firm has two cars, which it hires out by the day. The number of demands for a car on each day is distributed as a Poisson distribution with mean 1·5. Calculate the proportion of days on which neither of the cars is used, and the proportion of days on which some demand is refused. If each car is used an equal amount, on what proportion of days is a given one of the cars not in use? What proportion of demands has to be refused? (R.S.S.)

4. Show that the sum of two Poisson variates is itself a Poisson variate with mean equal to the sum of the separate means.

5. Pearson and Morel (*Ann. Eugenics*, Vol. 1, 1925) give the following table showing the number of boys at given ages possessing 0, 1, 2, 3 . . . defective teeth:

Number of teeth affected.	Central ages (years).					Total.
	$7\frac{5}{24}$	$8\frac{17}{24}$	$10\frac{5}{24}$	$11\frac{17}{24}$	$13\frac{5}{24}$	
0	12	16	27	61	67	183
1	4	14	13	47	69	147
2	6	23	28	43	50	150
3	4	11	20	35	41	111

Number of teeth affected.	Central ages (years).					Total.
	$7\frac{5}{24}$	$8\frac{17}{24}$	$10\frac{5}{24}$	$11\frac{17}{24}$	$13\frac{5}{24}$	
4	7	21	14	28	22	92
5	5	15	7	15	10	52
6	3	16	7	20	8	54
7	4	5	3	5	2	19
8	4	11	5	5	7	32
9	1	6	—	2	3	12
10	1	4	1	1	1	8
11	—	2	—	2	—	
12	1	1	—	1	2	5
Totals	52	145	125	265	282	869

Estimate the probability of a defective tooth for each age group. Plot this probability against age. Fit a negative binomial to each age group and also to the total. Fit a Poisson distribution to any group and to the total. Comment on your findings. (E.S.E.1)

Solutions

2. *Complete Solution* : If there are on the average m emissions in 1 second, there will be $m\delta t$ on the average in δt seconds. The probability of no emissions in δt will then be $\exp(-m\delta t)$ and that of 1 emission $e^{-m\delta t}m\delta t$. Therefore the probability of 0 emissions in n intervals of δt and of 1 in the next such interval will be

$$\delta p = \exp(-mn\delta t)\exp(-m\delta t)m\delta t.$$

Let

$$n\delta t \to t \text{ as } n \to \infty \text{ and } \delta t \to 0, \text{ and we have } \frac{dp}{dt} = me^{-mt}$$

or

$$dp = me^{-mt}\,dt.$$

3. 0·223; 0·191; 0·390; 0·187.

4. We use the fact (see Chapter Two) that the generating function of the sum of two independent variates is the product of the generating functions of the two variates. The m.g.f. of a Poisson variate with mean m_1 is $\exp(m_1(t-1))$; that of a Poisson variate with mean m_2 is $\exp(m_2(t-1))$. Hence the m.g.f. of the sum of these two variates is $\exp(m_1+m_2)(t-1)$, i.e., that of a Poisson variate whose mean is the sum of the separate means.

CHAPTER FIVE

STATISTICAL MODELS
III : THE NORMAL DISTRIBUTION

5.1. Continuous Distributions. So far our model distributions have been those of a *discrete variate*. Put rather crudely : up till now we have been concerned with the distribution of "countables". Now we must consider distributions of what, equally crudely, we may call "measurables", or *continuous variates*.

Table 5.1 shows the distribution of heights of National Servicemen born in 1933 (mostly aged about 18 years 3 months).

TABLE 5.1

(From "Heights and Weights of the Army Intake, 1951", by S. Rosenbaum (Directorate of Army Health), *Journal of the Royal Statistical Society*, Series A, vol. 117, Part 3, 1954.)

Height (in.).	Number.
59 and under	23
60–	169
61–	439
62–	1,030
63–	2,116
64–	3,947
65–	5,965
66–	8,012
67–	9,089
68–	8,763
69–	7,132
70–	5,314
71–	3,320
72–	1,884
73–	876
74–	383
75–	153
76–	63
77 and over	25
Total	58,703

The heights, we are told, were only taken to whole inches, the 67-in. class representing heights from $66\frac{7}{8}$in. to $67\frac{7}{8}$ in.

Smaller class intervals could, of course, have been taken. In such a case, some of the classes might well have been null or empty. But, had the total number of men been indefinitely increased, there is theoretically no reason why any of these classes should have been null. By increasing the size of our sample and reducing the class interval, we make the steps of our histogram narrower and shallower.

The fact remains, however, that all measurement is approximate. We never, in fact, measure the "true value" of any quantity. No matter how fine our unit of measurement, the most we can ever say is that "the height" of a certain man, for instance, lies within some specified interval. The smaller our unit, the smaller, of course, that interval will be, but there will always be an interval. In practice, of course, we cannot reduce the interval indefinitely, for, below a certain limit, that which we are attempting to "measure" no longer exhibits "definite" boundaries. If, however, we idealise the situation and ignore the existence of such a lower limit, then we can conceive of a position such that, no matter how small our interval, there will always be at least one value of our variate, whatever it is, lying within that interval. For instance, we can conceive of an infinite population of heights such that, no matter how small we chose our class intervals, there will always be at least one height lying within each interval. We then say that our variate (height in this case) varies continuously, and we come to the idea of a *continuous distribution*, where the relative frequency of the variate varies continuously as the variate itself varies continuously over its range.

Such a distribution is essentially ideal, but we may regard any actual finite sample of measured quantities as a sample from such an infinite, continuous parent population of measurable items.

One of the most important continuous distributions is that to which the distribution of heights in Table 5.1 approximates. It is called the *Normal distribution*. In his book *The Advanced Theory of Statistics*, M. G. Kendall has commented as follows:

> "The normal distribution has had a curious history. It was first discovered by de Moivre in 1753 as the limiting form of the binomial, but was apparently forgotten and rediscovered later in the eighteenth century by workers engaged in investigating the theory of probability and the theory of errors. The discovery that errors ought, on certain plausible hypotheses, to be distributed normally led to a general belief that they *were* so distributed. . . .

Vestiges of this dogma are still found in textbooks. It was found in the latter half of the nineteenth century that the frequency distributions occurring in practice are rarely of the normal type and it seemed that the normal distribution was due to be discarded as a representation of natural phenomena. But as the importance of the distribution declined in the observational sphere it grew in the theoretical, particularly in the theory of sampling. It is in fact found that many of the distributions arising in that theory are either normal or sufficiently close to normality to permit satisfactory approximations by the use of the normal distribution. . . . For these and other reasons . . . the normal distribution is pre-eminent among distributions of statistical theory " (vol. I, pp. 131–2).

5.2. From the Binomial to the Normal Distribution. Consider two adjacent cells of a Binomial *relative-frequency* histogram (Fig. 5.2). We take the equal class-intervals to be unit intervals and the mid-point of each interval to correspond to the appropriate value of the variate. The relative-frequency of any one value of the variate is then represented by the area of the corresponding cell. Let the height of the cell corresponding to the value x of the variate be y_x. Then, since the class-intervals are unit intervals, the relative-frequency of the value x of our variate will be y_x. When the value of the variate changes from x to $x + 1$, the corresponding increase in the relative frequency is $y_{x+1} - y_x$. Denoting the increase in y_x corresponding to an increase of Δx ($= 1$) by Δy_x, we may write

$$\frac{\Delta y_x}{\Delta x} = y_x(y_{x+1}/y_x - 1)$$

The relative-frequency of the value x of a binomial variate is precisely the probability of exactly x occurrences of an event E in n occurrences of $C(E, \bar{E})$, i.e., $y_x = p_n(x)$. Consequently,

$$\frac{\Delta y_x}{\Delta x} = y_x\left[\frac{p_n(x+1)}{p_n(x)} - 1\right]$$

and, using (3.3.1),

$$= y_x\left[\frac{n-x}{x+1}\cdot\frac{p}{q} - 1\right] = y_x\left[\frac{np - xp - xq - q}{q(x+1)}\right]$$

$$\text{or } \frac{\Delta y_x}{\Delta x} = y_x\left[\frac{p(n+1)}{q(x+1)} - \frac{1}{q}\right], \text{ since } p + q = 1 \quad . \quad . \quad (5.2.1)$$

The Binomial mean is np, and if we transfer our origin of co-ordinates to the mean value of our variate, our new variate will be $X = x - np$. Thus we may put $x = X + np$, where X is the deviation of the original variate from its mean value.

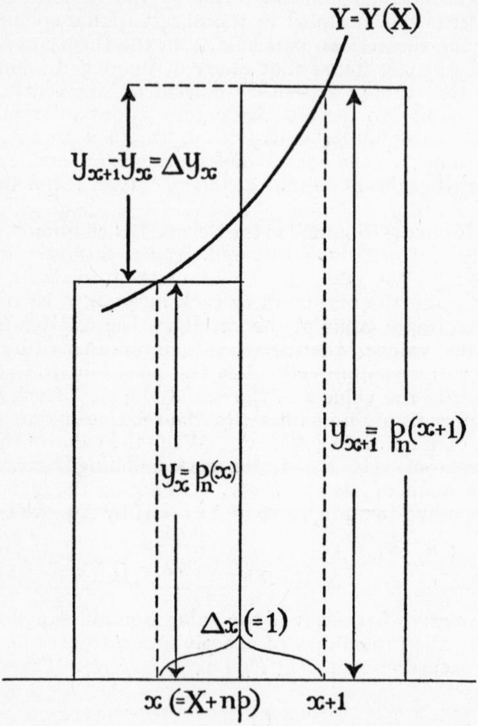

FIG. 5.2.

Moreover, $p_n(X) = p_n(x)$ and so $y_X = y_x$, while ΔX being still unity is equal to Δx. Therefore,

$$\Delta y_X/\Delta X = y_X\left[\frac{p(n+1)}{q(X+np+1)} - \frac{1}{q}\right] \quad . \quad (5.2.2)$$

But when n is large and p is not of the order $1/n$, both p and 1 are small compared with np.

Thus
$$\Delta y_X/\Delta X \simeq y_X\left[\frac{np}{q(X + np)} - \frac{1}{q}\right]$$
$$\simeq y_X(1/(1 + X/np)q - 1/q)$$

Now let $Y = Y(X)$ be the equation of a suitable continuous curve fitted to the vertices of the Binomial relative frequency polygon. Then we may put

$$\frac{dY}{dX} \simeq \frac{\Delta Y}{\Delta X} = \frac{\Delta y_X}{\Delta X} \simeq y_X\left[\frac{1}{q(1 + X/np)} - \frac{1}{q}\right]$$

or
$$\frac{1}{Y}\frac{dY}{dX} \simeq \frac{1}{q}\left[\frac{1}{1 + X/np} - 1\right]. \quad . \quad . \quad . \quad . \quad (5.2.3)$$

Integrating from $X = 0$ to $X = X$ (see Abbott, *Teach Yourself Calculus*, p. 158),

$$\log_e Y = \frac{np}{q}\log_e(1 + X/np) - X/q + \log_e Y_0 \quad . \quad (5.2.4)$$

where Y_0 is the value of Y at $X = 0$, i.e., the value of Y at the mean of the distribution.

Over the greater portion of the curve $Y = Y(X)$, X will be small compared with np. Since we are approximating, anyway, we may, therefore, expand $\log_e(1 + X/np)$ in terms of X/np (see Abbott, *op. cit.*, p. 332) and neglect powers of X/np greater than the second; thus

$$\log_e(1 + X/np) \simeq X/np - X^2/2n^2p^2$$

(5.2.4) then becomes

$$\log_e(Y/Y_0) \simeq \frac{np}{q}(X/np - X^2/2n^2p^2) - X/q = - X^2/2npq$$

or
$$Y \simeq Y_0 \exp(- X^2/2npq) \quad . \quad . \quad . \quad . \quad . \quad (5.2.5)$$

Let us be quite sure what this equation says. For positive and negative integral values of X ($X = 0, \pm 1, \pm 2, \pm 3 \ldots$) it gives us the approximate relative-frequency, or probability, $Y\Delta X = Y$ ($\because \Delta X = 1$), with which the variate assumes the value X. But we have not yet reached the *continuous distribution* to which the binomial distribution tends as n increases indefinitely and as the class intervals diminish indefinitely. For values of X not positive or negative integers (5.2.5) is meaningless. And, in any case, the formula, as it stands, is valueless, since we have not evaluated Y_0. Clearly, Y_0 is the probability that X assumes the value 0, or, what is the same, that x assumes its mean value np. This, by (3.2.1), gives

$$Y_0 = \frac{n!}{np!\,(n - np)!} \cdot p^{np} \cdot q^{(n-np)}$$

$$= \frac{n!}{np!\,nq!} \cdot p^{np} \cdot q^{nq} \quad . \quad (5.2.6)$$

When N is large, we have an approximation, named after Stirling, for $N!$

$$N! \simeq \sqrt{2\pi N} \cdot N^N \cdot e^{-N} \quad . \quad . \quad . \quad (5.2.7)$$

(see Nicholson, *Fundamentals and Techniques of Mathematics for Scientists*, p. 363). Using this approximation for $n!$, $np!$ and $nq!$ in (5.2.6), the reader will verify that, with some easy simplification, this gives $Y_0 \simeq 1/(2\pi npq)^{\frac{1}{2}}$, Therefore,

$$Y \simeq \frac{1}{\sqrt{2\pi npq}} \exp\left(-X^2/2\sigma^2\right) \quad . \quad . \quad (5.2.8)$$

5.3. The Normal Probability Function. We now replace X in 5.2.8 by $zn^{\frac{1}{2}}$. This has the effect of replacing the unit class-interval of the X-distribution by one of $n^{-\frac{1}{2}}$ for the new z-distribution. Thus, as n increases, the internal for z, corresponding to unit interval for X, diminishes. Furthermore, the probability that X lies in a particular unit interval will be the probability that z lies in the z-interval corresponding to that particular X-interval, and this is $Y\Delta X = \frac{1}{\sqrt{2\pi npq}} \exp\left(-X^2/2npq\right) \cdot \Delta X$. But $\Delta X = n^{\frac{1}{2}} \cdot \Delta z$, and so the probability of z lying in the interval Δz is $\frac{1}{\sqrt{2\pi npq}} \exp\left(-z^2/2pq\right) \cdot n^{\frac{1}{2}}\Delta z$, i.e.,

$$\frac{1}{\sqrt{2\pi pq}} \exp\left(-z^2/2pq\right) \cdot \Delta z$$

Calling this probability $\Delta p(z)$, we have

$$\frac{\Delta p(z)}{\Delta z} \simeq \frac{1}{\sqrt{2\pi pq}} \exp\left(-z^2/2pq\right)$$

or, as n tends to infinity,

$$\frac{dp(z)}{dz} = \frac{1}{\sqrt{2\pi pq}} \exp\left(-z^2/2pq\right)$$

Now npq was the variance of the original Binomial distribution. Since we have put $z = Xn^{-\frac{1}{2}}$, the variance of the new continuous distribution of z will be pq. Calling this σ^2, we have the probability density of the new distribution

$$\phi(x) = \frac{1}{\sigma\sqrt{2\pi}} \exp\left(-x^2/2\sigma^2\right) \quad . \quad . \quad (5.3.1)$$

This is the Normal probability density function, defining the *Normal distribution.*

5.4. Some Properties of the Normal Distribution.

(*a*) The range of a normally distributed variate with zero mean and variance σ^2 is from $-\infty$ to $+\infty$.

(*b*) When the mean of the distribution is at $x = \mu$, the p.d.f. is

$$\phi(x) = \frac{1}{\sigma\sqrt{2\pi}} \exp\left(-(x-\mu)^2/2\sigma^2\right) \quad . \quad (5.4.1)$$

(*c*) The equation of the probability curve referred to its

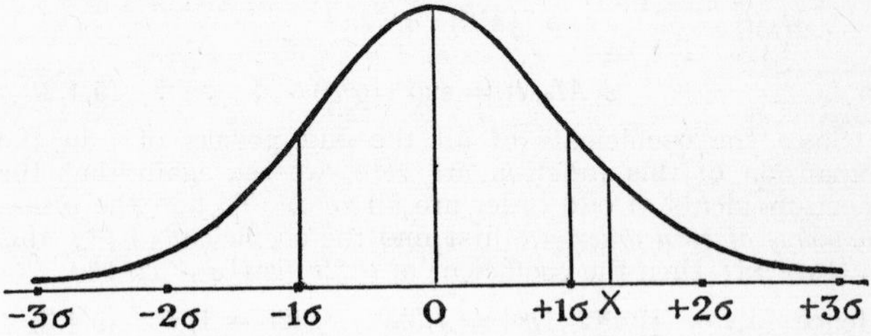

FIG. 5.4.1.—Normal Distribution.

mean as origin, the continuous curve, to which the binomial distribution approximates when n is very large, is

$$y = \phi(x)$$

this curve is symmetrical (since $\phi(-x) = \phi(x)$), unimodal (mode, median and mean coincide) and such that y decreases rapidly as the numerical value of x increases.

(*d*) It follows from the symmetry of the distribution that *the mean-moments of odd order are all zero.* Since $\phi(x)$ is an even function of x, $x^{2r+1}\phi(x)$ is an odd function and, consequently,

$$\mu_{2r+1} = \int_{-\infty}^{+\infty} x^{2r+1}\phi(x)dx = 0$$

(*e*) The *mean-moment generating function* is

$$M_m(t) \equiv \mathcal{E}(e^{tx}) = \int_{-\infty}^{+\infty} e^{tx}\phi(x)dx$$

$$= \frac{1}{\sigma\sqrt{2\pi}}\int_{-\infty}^{+\infty} \exp\,[tx - x^2/2\sigma^2]dx$$

$$= \frac{1}{\sigma\sqrt{2\pi}}\int_{-\infty}^{+\infty} \exp\left[-\frac{1}{2\sigma^2}(x^2 - 2\sigma^2xt + \sigma^4t^2) + \frac{\sigma^2t^2}{2}\right]dx$$

$$= \frac{1}{\sigma\sqrt{2\pi}}\exp\,(\tfrac{1}{2}\sigma^2t^2)\int_{-\infty}^{+\infty} \exp\left[-\frac{1}{2\sigma^2}\,(x - \sigma^2t)^2\right]dx$$

$$= \frac{1}{\sigma\sqrt{2\pi}}\exp\,(\tfrac{1}{2}\sigma^2t^2)\int_{-\infty}^{+\infty} \exp\,(-\,y^2/2\sigma^2)dy$$

where $y = x - \sigma^2t$.

$$\therefore M_m(t) = \frac{1}{\sigma\sqrt{2\pi}}\exp\,(\tfrac{1}{2}\sigma^2t^2)\,.\,\sigma\sqrt{2\pi}$$ [1]

or

$$\mathbf{M_m(t) = \exp\,(\tfrac{1}{2}\sigma^2t^2)} \quad . \quad . \quad . \quad (5.4.2)$$

Since the coefficients of all the odd powers of t in the expansion of this function are zero, we see again that the mean-moments of odd order are all zero. To find the *mean-moments of even order*, we first find the coefficient of t^{2r}; this is $(\frac{1}{2}\sigma^2)^r/r\,!$; then the coefficient of $t^{2r}/2r\,!$ is $(\frac{1}{2}\sigma^2)^r\,.\,2r\,!/r\,!$

Hence $\mu_{2r} = (\frac{1}{2})^r\sigma^{2r}2r\,!/r\,! = 1.3.5\,.\,.\,.\,(2r - 1)\sigma^{2r}$ (5.4.3)

In particular, $\mu_2 = \sigma^2$ and $\mu_4 = 3\sigma^4$.

We also have a useful recurrence relation

$$\mu_{2r} = (2r - 1)\sigma^2\mu_{2r-2} \quad . \quad . \quad . \quad (5.4.4)$$

---

[1] By 3.C.3.; alternatively, the probability that x shall take a value somewhere between $-\infty$ and $+\infty$ to the total area under the probability curve, i.e., $\int_{-\infty}^{+\infty} \frac{1}{\sigma\sqrt{2\pi}}\exp\,(-\,x^2/2\sigma^2)dx$. But this is certain. Hence

$$\int_{-\infty}^{+\infty} \frac{1}{\sigma\sqrt{2\pi}}\exp\,(-\,x^2/2\sigma^2)dx = 1$$

or

$$\int_{-\infty}^{+\infty} \exp\,(-\,x^2(2\sigma^2)dx = \sigma\sqrt{2\pi}$$

(*f*) Since the area under the probability curve between $x = 0$ and $x = X$ is the probability that the variate x will assume some value between these two values,

$$\mathbf{P}(0 < x \leqslant \mathbf{X}) = \frac{1}{\sigma\sqrt{2\pi}}\int_0^X \exp\,(-x^2/2\sigma^2)\,dx \quad . \qquad (5.4.5)$$

Now, referring to Fig. 5.4.1, we see that

$$\frac{1}{\sigma\sqrt{2\pi}}\int_0^\infty \exp\,(-\,x^2/2\sigma^2)\,dx$$

$$= \frac{1}{\sigma\sqrt{2\pi}}\int_0^X \exp\,(-x^2/2\sigma^2)\,dx + \frac{1}{\sigma\sqrt{2\pi}}\int_X^\infty \exp\,(-x^2/2\sigma^2)\,dx$$

But the integral on the left-hand side of this equation gives the half the area under the entire curve and is, therefore, equal to $\frac{1}{2}$; also $\frac{1}{\sigma\sqrt{2\pi}}\int_0^X \exp\,(-x^2/2\sigma^2)\,dx = P(0 < x \leqslant X)$ and

$$\frac{1}{\sigma\sqrt{2\pi}}\int_X^\infty \exp\,(-\,x^2/2\sigma^2)\,dx = P(x > X).$$

Therefore

$$P(x > X) = \tfrac{1}{2} - P(x \leqslant X) \quad . \quad . \qquad (5.4.6)$$

If, however, we are concerned only with the *absolute value* of the variate, measured from its mean, then

$$P(|x| \geqslant X > 0) = 1 - 2P(0 < x \leqslant X) \qquad (5.4.7)$$

This is frequently the case. Consider the following, hypothetical, problem:

> In a factory producing ball-bearings a sample of each day's production is taken, and from this sample the mean diameter and the standard deviation of the day's output are estimated. The mean is in fact the specified diameter, say 0·5 in.; the standard deviation is 0·0001 in. A bearing whose diameter falls *outside* the range 0·5 ± 0·0002 in. is considered substandard. What percentage of the day's output may be expected to be substandard?

This is what is generally called a *two-tail problem*, for we are concerned with the probability of a bearing having a diameter which deviates from the mean by more than 0·0002 in. *above* the mean *and* of a bearing having a diameter which deviates by more than 0·0002 in. from the mean *below* the mean, i.e., we are concerned with finding the *two* (in this case, equal) areas under the Normal curve between $-\infty$ and $-$ 0·0002 in. and between $+$ 0·0002 in. and $+\infty$. This will be given by $1 - 2P(0 < x \leqslant 0{\cdot}0002)$. How, then, do we find probabilities such as $P(0 < x \leqslant 0{\cdot}0002)$?

Consider (5.4.5) again. Let us take the standard deviation of the distribution as the unit for a new variate and write $t = x/\sigma$. Then (5.4.5) becomes

$$P(0 < t \leqslant T) = \frac{1}{\sqrt{2\pi}}\int_0^T \exp(-t^2/2)dt \quad . \quad (5.4.8)$$

where $T = X/\sigma$.

TABLE 5.4. *Area under the Normal Curve:*

$$P(t \leqslant T) = \frac{1}{\sqrt{2\pi}}\int_0^T \exp(-t^2/2)dt$$

T (= X/σ).	0.	1.	2.	3.	4.	5.	6.	7.	8.	9.
0·0	·0000	·0040	·0080	·0120	·0159	·0199	·0239	·0279	·0319	·0359
0·1	·0398	·0438	·0478	·0517	·0557	·0596	·0636	·0675	·0714	·0753
0·2	·0793	·0832	·0871	·0910	·0948	·0987	·1026	·1064	·1103	·1141
0·3	·1179	·1217	·1255	·1293	·1331	·1368	·1406	·1443	·1480	·1517
0·4	·1554	·1591	·1628	·1664	·1700	·1736	·1772	·1808	·1844	·1879
0·5	·1915	·1950	·1985	·2019	·2054	·2088	·2123	·2157	·2190	·2224
0·6	·2257	·2291	·2324	·2357	·2389	·2422	·2454	·2486	·2518	·2549
0·7	·2580	·2611	·2642	·2673	·2704	·2734	·2764	·2794	·2823	·2852
0·8	·2881	·2910	·2939	·2967	·2995	·3023	·3051	·3078	·3106	·3133
0·9	·3159	·3186	·3212	·3238	·3264	·3289	·3315	·3340	·3365	·3389
1·0	·3413	·3438	·3461	·3485	·3508	·3531	·3554	·3577	·3599	·3621
1·1	·3643	·3665	·3686	·3708	·3729	·3749	·3770	·3790	·3810	·3830
1·2	·3849	·3869	·3888	·3907	·3925	·3944	·3962	·3980	·3997	·4015
1·3	·4032	·4049	·4066	·4082	·4099	·4115	·4131	·4147	·4162	·4177
1·4	·4192	·4207	·4222	·4236	·4251	·4265	·4279	·4292	·4306	·4319
1·5	·4332	·4345	·4357	·4370	·4382	·4394	·4406	·4418	·4430	·4441
1·6	·4452	·4463	·4474	·4485	·4495	·4505	·4515	·4525	·4535	·4545
1·7	·4554	·4564	·4573	·4582	·4591	·4599	·4608	·4616	·4625	·4633
1·8	·4641	·4649	·4656	·4664	·4671	·4678	·4686	·4693	·4699	·4706
1·9	·4713	·4719	·4726	·4732	·4738	·4744	·4750	·4756	·4762	·4767
2·0	·4772	·4778	·4783	·4788	·4793	·4798	·4803	·4808	·4812	·4817
2·1	·4821	·4826	·4830	·4834	·4838	·4842	·4846	·4850	·4854	·4857
2·2	·4861	·4865	·4868	·4871	·4875	·4878	·4881	·4884	·4887	·4890
2·3	·4893	·4896	·4898	·4901	·4904	·4906	·4909	·4911	·4913	·4916
2·4	·4918	·4920	·4922	·4925	·4927	·4929	·4931	·4932	·4934	·4936
2·5	·4938	·4940	·4941	·4943	·4945	·4946	·4948	·4949	·4951	·4952
2·6	·4953	·4955	·4956	·4957	·4959	·4960	·4961	·4962	·4963	·4964
2·7	·4965	·4966	·4967	·4968	·4969	·4970	·4971	·4972	·4973	·4974
2·8	·4974	·4975	·4976	·4977	·4977	·4978	·4979	·4980	·4980	·4981
2·9	·4981	·4982	·4983	·4983	·4984	·4984	·4985	·4985	·4986	·4986
T	3·0	3·1	3·2	3·3	3·4	3·5	3·6	3·7	3·8	3·9
$P(t \leqslant T)$	·4987	·4990	·4993	·4995	·4997	·4998	·4998	·4999	·4999	·5000

Now $P(t \leqslant T)$ is the area under the curve $y = \frac{1}{\sqrt{2\pi}} . \exp(-t^2/2)$ between $t = 0$ and $t = T$. The integral

$$\frac{1}{\sqrt{2\pi}}\int_0^T \exp(-t^2/2)dt$$

frequently called the *probability integral,* is a function of T. It cannot, however, be evaluated in finite form, but if we expand the integrand and integrate term by term, the integral can be computed to any degree of accuracy required. Table 5.4 gives values of this integral for $T = 0$ to $T = 3{\cdot}9$, correct to four decimal places.

Worked Example : *Find the value of* $\frac{1}{\sqrt{2\pi}}\int_0^{0{\cdot}500} \exp(-t^2/2)dt$ *correct to four decimal places using four terms of the expansion of the integrand.*

We have

$$\exp(-t^2/2) = 1 - t^2/2 + t^4/4.2! - t^6/8.3! + \ldots$$

Therefore

$$\frac{1}{\sqrt{2\pi}}\int_0^T \exp(-t^2/2)dt = \frac{1}{\sqrt{2\pi}}(T - T^3/6 + T^5/40 - T^7/336 \ldots)$$

Now $T = 0{\cdot}50000$; $T^3 = 0{\cdot}12500$ and $T^3/6 = 0{\cdot}02083$; $T^5 = 0{\cdot}03125$ and $T^5/40 = 0{\cdot}00078$; $T^7 = 0{\cdot}00781$ and $T^7/336 = 0{\cdot}00002$

Taking $1/\sqrt{2\pi} = 0{\cdot}39894$, we have $\frac{1}{\sqrt{2\pi}}\int_0^{0.500} \exp(-t^2/2)dt \simeq 0{\cdot}1914$, which should be compared with that of $0{\cdot}1915$ given in Table 5.4. This method is satisfactory when $T \leqslant 1$, but, for larger values, we use what is called an *asymptotic expansion* (see Whittaker and Watson, *Modern Analysis,* Ch. 8, or Nicholson, *Fundamentals and Techniques of Mathematics for Scientists,* Ch. 14).

$$\frac{1}{\sqrt{2\pi}}\int_0^T \exp(-t^2/2)dt = \frac{1}{\sqrt{2\pi}}\int_0^\infty \exp(-t^2/2)dt$$

$$- \frac{1}{\sqrt{2\pi}}\int_T^\infty \exp(-t^2/2)dt = 0{\cdot}5 - \frac{1}{\sqrt{2\pi}}\int_T^\infty \frac{1}{t} . \exp(-t^2/2)tdt$$

and, integrating successively by parts, we have, for $T > 1$,

$$\frac{1}{\sqrt{2\pi}}\int_0^T \exp(-t^2/2)dt = 0{\cdot}5 - \frac{\exp(-T^2/2)}{T\sqrt{2\pi}} \times$$

$$[1 - 1/T^2 + 1 . 3/T^4 - 1 . 3 . 5/T^6 + 1 . 3 . 5 . 7/T^8 - \ldots]$$

where $1/\sqrt{2\pi} = 0{\cdot}39894228\ldots$

Exercise : *Find* $\frac{1}{\sqrt{2\pi}}\int_0^3 \exp(-t^2/2)dt$ *correct to four decimal places and check the result with the value given in Table* 5.4.

We may now return to our ball-bearing problem. The standard deviation of the sample was 0·0001 in. Since we have to find $P(x > 0{\cdot}0002)$, $X = 0{\cdot}0002$ and $T = 0{\cdot}0002/0{\cdot}0001 = 2$. Hence the probability that the diameter of a bearing will lie between 0·5 and 0·5002 in. is 0·4772. Therefore the probability that the diameter will exceed 0·5002 in. is $0{\cdot}5 - 0{\cdot}4772 = 0{\cdot}0228$. Since the Normal distribution is symmetrical, the probability of a bearing with a diameter less than 0·4998 in. will also be 0·0228. Hence the probability that the diameter of a bearing will lie outside the tolerance limits will be 0·0456. This means that we should expect, on the data available, just over $4\frac{1}{2}\%$ of the bearings produced on the day in question to be substandard.

(*g*) *If we pick at random a value of a variate known to be distributed normally about zero-mean with variance* σ^2, *what is the probability that this random value will deviate by more than* σ, 2σ, 3σ, *from the mean?*

Entering Table 5.4 at $T = 1{\cdot}00$, we find that the area between the mean ordinate and that for $T = 1{\cdot}00$ is 0·3413. This is the probability that the random value of the variate will lie between 0 and σ. By symmetry, the probability that it will lie between 0 and $-\sigma$ is also 0·3413. Thus the probability of it lying between $-\sigma$ and $+\sigma$ is $2 \times 0{\cdot}3413 = 0{\cdot}6826$. Consequently the probability that it will deviate from the mean by more than σ in either direction is $1 - 0{\cdot}6826 = 0{\cdot}3174$, or less than $\frac{1}{3}$.

Similarly, the probability that a random value will lie between -2σ and $+2\sigma$ is 0·9544; this means that the probability that it will lie *outside* this range is 0·0456, or only about $4\frac{1}{2}\%$ of a normally distributed population deviate from the mean by more than 2σ.

Likewise, as the reader may ascertain for himself, the probability of a deviation greater than 3σ is only 0·0027.

(*h*) Suppose now that we were to plot values of the integral

$$\frac{1}{\sigma\sqrt{2\pi}}\int_{-\infty}^{X} \exp(-x^2/2\sigma^2)dx$$

against the value of X. This is not possible over the full range, $-\infty$ to $+\infty$, but since we have just found that deviations of more than 3σ from the mean are very rare, we can confine our attention to that section of the range lying between $-3{\cdot}9\sigma$ and $+3{\cdot}9\sigma$, the range covered by Table 5.4. If we do this we obtain a *cumulative probability curve* for the Normal distribution. The function $F(X)$ defined by

$$F(X) \equiv \frac{1}{\sigma\sqrt{2\pi}}\int_{-\infty}^{X} \exp\,(-x^2/2\sigma^2)dx \quad . \quad (5.4.9)$$

is called the *Normal distribution function*. Clearly

$$F(X) = \tfrac{1}{2} + P(0 < x \leqslant X) \quad . \quad (5.4.10)$$

The graph of a typical $F(X)$ is shown in Fig. 5.4.2. From (5.4.9) it follows that the value of the ordinate of this graph at X is equal to the area under the curve of the probability

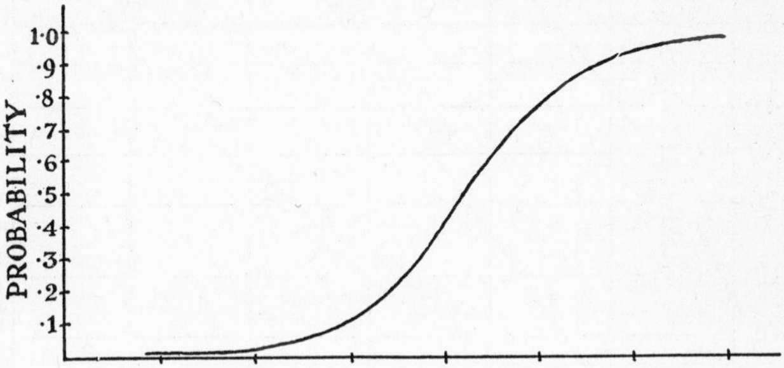

FIG. 5.4.2.—Curve of Normal Distribution Function.

density function $\phi(x)$ from $-\infty$ to X. If, however, we plot $F(X)$ against X on *probability graph paper* (Fig. 5.4.3) the resultant cumulative probability curve is a straight line. There is nothing strange in this, for probability paper is deliberately designed to ensure that this will happen !

5.5. Binomial, Poisson, Normal. When n is large the Binomial distribution tends towards the Normal distribution with mean at the Binomial mean value and variance equal to that of the discrete distribution. Furthermore, as we have also seen, when the mean of the Poisson distribution—also a discrete distribution—is very large, the Poisson probability polygon tends towards symmetry. In fact, when m is large, the Poisson distribution also tends to normality.

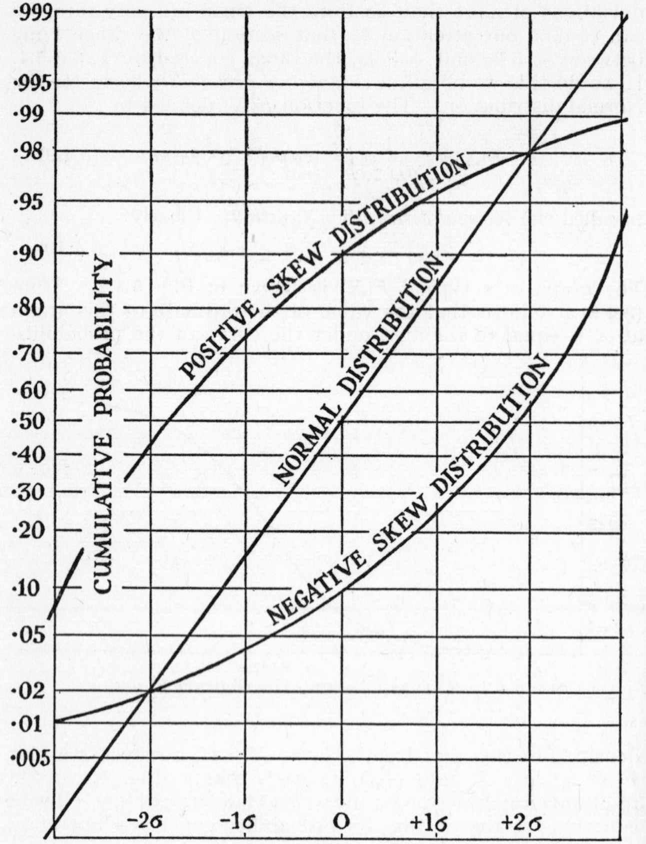

FIG. 5.4.3.—Cumulative Probability Curves on Normal Probability Paper.

Worked Example : *Use the Normal distribution to find approximately the frequency of exactly* 5 *successes in* 100 *trials, the probability of a success in each trial being* $p = 0{\cdot}1$.

The mean of the binomial distribution is $np = 10$ and the variance, npq, $= 9$. The standard deviation is, therefore, 3. The binomial class-interval for 5 will then correspond to the interval $-4\cdot5$ to $-5\cdot5$ of the normal distribution (referred to its mean as origin) and dividing by $\sigma = 3$, this, in standardised units, is $-1\cdot50$ to $-1\cdot83$. Owing to the symmetry of the normal curve, we may disregard the negative signs, and entering Table 5·4 at 1·50 and 1·83, we read 0·4332 and 0·4664 respectively. Hence the probability of 5 successes is approximately $0\cdot4664 - 0\cdot4332 = 0\cdot0332$. Thus in 100 trials the frequency of 5 successes will be approximately 3·32. The reader should verify for himself that direct calculation of the binomial frequency gives 3·39, while the frequency obtained from the Poisson series with $m = 10$ gives 3·78.

5.6. Three Examples. We conclude this chapter with two other typical problems in the treatment of which we make use of some of the properties of the Normal distribution. The reader should work each step himself, following carefully the directives given.

Example 1 : *To fit a Normal curve to the distribution given in Table 5·1.*

First Treatment : (1) Draw the frequency histogram for the data. The height 67 in. represents heights between $66\frac{7}{8}$ and $67\frac{7}{8}$ in.

(2) Calculate the *Mean* and *Standard Deviation*, correcting for grouping (2.15) the value of the latter. It will be found that the mean is 67·852 in., and the standard deviation 2.60 in.

(3) The normal curve corresponding to these values for the mean and standard deviation is drawn using Table 5.5 on page 90. For each class-interval, work out the deviation, from the mean, of each of the boundary values. For instance, the boundary values for the interval " 69 in." are 68·975 and 69·975. The respective deviations from the mean are 1·123 and 2·123. Making the transformation $T = X/\sigma$, we divide each of these by 2·60, obtaining, correct to three decimal places, 0·432 and 0·817. Now Table 5.5 gives the values of σ times the ordinate of the normal curve, $y = \phi(x)$. But since the total frequency of the distribution is 58,703 and the area under the normal curve is unity, each of the two values read from Table 5.5 must be multiplied by the factor $58{,}703/2.60 = 22{,}578$. Entering Table 5·5 at 0·432 and interpolating, we have 0·3634, and at 0·817, 0·2857. The ordinates corresponding to the end points of the interval " 69 in." for the fitted normal frequency curve are thus $22{,}578 \times 0\cdot3634 = 8205$, and $22{,}578 \times 0\cdot2857 = 6450$. Proceeding in this way, we plot the required curve.

(4) We now calculate the *theoretical* frequency for each class-interval in order to compare it with the corresponding *observed* frequency. This time we use Table 5·4. The area under the normal curve from the mean to the right-hand class-boundary (0·817) is, from this table, 0·2930; the area from the mean to the left-hand boundary (0·432) is 0·1671. The difference between these two values multiplied by the total frequency, $0\cdot1259 \times 58{,}703 = 7{,}391$, is our theoretical frequency for this interval. The corresponding *observed* frequency, note, is 7,132. The reader should

TABLE 5.5. *Ordinates of Normal Curve Multiplied by Standard Deviation*

Divide each value by σ to obtain $y = \phi(x)$

$T (= X/\sigma)$.	0.	1.	2.	3.	4.	5.	6.	7.	8.	9.
0·0	·3989	·3989	·3989	·3988	·3986	·3984	·3982	·3980	·3977	·3973
0·1	·3970	·3965	·3961	·3956	·3951	·3945	·3939	·3932	·3925	·3918
0·2	·3910	·3902	·3894	·3885	·3876	·3867	·3857	·3847	·3836	·3825
0·3	·3814	·3802	·3790	·3778	·3765	·3752	·3739	·3725	·3712	·3697
0·4	·3683	·3668	·3653	·3637	·3621	·3605	·3589	·3572	·3555	·3538
0·5	·3521	·3503	·3485	·3467	·3448	·3429	·3410	·3391	·3372	·3352
0·6	·3332	·3312	·3292	·3271	·3251	·3230	·3209	·3187	·3166	·3144
0·7	·3123	·3101	·3079	·3056	·3034	·3011	·2989	·2966	·2943	·2920
0·8	·2897	·2874	·2850	·2827	·2803	·2780	·2756	·2732	·2709	·2685
0·9	·2661	·2637	·2613	·2589	·2565	·2541	·2516	·2492	·2468	·2444
1·0	·2420	·2396	·2371	·2347	·2323	·2299	·2275	·2251	·2227	·2203
1·1	·2179	·2155	·2131	·2107	·2083	·2059	·2036	·2012	·1989	·1965
1·2	·1942	·1919	·1895	·1872	·1849	·1826	·1804	·1781	·1758	·1736
1·3	·1714	·1691	·1669	·1647	·1626	·1604	·1582	·1561	·1539	·1518
1·4	·1497	·1476	·1456	·1435	·1415	·1394	·1374	·1354	·1334	·1315
1·5	·1295	·1276	·1257	·1238	·1219	·1200	·1182	·1163	·1145	·1127
1·6	·1109	·1092	·1074	·1057	·1040	·1023	·1006	·0989	·0973	·0957
1·7	·0940	·0925	·0909	·0893	·0878	·0863	·0848	·0833	·0818	·0804
1·8	·0790	·0775	·0761	·0748	·0734	·0721	·0707	·0694	·0681	·0669
1·9	·0656	·0644	·0632	·0620	·0608	·0596	·0584	·0573	·0562	·0551
2·0	·0540	·0529	·0519	·0508	·0498	·0488	·0478	·0468	·0459	·0449
2·1	·0440	·0431	·0422	·0413	·0404	·0395	·0387	·0379	·0371	·0363
2·2	·0355	·0347	·0339	·0332	·0325	·0317	·0310	·0303	·0297	·0290
2·3	·0283	·0277	·0270	·0264	·0258	·0252	·0246	·0241	·0235	·0229
2·4	·0224	·0219	·0213	·0208	·0203	·0198	·0194	·0189	·0184	·0180
2·5	·0175	·0171	·0167	·0163	·0158	·0154	·0151	·0147	·0143	·0139
2·6	·0136	·0132	·0129	·0126	·0122	·0119	·0116	·0113	·0110	·0107
2·7	·0104	·0101	·0099	·0096	·0093	·0091	·0088	·0086	·0084	·0081
2·8	·0079	·0077	·0075	·0073	·0071	·0069	·0067	·0065	·0063	·0061
2·9	·0060	·0058	·0056	·0055	·0053	·0051	·0050	·0048	·0047	·0046
3·0	·0044	·0043	·0042	·0040	·0039	·0038	·0037	·0036	·0035	·0034
3·1	·0033	·0032	·0031	·0030	·0029	·0028	·0027	·0026	·0025	·0025
3·2	·0024	·0023	·0022	·0022	·0021	·0020	·0020	·0019	·0018	·0018
3·3	·0017	·0017	·0016	·0016	·0015	·0015	·0014	·0014	·0013	·0013
3·4	·0012	·0012	·0012	·0011	·0011	·0010	·0010	·0010	·0009	·0009
3·5	·0009	·0008	·0008	·0008	·0008	·0007	·0007	·0007	·0007	·0006
3·6	·0006	·0006	·0006	·0005	·0005	·0005	·0005	·0005	·0005	·0004
3·7	←		·0004			→	←		·0003	→
3·8	←		·0003		→	←			·0002	→
3·9	←		·0002					→	·0001	→

complete the calculations and draw the theoretical frequency polygon.

Second Treatment : (1) Draw the *cumulative frequency polygon* for the data of Table 5.1.

(2) Draw the theoretical cumulative normal frequency curve with mean 67·852 and s.d. 2·60. This is done using Table 5.4 as follows :

To find the ordinate of the cumulative frequency curve at, say, the lower end-point of the interval " 64 in.," i.e., at 63·975 in., we have to find the area under the normal curve from $-\infty$ to $X =$ 63·975. But this is $\frac{1}{2}$ − (area under curve between mean, 67·852, and the ordinate at 63·975). The deviation from the mean is

$-3\cdot877$. But the area under the normal curve between $X = 0$ and $X = -3\cdot877$ is, by symmetry, the area under the curve between $X = 0$ and $X = +3\cdot877$. Dividing $3\cdot877$ by $2\cdot60$, we obtain $1\cdot491$; entering Table 5·4 at this value, we read $0\cdot4319$. The required ordinate of the cumulative frequency curve is then given by $58{,}703 \times (0\cdot5000 - 0\cdot4319) = 3{,}997$. The reader should calculate the other ordinates in a similar manner and complete the curve.

(3) If now we mark upon the vertical axis percentage cumulative frequencies (with 58,703 as 100%), we can find the position of the median and other percentiles. (Median: 67·7 in.; quartiles: 66·0 and 69·5 in.; deciles: 64·4 and 71·1 in.)

Example 2: *To find, using probability graph paper, approximate values for the mean and standard deviation of an observed frequency distribution which is approximately normal.*

Treatment: When plotted on probability graph paper, the cumulative frequency curve of a normal distribution is a straight line. If, then, we draw the cumulative relative-frequency polygon of an observed distribution on such paper and find that it is approximately a straight line, we may assume that the distribution is approximately normal. We next draw the straight line to which the polygon appears to approximate. Then, working with this "filled" line:

(*a*) since, for the normal distribution, mean and median coincide and the median is the 50th percentile, if we find the 50th percentile, we shall have a graphical estimate of the mean of the observed distribution;

(*b*) the area under the normal curve between $-\infty$ and $\mu + \sigma$ is $0\cdot5000 + 0\cdot3413 = 0\cdot8413$. Thus 84·13% of the area under the normal curve lies to the left of the ordinate at $\mu + \sigma$. So the 84·13 percentile corresponds to a deviation of $+\sigma$ from the mean. If, therefore, from the *fitted cumulative frequency line* we find the position of the 84th percentile, the difference between this and the mean will give us an estimate of σ for the observed distribution. Likewise, the difference between the 16th percentile and the median will also be an estimate of σ.

Example 3: *The frequency distribution* $f(x)$ *in obtained from the normal distribution* $N(t) = \dfrac{1}{\sqrt{2\pi}} \exp(-\tfrac{1}{2}t^2)$, *by means of the equations*

$$\text{(i)} \int_1^x f(x)dx = \int_{-\infty}^{t} N(t)dt, \quad \text{and} \quad \text{(ii) } t = a \log (x - 1).$$

If $\exp(1/a^2) = 4$, *show that the median of* $f(x)$ *is* 2, *the mean is* 3 *and the mode is* 1·25. (L.U.)

Treatment: As $x \rightarrow 1$, $t \rightarrow -\infty$; as $x \rightarrow +\infty$, $t \rightarrow +\infty$.

Also $\int_1^{\infty} f(x)dx = \int_{-\infty}^{+\infty} N(t)dt = 1$. Hence the median value of $f(x)$ is given by $\int_1^{x} f(x)dx = \frac{1}{2} = \int_{-\infty}^{0} N(t)dt$, i.e., by $0 = a\log(x-1)$, i.e., since $\log 1 = 0$, $\underline{x = 2}$.

$$\bar{x} = \int_1^{\infty} xf(x)dx. \quad \text{But} \quad x = 1 + e^{t/a}.$$

Hence

$$\bar{x} = \int_{-\infty}^{+\infty} (1 + e^{t/a})N(t)dt = 1 + \frac{1}{\sqrt{2\pi}}\int_{-\infty}^{+\infty} e^{-\frac{1}{2}\left(t^2 - \frac{2t}{a}\right)} dt$$

$$= 1 + \frac{e^{\frac{1}{2}/a^2}}{\sqrt{2\pi}}\int_{-\infty}^{+\infty} \exp\left[-\frac{1}{2}\left(t - \frac{1}{a}\right)^2\right]dt$$

i.e.,

$$\bar{x} = 1 + e^{\frac{1}{2}/a^2} = 1 + (4)^{\frac{1}{2}} = 3.$$

Differentiating (i) with respect to t, we have

$$N(t) = \frac{d}{dt}\int_1^{x} f(x)dx = \left[\frac{d}{dx}\int_1^{x} f(x)dx\right]\frac{dx}{dt} = f(x) \cdot \frac{1}{a}e^{t/a}$$

or

$$f(x) = ae^{-t/a}N(t) = \frac{a}{\sqrt{2\pi}}\exp\left[-\frac{1}{2}\left(t^2 + \frac{2t}{a}\right)\right]$$

$$\therefore \quad \frac{df(x)}{dx} = \frac{d}{dt}\left[\frac{a}{\sqrt{2\pi}}\exp\left(-\frac{1}{2}\{t^2 + 2t/a\}\right)\right] \times ae^{-t/a}$$

$$= \frac{a^2}{\sqrt{2\pi}}e^{-t/a} \cdot \exp\left[-\frac{1}{2}(t^2 + 2t/a)\right] \cdot -\left[t + \frac{1}{a}\right].$$

If then $\frac{df(x)}{dx} = 0$, which defines the modal value, we must have $t = -\frac{1}{a}$.

Thus $\quad x - 1 = e^{-\frac{1}{a^2}} = \frac{1}{4}$ or $\underline{x = 1{\cdot}25}$.

EXERCISES ON CHAPTER FIVE

1. Fit a normal curve to the distribution of lengths of metal bars given in 2.1.

2. The wages of 1,000 employees range from 4*s*. 6*d*. to 19*s*. 6*d*. They are grouped in 15 classes with a common class interval of 1*s*. The class frequencies, from the lowest class to the highest, are 6, 17, 35, 48, 65, 90, 131, 173, 155, 117, 75, 52, 21, 9, 6. Show that the

mean wage is 12·006*s.* and the standard deviation 2·626*s.* Fit a normal distribution, showing that the class frequencies per thousand of the normal distribution are approximately 6·7, 11·3, 25·0, 48·0, 79·0, 113·1, 140·5, 151·0, 140·8, 113·5, 79·5, 48·1, 25·3, 11·5 and 6·7.
(Weatherburn, *Mathematical Statistics.*)

3. A machine makes electrical resistors having a mean resistance of 50 ohms with a standard deviation of 2 ohms. Assuming the distribution of values to be normal, find what tolerance limits should be put on the resistance to secure that no more than $\frac{1}{1000}$ of the resistors will fail to meet the tolerances. (R.S.S.)

4. Number of individual incomes in different ranges of net income assessed in 1945–46 :

Range of Income after tax (x). £	Number of Incomes.
150–500	13,175,000
500–1,000	652,000
1,000–2,000	137,500
2,000 and over	35,500
Total	14,000,000

Assume that this distribution of incomes, $f(x)$, is linked with the normal distribution

$$N(t) = \frac{1}{\sqrt{2\pi}} \exp\left(-\tfrac{1}{2}t^2\right)$$

by the relationship

$$\int_{-\infty}^{t} N(t)dt = \int_{150}^{x} f(x)dx, \text{ where } t = a \log(x - 150) + b.$$

Obtain estimates for a and b from the data, and find the number of incomes between £250 and £500.

5. Show that β_2 for a normal distribution is equal to 3.

6. If $p = \frac{1}{5}$, use the normal distribution to estimate the probability of obtaining less than five or more than 15 successes in 50 trials. What is the actual probability?

Solutions

3. ± 6·6 ohms.

4. See Example 3 of 5.6. $a = 0{\cdot}71(5)$ $b = -2{\cdot}58$; number of incomes between £250 and £500 is $2{\cdot}5 \times 10^6$, (2·48), to two significant figures.

6. 0·0519; 0·0503.

CHAPTER SIX

MORE VARIATES THAN ONE: BIVARIATE DISTRIBUTIONS, REGRESSION AND CORRELATION

6.1. Two Variates. In the last chapter we discussed the distribution of height among 58,703 National Servicemen born in 1933 who entered the Army in 1951. We could have discussed the distribution of weight among them. In either case, the distribution would have been *univariate*, the distribution of one measurable characteristic of the population or sample. But had we considered the distribution of *both* height *and* weight, a joint distribution of two variates, we should have had a *bivariate* distribution.

6.2. Correlation Tables. How do we tabulate such a distribution? To each National Serviceman in the total of 58,703, there corresponds a pair of numbers, his weight, x lb. say, and his height, y in. Let us group the heights in 2-in. intervals and the weights in 10-lb. intervals. Some men will be classed together in the same weight-group (call it the x_i group) but will be in different height-groups; others will occupy the same height-group (the y_j group, say) but different weight groups; but there will be some in the same weight-group and the same height-group, the group (x_i, y_j) for short. Denote the number of men in this *class-rectangle* by f_{ij}. The joint distribution may then be tabulated as in Table 6.2. A general scheme is given in Table 6.2.2.

NOTE:

(i) x_i is the mid-value of the class-interval of the ith x-array; y_j is the mid-value of the jth y-array.

(ii) If the data is not grouped—to each value of x corresponds but one value of y and to each y corresponds but one value of x, the correlation Table becomes:

x	x_1	x_2	x_3	...	x_i	...	x_N
y	y_1	y_2	y_3	...	y_i	...	y_N

The (x_6, y_7) group in Table 6.2.2, for instance, corresponds to that of those men whose weights are in the 130–139-lb. weight class and whose heights are in the 65-in. height class, and $f_{67} = 3,879$. Such a table is called *a correlation table*. Each row

TABLE 6.2.1. *Joint Frequency Distribution of Heights and Weights of National Servicemen born in* 1933, *Army Intake* 1951

(From " Heights and Weights of Army Intake, 1951 ", by S. Rosenbaum (Directorate of Army Health), *Journal of Royal Statistical Society*, Series A, Vol. 117, Part 3, 1954.)

Lb. \ In.	53	55	57	59	61	63	65	67	69	71	73	75	77	79
80–89	—	—	—	—	1	4	—	—	—	—	—	—	—	—
90–99	—	—	—	18	73	35	12	5	1	—	—	—	—	—
100–109	—	—	1	59	358	529	331	71	10	1	—	—	—	—
110–119	1	—	4	54	616	2,031	2,534	1,104	209	13	2	—	—	—
120–129	—	3	—	21	275	2,008	4,528	3,924	1,275	180	10	5	—	—
130–139	1	—	2	16	98	994	3,879	5,737	3,003	702	88	5	2	—
140–149	—	—	2	5	33	321	1,849	4,304	3,912	1,428	223	22	1	—
150–159	—	—	1	4	8	84	549	1,778	2,326	1,400	335	50	2	—
160–169	—	—	—	—	4	31	191	600	1,065	820	316	43	8	1
170–179	—	—	—	—	2	16	55	183	371	365	163	44	4	—
180–189	—	—	—	—	—	7	30	72	154	170	63	26	3	1
190–199	—	—	—	—	1	2	13	43	65	64	31	12	1	—
200–209	—	—	—	—	—	1	5	12	24	27	12	5	1	—
210–219	—	—	—	—	—	—	1	12	18	16	9	3	1	—
220–229	—	—	—	—	—	—	—	6	9	11	1	1	—	—
230–239	—	—	—	—	—	—	—	1	2	3	3	—	—	—
240–249	—	—	—	—	—	—	—	—	1	3	2	—	—	—
250–259	—	—	—	—	—	—	—	—	1	—	—	—	—	—
260–269	—	—	—	—	—	—	—	—	—	1	1	—	—	—

and each column tabulates the distribution of one of the variates for a given value of the other. Thus each row (or column) gives a univariate frequency distribution. A row or column is often called an *array*: the x_6 array, for example, is that row of y-values for which $x = x_6$.

TABLE 6.2.2. *Correlation Table for Grouped Data*

x \ y	y_1	y_2	y_3	...	y_j	...	y_q	TOTALS
x_1	f_{11}	f_{12}	f_{13}	...	f_{1j}	...	f_{1q}	$f_{1\cdot}$
x_2	f_{21}	f_{22}	f_{23}	...	f_{2j}	...	f_{2q}	$f_{2\cdot}$
x_3	f_{31}	f_{32}	f_{33}	...	f_{3j}	...	f_{3q}	$f_{3\cdot}$
$\vdots$	$\vdots$	$\vdots$	$\vdots$	...	$\vdots$	...	$\vdots$	$\vdots$
x_i	f_{i1}	f_{i2}	f_{i3}	...	f_{ij}	...	f_{iq}	$f_{i\cdot}$
$\vdots$	$\vdots$	$\vdots$	$\vdots$	...	$\vdots$	...	$\vdots$	$\vdots$
x_p	f_{p1}	f_{p2}	f_{p3}	...	f_{pj}	...	f_{pq}	$f_{p\cdot}$
TOTALS	$f_{\cdot 1}$	$f_{\cdot 2}$	$f_{\cdot 3}$	...	$f_{\cdot j}$	...	$f_{\cdot q}$	N

6.3. Scatter Diagrams, Stereograms. How do we display such a distribution? If we confine ourselves to two dimensions, we make a *scatter-diagram*. A pair of rectangular axes is taken, the abscissæ being values of one of the variates, the ordinates those of the other. So to every pair of values (x_i, y_j) there will correspond a point in the plane of the axes. If we plot these points, we have a scatter-diagram. The main disadvantage of this method of display is that it is not well suited to the representation of *grouped* data, for it is difficult to exhibit a number of coincident points! Nevertheless, a scatter-diagram is very often suggestive of directions along which further investigation may prove fruitful. (Figs. 6.3.1 (*a*), (*b*), (*c*) and (*d*).)

To represent a grouped bivariate distribution in three dimensions, mark off on mutually perpendicular axes in a horizontal plane the class-intervals of the two variates. We thus obtain a network of *class-rectangles*. On each of these rectangles we erect a right prism of volume proportional to the occurrence-frequency of the value-pair represented by the rectangle in question. In this way we obtain a surface composed of horizontal rectangular planes. This is a *prismogram* or *stereogram*, corresponding in three dimensions to the histogram in two. Alternatively, at the centre of each class rectangle, we may erect a line perpendicular to the horizontal plane proportional in length to the frequency of the variates in that class-rectangle. If we then join up all the points so obtained by straight lines, we obtain the three-dimensional analogue of the two-dimensional frequency polygon. Now, if we regard our distribution as a sample from a continuous bivariate population parent distribution, we can also think of a relative-frequency prismogram as a rough sample approximation to that ideal, continuous surface—the *correlation surface*—

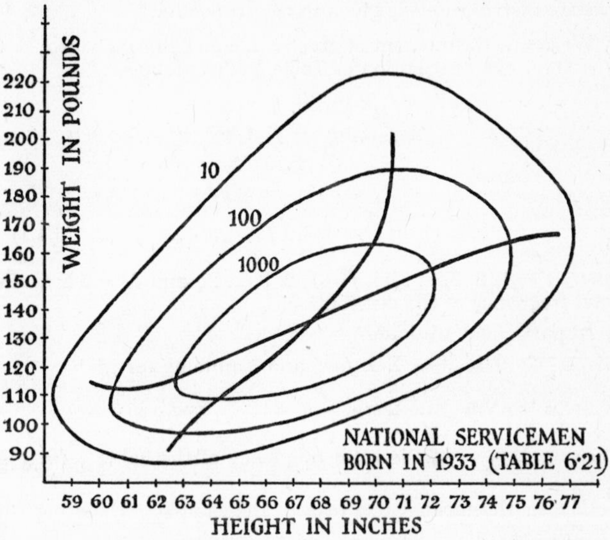

FIG. 6.3.2.—Frequency Contours of Bivariate Distribution.

which represents the continuous bivariate probability distribution in the parent population.

Three-dimensional figures, however, also have their disadvantages, and we frequently find it convenient to return to two-dimensional diagrams representing sections through the three-dimensional surface. Thus if we cut the surface with a horizontal plane we obtain a *contour* of the surface corresponding to the particular frequency (or probability) represented by the height of the plane above the plane of the variate axes. Fig. 6.3.2 shows frequency contours of ten, a hundred and a thousand men in the groups of Table 6.2.1. It also shows mean weights at each height and mean heights at each weight.

If, however, we cut the surface by a plane corresponding to a given value of one of the variates, we obtain the frequency (or probability) curve of the other variate for that given value of the first.

6.4. Moments of a Bivariate Distribution. We confine ourselves here to the discussion of bivariate distributions with both variates discrete. A brief treatment of continuous bivariate distributions is given in the Appendix.

We define the moment of order r in x and s in y about $x = 0$, $y = 0$ for the distribution of Table 6.2.2 as follows:

$$\begin{aligned} Nm_{rs}' = & f_{11}x_1^r y_1^s + f_{12}x_1^r y_2^s + \ldots \\ & + f_{21}x_2^r y_1^s + f_{22}x_2^r y_2^s + \ldots \\ & \ldots + f_{ij}x_i^r y_j^s + \ldots \\ & \ldots + f_{pq}x_p^r y_q^s \end{aligned}$$

or

$$m_{rs}' = \frac{1}{N}\sum_i \sum_j f_{ij}x_i^r y_j^s \quad . \quad . \quad . \quad (6.4.1)$$

where $i = 1, 2, 3, \ldots p$; $j = 1, 2, 3, \ldots q$ and $N = \sum_i \sum_j f_{ij}$, the total frequency of the distribution.

In particular, we have

$$Nm_{10}' = \sum_i \sum_j f_{ij}x_i, \text{ and, summing for } j,$$

$$Nm_{10}' = \sum_i (f_{i1} + f_{i2} + \ldots + f_{iq})x_i.$$

Writing $\sum_j f_{ij} = f_{i\cdot}$, the total frequency of the value x_i, $m_{10}' = \frac{1}{N}\sum_i f_{i\cdot}x_i$, the mean value of x in the sample. Denoting this mean by $\bar{x}$, we have

$$m_{10}' = \bar{x} \quad . \quad . \quad . \quad . \quad . \quad (6.4.2)$$

and, likewise,

$$m_{01}' = \bar{y} \quad . \quad . \quad . \quad . \quad . \quad (6.4.3)$$

Again, $m_{20}' = \frac{1}{N}\sum_i \sum_j f_{ij}x_i^2 = \frac{1}{N}\sum_i f_{i\cdot}x_i^2$, the second moment of x about the origin. Writing $X_i = x_i - \bar{x}$, $Y_j = y_j - \bar{y}$,

$$m_{20}' = \frac{1}{N}\sum_i f_{i\cdot}(X_i + \bar{x})^2 = \frac{1}{N}\sum_i f_{i\cdot}(X_i^2 + 2\bar{x}X_i + \bar{x}^2)$$

$$= \frac{1}{N}\sum_i f_{i\cdot}X_i^2 + \bar{x}^2, \text{ since } \frac{1}{N}\sum_i f_{i\cdot}X_i = 0.$$

Denoting the variance of x by s_x^2 and var (y) by s_y^2, we have

$$m_{20}' = s_x^2 + \bar{x}^2 = m_{20} + (m_{10}')^2 \quad . \quad (6.4.4)$$

and, similarly, $m_{02}' = s_y^2 + \bar{y}^2 = m_{02} + (m_{01}')^2 \quad . \quad (6.4.5)$

where, of course, m_{20} and m_{02} are the moments of order 2, 0 and 0, 2 about the mean.

Now consider

$$m_{11}' = \frac{1}{N}\sum_i\sum_j f_{ij}\,x_i y_j = \frac{1}{N}\sum_i\sum_j f_{ij}\,(X_i + \bar{x})(Y_j + \bar{y})$$

$$= \frac{1}{N}\sum_i\sum_j (f_{ij}X_iY_j + \bar{x}\,f_{ij}Y_j + \bar{y}f_{ij}X_i + f_{ij}\bar{x}\bar{y})$$

$$= \frac{1}{N}\sum_i\sum_j f_{ij}X_iY_j + \bar{x}\bar{y}$$

The quantity $\frac{1}{N}\sum_i\sum_j f_{ij}X_iY_j$ is called the *covariance of x and y* and is variously denoted by s_{xy} or cov (x, y). We may therefore write

$$m_{11}' = m_{11} + m_{10}' \cdot m_{01}'$$

or $\quad \text{cov}\,(x, y) \equiv s_{xy} = m_{11}' - m_{10}' \cdot m_{01}' = m_{11}' - \bar{x}\bar{y} \quad (6.4.6)$

6.5. Regression. When we examine the data provided by a sample from a bivariate population, one of the things we wish to ascertain is whether there is any evidence of association between the variates of the sample, and whether, if such an association is apparent, it warrants the inference that a corresponding association exists between the variates in the population. We also wish to know what type of association, if any, exists.

Frequently, if our sample is of sufficient size, a scatter-diagram of the sample data provides a clue. If, for instance, there is a fairly well-defined locus of maximum " dot-density " in the diagram, and if, when we increase the sample size, this locus " condenses ", as it were, more and more to a *curve*, we may reasonably suspect this curve to be the smudged reflection of a *functional relationship* between the variates in the population, the smudging resulting from the hazards of random sampling. In Fig. 6.3.1 (a) and (b) we have scatter diagrams of samples from populations in which the variates are linearly related. If, however, the dots do not appear to cluster around or condense towards some fairly definitely indicated curve, and yet are not distributed at random all over the range of the

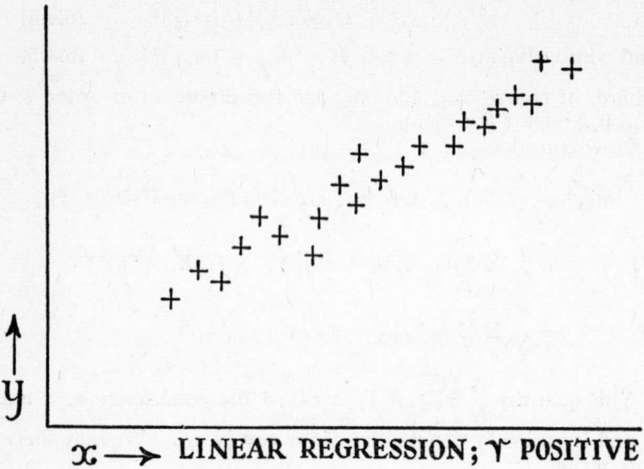

FIG. 6.3.1 (*a*).—Scatter Diagram (I).

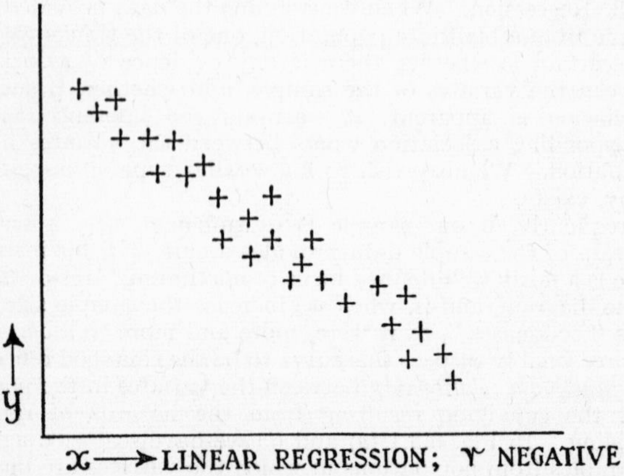

FIG. 6.3.1 (*b*).—Scatter Diagram (II).

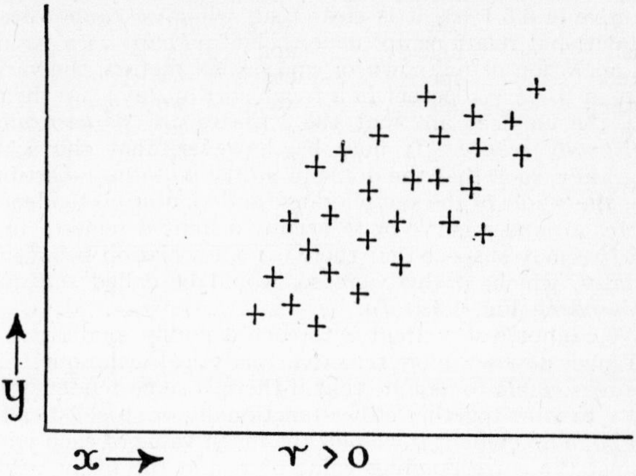

FIG. 6.3.1 (*c*).—Scatter Diagram (III).

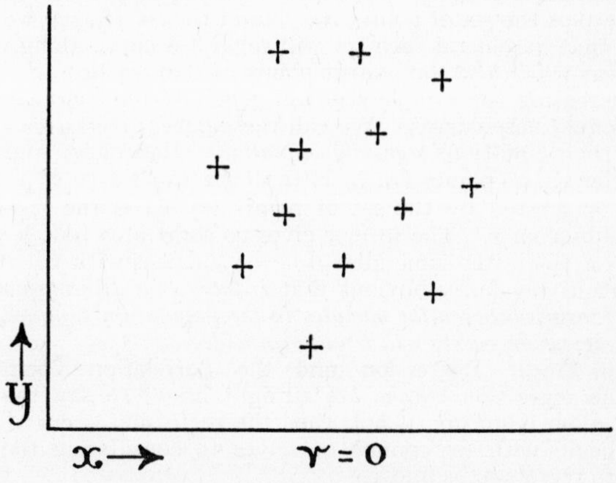

FIG. 6.3.1 (*d*).—Scatter Diagram (IV).

sample, occupying rather a fairly well-limited *region*, as for example in 6.3.1 (*c*), it is clear that, while we cannot assume a functional relationship, nevertheless perhaps as a result of the operation of unknown or unspecified factors, the variates do tend to vary together in a rough sort of way; we then say that the chances are that the variates are *stochastically or statistically related*. It may be, however, that the scatter-diagram is such that the dots are pretty uniformly distributed over the whole of the sample range and exhibit no tendency to cluster around a curve or to occupy a limited region; in this case, we may suspect that there is no association between the variates, which, if this were so, would be called *statistically independent* (Fig. 6.3.1 (*d*)).

We cannot rest content with such a purely qualitative test and must devise a more sensitive, analytical technique. Now it is reasonable to assume that if there is some tendency for x and y to vary together either functionally or stochastically, it will be more evident if we plot the mean value of each y-array against the corresponding value of x, and the mean value of each x-array against the corresponding value of y. In practice, it is customary to denote the means of x-arrays by small circles and those of y-arrays by small crosses.

Let the mean of the y-array corresponding to the value $x = x_i$ be $\bar{y}_i$, and the mean of the x-array corresponding to $y = y_j$ be $\bar{x}_j$. If we plot the set of points $(x_i, \bar{y}_i)$ and the set $(\bar{x}_j, y_j)$, we shall find that in general each set will suggest a curve along which or near which the component points of that set lie.

Increasing the sample size will generally tend more clearly to define these curves. We call these curves *regression curves* and their equations *regression equations*: that curve suggested by the set of points $(x_i, \bar{y}_i)$ is the *regression curve of y on x*; that suggested by the set of points $(\bar{x}_j, y_j)$ is the *regression curve of x on y*. The former gives us some idea how y varies with x, the latter some idea of how x changes with y. And it is intuitively fairly obvious that *if there is a direct functional relationship between the variates in the population sampled these two regression curves will tend to coincide*.

6.6. Linear Regression and the Correlation Coefficient. If the regression curves are straight lines, we say that the regression is linear; if not, then the regression is curvilinear. To begin with we confine ourselves to considering the case where regression is linear.

Clearly, although the set of points $(x_i, \bar{y}_i)$ *tend* to lie on a straight line, they do not do so exactly and our problem is to find that line about which they cluster most closely. Assume the line to be $\bar{y}_i = Ax_i + B$, where A and B are constants to be determined accordingly. To do this we use the *Method of Least Squares.*

The value of $\bar{y}_i$ corresponding to x_i should be $Ax_i + B$. The difference between the actual value of $\bar{y}_i$ and this *estimated* value is $\bar{y}_i - Ax_i - B$. Now to each x_i there corresponds $f_{i\cdot}$ values of y. To allow for this fact we form the sum

$$S^2_{\bar{y}} = \sum_i f_{i\cdot} (\bar{y}_i - Ax_i - B)^2 \quad . \quad . \quad (6.6.1)$$

Now since all the terms making up $S_{\bar{y}}^2$ are positive, $S_{\bar{y}}^2 = 0$ if and only if all the means of the y-arrays lie on this line. Thus $S_{\bar{y}}^2$ would appear to be a satisfactory measure of the overall discrepancy between the set of points $(x_i, \bar{y}_i)$ and this theoretical straight line. The " best " line we can draw, using this criterion—there are others—so that these points cluster most closely about it will, then, be that line for which $S_{\bar{y}}^2$ is a minimum.

Now $S_{\bar{y}}^2$ is a function of the two quantities A and B. To find the values of A and B which minimise $S_{\bar{y}}^2$, we equate to zero the two partial derivatives of $S_{\bar{y}}^2$ (see Abbott, *Teach Yourself Calculus*, Chapter XVIII, for an introduction to partial differentiation), with respect to A and B. Thus we have

$$\frac{\partial}{\partial A}(S_{\bar{y}}^2) = -2\sum_i f_{i\cdot} (\bar{y}_i - Ax_i - B)x_i = 0 \quad (6.6.2)$$

and

$$\frac{\partial}{\partial B}(S_{\bar{y}}^2) = -2\sum_i f_{i\cdot} (\bar{y}_i - Ax_i - B) = 0 \quad (6.6.3)$$

The latter equation gives us—remembering that $f_{i\cdot} = \sum_j f_{ij}$—

$$\sum_i \sum_j f_{ij}y_j - A \sum_i \sum_j f_{ij}x_i - B \sum_i \sum_j f_{ij} = 0. \quad (6.6.4)$$

Dividing through by $N = \sum_i \sum_j f_{ij}$, we have

$$\bar{y} = A\bar{x} + B \quad . \quad . \quad . \quad . \quad (6.6.5)$$

Showing that the mean of the sample $(\bar{x}, \bar{y})$ lies on the line $\bar{y}_i = Ax_i + B$

Likewise (6.6.2) may be written

$$\sum_i \sum_j f_{ij}x_iy_j - A \sum_i \sum_j f_{ij}x_i^2 - B \sum_i \sum_j f_{ij}x_i = 0 \quad (6.6.6)$$

and, again dividing by N, this is

$$m_{11}' - Am_{20}' - B\bar{x} = 0. \quad . \quad . \quad (6.6.7)$$

Solving for A between (6.6.5) and (6.6.7), we have

$$A = \frac{m_{11}' - \bar{x}\bar{y}}{m_{20}' - \bar{x}^2} = \frac{m_{11}}{m_{20}} = \frac{s_{xy}}{s_x^2} \quad . \quad . \quad (6.6.8)$$

Finally, subtracting (6.6.5) from $\bar{y}_i = Ax_i + B$, we have

$$\bar{y}_i - \bar{y} = (s_{xy}/s_x^2)(x_i - \bar{x}) . \quad . \quad . \quad (6.6.9)$$

as the line about which the set of means of the y-arrays cluster most closely, the line of regression of y on x. Thus, from 6.6.9, $(x_i, \bar{y}_i)$ lies on the line

$$(y - \bar{y})/s_y = (s_{xy}/s_x s_y)(x - \bar{x})/s_x$$

If, therefore, we transfer our origin to the mean of the sample distribution and measure the deviation of each variate from the mean in terms of the standard deviation of that variate as unit, i.e., if we put

$$Y = (y - \bar{y})/s_y \text{ and } X = (x - \bar{x})/s_x$$

the equation of our regression line of y on x is

$$Y = (s_{xy}/s_x s_y)X . \quad . \quad . \quad . \quad (6.6.10)$$

and this may be further simplified by putting

$$r = s_{xy}/s_x s_y \quad . \quad . \quad . \quad . \quad (6.6.11)$$

Thus

$$Y = rX \quad . \quad . \quad . \quad . \quad . \quad (6.6.12)$$

and in this form the regression line of Y on X gives us a measure, r, of the change in Y for unit change in X.

The line of regression of x on y is immediately obtained by interchanging x and y, thus

$$(x - \bar{x})/s_x = (s_{xy}/s_y s_x)(y - \bar{y})/s_y \quad . \quad (6.6.9a)$$

or

$$X = rY, \text{ i.e., } Y = (1/r)X \quad . \quad (6.6.12a)$$

We now have our two regression lines, one with gradient r, the other with gradient $1/r$, passing through the mean of the sample distribution (see Fig. 6.6). The angle between them, θ, is obtained by using a well-known formula of trigonometry (see Abbott, *Teach Yourself Trigonometry*, p. 101), viz.,

$$\tan(\phi_1 - \phi_2) = \frac{\tan\phi_1 - \tan\phi_2}{1 + \tan\phi_1 \tan\phi_2}.$$

In this case,

$$\tan\theta = (1/r - r)/(1 + (1/r) . r) = (1 - r^2)/2r \quad (6.6.13)$$

We see immediately that if $r^2 = 1$, i.e., $r = \pm 1$, $\theta = 0$ and the two lines coincide. This means that in the sample the two variates x and y are functionally related by a linear relationship and in the population which has been sampled it may also be the case. We say, then, that the two variates are *perfectly correlated*, positively if $r = +1$ and negatively if $r = -1$. On the other hand, if $r = 0$, $\theta = 90°$, and there is no functional relationship between the variates in the sample and hence, probably, little or none in the parent population : the variates are *uncorrelated*. It is natural, therefore, that, *when regression is linear or assumed to be linear*, we should regard r as a measure

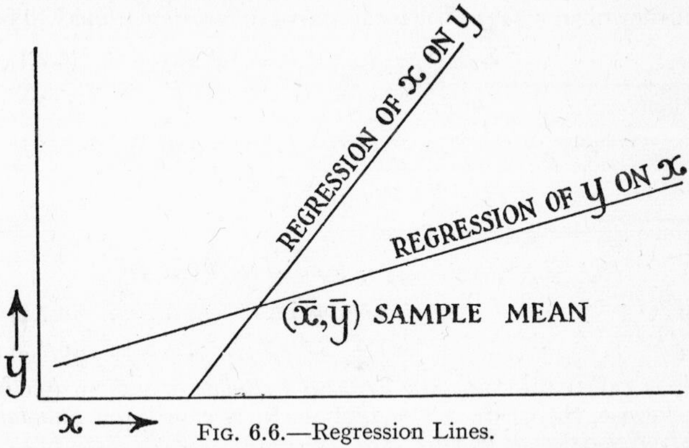

FIG. 6.6.—Regression Lines.

of the degree to which the variates are related in the sample by a linear functional relationship. We accordingly call r the sample *coefficient of product-moment correlation of x and y* or, briefly, the sample *correlation-coefficient*.

The gradient of the line given by (6.6.9), the regression line of y on x, is (s_{xy}/s_x^2) or, as it is often written, cov (x, y)/var (x). This quantity, called the sample *coefficient of regression of y on x*, is denoted by b_{yx}; similiarly, s_{xy}/s_y^2 or cov (x, y)/var (y) is the coefficient of regression of x on y and is denoted by b_{xy}. It follows that

$$b_{yx} \,.\, b_{xy} = s_{xy}^2/s_x^2 \,.\, s_y^2 = r^2 \quad . \quad . \quad (6.6.14)$$

It should be noted that *regression* is a relation of dependence and is not symmetrical, while *correlation* is one of *interdependence* and is symmetrical.

6.7. Standard Error of Estimate. We must now examine r in a little more detail so as to substantiate our statement that it is a measure of the degree to which the association between x and y in the sample does tend toward a linear functional relationship.

Taking the mean of the distribution as our origin of co-ordinates, we may write the equation of the line of regression of y on x is the form $y = b_{yx}x$. We now form the sum of the squared deviations not of the array-means from the corresponding values predicted from this equation, but of *all* the points (x_i, y_j) from the points on the line $y = b_{yx}x$ corresponding to $x = x_i$, i.e., from $(x_i, b_{yx}x_i)$. Remembering that the frequency of (x_i, y_j) is f_{ij}, the total sum of square deviations will be

$$\sum_i \sum_j f_{ij} (y_j - b_{yx}x_i)^2 = NS_y^2, \text{ say.} \quad . \quad (6.7.1)$$

Then

$$NS_y^2 = \sum_i \sum_j f_{ij}y_j^2 - 2b_{yx} \sum_i \sum_j f_{ij}x_iy_j + b_{yx}^2 \sum_i \sum_j f_{ij}x_i^2$$

$$= Ns_y^2 - 2b_{yx}Ns_{xy} + Nb_{yx}^2s_x^2$$

Since $b_{yx} = s_{xy}/s_x^2$, we have

$$NS_y^2 = Ns_y^2 (1 - s_{xy}^2/s_x^2s_y^2) = Ns_y^2(1 - r^2)$$

or

$$S_y^2 = s_y^2(1 - r^2) \quad . \quad . \quad . \quad . \quad (6.7.2)$$

or

$$r^2 = 1 - S_y^2/s_y^2 \quad . \quad . \quad . \quad . \quad (6.7.3)$$

S_y is called the *Standard Error of Estimate of* y from (6.6.9). Likewise, S_x, where $S_x^2 = s_x^2(1 - r^2)$, is called the *Standard Error of Estimate of* x.

Since S_y^2 is the mean of a sum of squares, it can never be negative. Therefore (6.7.2) shows that r^2 cannot be greater than 1. When $r = \pm 1$, $S_y^2 = 0$ and so *every* deviation, $(y_j - b_{yx}x_i) = 0$; this means that *every* point representing an *observed* value, every (x_i, y_j), lies on the regression line of y upon x. But if $r = \pm 1$, the line of regression of y on x and that of x on y coincide. Consequently, *all* the points representing the different observed values (x_i, y_j), and not just the points representing the array-means, lie on a single line. There is then a straight-line relationship between the variates in the sample and the correlation in the sample is perfect. We see then that the nearer r approaches unity, the more closely the observed values cluster about the regression lines and the closer these lines lie to each other. *r is therefore a measure of the extent to which any relationship there may be between the variates tends towards linearity.*

Exercise : *Show that the line of regression of y on x as defined above is also the line of minimum mean square deviation for the set of points* (x_i, y_j).

6.8. Worked Example.

The marks, x and y, gained by 1,000 *students for theory and laboratory work respectively, are grouped with common class intervals of* 5 *marks for each variable, the frequencies for the various classes being shown in the correlation-table below. The values of x and y indicated are the mid-values of the classes. Show that the coefficient of correlation is* 0·68 *and the regression equation of y on x is* $y = 29{\cdot}7 + 0{\cdot}656x$ (Weatherburn.)

y \ x	42	47	52	57	62	67	72	77	82	TOTALS
52	3	9	19	4	—	—	—	—	—	35
57	9	26	37	25	6	—	—	—	—	103
62	10	38	74	45	19	6	—	—	—	192
67	4	20	59	96	54	23	7	—	—	263
72	—	4	30	54	74	43	9	—	—	214
77		—	7	18	31	50	19	5	—	130
82	—	—	—	2	5	13	15	8	3	46
87	—	—	—	—	—	2	5	8	2	17
TOTALS	26	97	226	244	189	137	55	21	5	1,000

Treatment : (1) To simplify working we select a working mean and new units. We take our working mean at (57, 67) and since the class-interval for both variates is 5 marks, we take new variates :

$$X = (x - 57)/5; \quad Y = (y - 67)/5$$

What will be the effect of these changes on our calculations?

Consider a general transformation,

$$x = a + cX; \; y = b + dY; \text{ then } \bar{x} = a + c\bar{X}; \; \bar{y} = b + d\bar{Y}$$

We have :

$$s_x^2 = \frac{1}{N}\sum_i f_{ij}(x_i - \bar{x})^2 = \frac{c^2}{N}\sum_i f_{ij}(X_i - \bar{X})^2$$

or

$$s_x^2 = c^2 s_X^2 \text{ and, likewise, } s_y^2 = d^2 s_Y^2 \quad . \quad . \quad (6.8.1)$$

Also

$$s_{xy} = \frac{1}{N}\sum_i\sum_j f_{ij}(x_i - \bar{x})(y_j - \bar{y}) = \frac{cd}{N}\sum_i\sum_j f_{ij}(X_i - \bar{X})(Y_j - \bar{Y}) = cds_{XY} \quad (6.8.2)$$

$$\therefore \; r = \frac{s_{xy}}{s_x s_y} = \frac{cds_{XY}}{cs_X ds_Y} = \frac{s_{XY}}{s_X s_Y} \quad . \quad . \quad . \quad (6.8.3)$$

Again

$$b_{yx} = s_{xy}/s_x^2 = cds_{XY}/c^2s_X^2 = (d/c)b_{YX}$$

and, similarly,

$$b_{xy} = (c/d)b_{XY} \quad . \quad . \quad . \quad . \quad . \quad . \quad (6\cdot8\cdot4)$$

We conclude, therefore, that such a transformation of variates does not affect our method of calculating r, while, if, as in the present case, the new units are equal (here $c = d = 5$), the regression coefficients may also be calculated directly from the new correlation table.

(2) We now set out the table on page 109.

(3) (i) $\bar{X} = 0\cdot239$; $\bar{Y} = 0\cdot177$. Consequently, $\bar{x} = 57 + 5 \times 0\cdot239 = \underline{58\cdot195}$, and $y = 67 + 5 \times 0\cdot177 = \underline{67\cdot885}$.

(ii) $\frac{1}{N}\sum_i\sum_j f_{ij}X_i^2 = 2\cdot541$. $\therefore s_X^2 = \frac{1}{N}\sum_i\sum_j f_{ij}X_i^2 - \bar{X}^2$ $= 2\cdot541 - (0\cdot239)^2 = \underline{2\cdot484}$, and $s_X = \underline{1\cdot576}$. Consequently, although we do not require it here, $s_x = 5 \times 1\cdot576 = 7\cdot880$.

(iii) $\frac{1}{N}\sum_i\sum_j f_{ij}Y_j^2 = 2\cdot339$. $\therefore s_Y^2 = 2\cdot338 - (0\cdot177)^2 = \underline{2\cdot308}$ and $s_Y = \underline{1\cdot519}$. Consequently, $s_y = 5 \times 1\cdot519 = 7\cdot595$.

(iv) $\frac{1}{N}\sum_i\sum_j f_{ij}X_iY_j = 1\cdot671$. $\therefore s_{XY} = \frac{1}{N}\sum_i\sum_j f_{ij}X_iY_j - \bar{X}\bar{Y}$ $= 1\cdot671 - (0\cdot239)(0\cdot177) = \underline{1\cdot629}$, giving s_{xy} (not here required) $= 5^2 \times 1\cdot629 = 40\cdot725$.

(v) The *correlation coefficient*, r, is given by

$$r = s_{XY}/s_X \, . \, s_Y = 1\cdot629/1\cdot576 \times 1\cdot519 = \underline{0\cdot679}.$$

(vi) *The line of regression of y on x* is given by

$$y - \bar{y} = b_{yx}(x - \bar{x}).$$

But

$$b_{YX} = s_{YX}/s_X^2 = 1\cdot629/2\cdot484 = 0\cdot656.$$

Hence the required equation is

$$\underline{y = 0\cdot656x + 29\cdot696.}$$

Exercise: *For the data of the above example, find the regression equation of x on y and the angle between the two regression lines. Use* 6.6.13 *and the value of* $\tan\theta$ *to find r.*

Check and Alternative Method of Finding the Product-moment: It will be noticed that along each diagonal line running from top right to bottom left of the correlation table, the value of $X + Y$ is constant. Thus along the line from $X = 4$, $Y = -3$ to $X = -3$, $Y = 4$, $X + Y = 1$. Likewise, along each diagonal line from top-left to bottom-right, the value of $X - Y$ is constant. For the line running from $X = -3$, $Y = -3$ to $X = 4$, $Y = 4$, for example, $X - Y = 0$.

y	$Y \backslash X$ (x)	42	47	52	57	62	67	72	77	82	Totals A	B	C	D
	X	−3	−2	−1	0	+1	+2	+3	+4	+5	$\sum_i f_{ij}$	$\sum_i f_{ij}X_i$	$\sum_i f_{ij}X_i^2$	$\sum_i f_{ij}X_iY_j$
52	−3	3	9	19	4	—	—	—	—	—	35	− 46	82	138
57	−2	9	26	37	25	6	—	—	—	—	103	−110	228	220
62	−1	10	38	74	45	19	6	—	—	—	192	−149	359	149
67	0	4	20	59	96	54	23	7	—	—	263	+10	384	0
72	+1	—	4	30	54	74	43	9	—	—	214	+149	373	149
77	+2	—	—	7	18	31	50	19	5	—	130	+201	489	402
82	+3	—	—	—	2	5	13	15	8	3	46	+123	395	369
87	+4	—	—	—	—	—	2	5	8	2	17	+ 61	231	244
TOTALS E	$\sum_j f_{ij}$	26	97	226	244	189	137	55	21	5	$N =$ 1,000	$N\bar{X} =$ 239	2,541	1,671
TOTALS F	$\sum_j f_{ji}Y_j$	−37	−113	−161	−11	+120	+184	+112	+66	+17	$N\bar{Y} =$ 177		Check	
TOTALS G	$\sum_j f_{ji}Y_j^2$	73	227	451	325	286	398	300	220	59	2,339			
TOTALS H	$\sum_j f_{ji}X_iY_j$	111	226	161	0	120	368	336	264	85	1,671			

Now

$$\sum_i \sum_j f_{ij}(X_i + Y_j)^2 = \sum_i \sum_j f_{ij}X_i^2 + \sum_i \sum_j f_{ij}Y_j^2 + 2\sum_i \sum_j f_{ij}X_iY_j,$$

and

$$\sum_i \sum_j f_{ij}(X_i - Y_j)^2 = \sum_i \sum_j f_{ij}X_i^2 + \sum_i \sum_j f_{ij}Y_j^2 - 2\sum_i \sum_j f_{ij}X_iY_j$$

If then, as in the present case, the entries in the table cluster around the leading diagonal, we may use the second of these identities to find the product-moment of X and Y. Tabulating, we have

$X_i - Y_j$.	-3	-2	-1	0	1	2	3
f_{ij} . .	17	85	209	346	217	103	23
$(X_i - Y_j)^2$.	9	4	1	0	1	4	9
$f_{ij}(X_i - Y_j)^2$	153	340	209	0	217	412	207

$$\sum_i \sum_j f_{ij}X_i^2 = 2{,}541, \quad \sum_i \sum_j f_{ij}Y_j^2 = 2{,}339,$$

From the table, $\sum_i \sum_j f_{ij}(X_i - Y_j)^2 = 1{,}538$. Therefore, $\sum_i \sum_j f_{ij}X_iY_j$ $= \frac{1}{2}(2{,}541 + 2{,}339 - 1{,}538) = 1{,}671$.

If the entries cluster about the other diagonal, the first of the above two identities is the more convenient with which to work.

6.9. Rank Correlation. Suppose we have n individuals which, in virtue of some selected characteristic A, may be arranged in order, so that to each individual a different ordinal number is assigned. The n individuals are then said to be *ranked* according to the characteristic A, and the ordinal number assigned to an individual is its *rank*. For example, "seeded" entries for the Wimbledon lawn-tennis championships are ranked: they are "seeded" 1, 2, 3 (first, second and third) and so on.

The concept of *rank* is useful in the following ways:

(*a*) We may reduce the arithmetic involved in investigating the correlation between two variates if, for each variate separately, we first rank the given values and then calculate the product-moment correlation coefficient from these rank-values. In this way we have an *approximation* to the correlation coefficient, r.

(*b*) We may wish to estimate how good a judge of some characteristic of a number of objects a man is by asking him to rank them and then comparing his ranking with some known objective standard.

(c) We may wish to investigate the degree of agreement between two judges of the relative merits of a number of objects each possessing some characteristic for which there is no known objective standard of measurement (e.g., two judges at a " Beauty Competition ".)

Assume a set of n individuals, $a_1, a_2, \ldots a_n$, each possessing two characteristics x and y, such that the n individuals may be ranked according to x and, separately, according to y. Let the rankings be as follows :

Individual . .	$a_1\ a_2 \ldots a_i \ldots a_n$
x-Rank . . .	$x_1\ x_2 \ldots x_i \ldots x_n$
y-Rank . . .	$y_1\ y_2 \ldots y_i \ldots y_n$

Here $x_1, x_2 \ldots x_i \ldots x_n$ are the numbers $1, 2, 3 \ldots n$ in some order without repetitions or gaps. Likewise the y's.

Now if there were perfect correlation between the rankings we should have, for all i, $x_i = y_i$. If this is not so, write $x_i - y_i = d_i$.

Then

$$\sum_i d_i^2 = \sum_i (x_i - y_i)^2 = \sum_i x_i^2 + \sum_i y_i^2 - 2\sum_i x_i y_i$$

But $\sum_i x_i^2 = \sum_i y_i^2 = 1^2 + 2^2 + 3^2 + \ldots + n^2$, the sum of the squares of the first n natural numbers. Consequently, $\sum_i x_i^2 = \sum_i y_i^2 = n(n+1)(2n+1)/6$. Therefore,

$$\sum_i x_i y_i = \tfrac{1}{2}(\sum_i x_i^2 + \sum_i y_i^2) - \tfrac{1}{2}\sum_i d_i^2$$
$$= n(n+1)(2n+1)/6 - \tfrac{1}{2}\sum_i d_i^2.$$

Now

$$\text{cov}\,(x, y) = \frac{1}{n}\sum_i x_i y_i - \bar{x}\bar{y};$$

and $$\text{var}\,x = \text{var}\,y = \frac{1}{n}(1^2 + 2^2 + \ldots + n^2) - \bar{y}^2;$$

But $$\bar{x} = \bar{y} = (1 + 2 + 3 + \ldots + n)/n = (n+1)/2.$$

Therefore,

$$\text{cov}(x, y) = (n + 1)(2n + 1)/6 - (\sum_i d_i^2)/2n - (n + 1)^2/4$$

$$= (n^2 - 1)/12 - (\sum_i d_i^2)/2n$$

and

$$\text{var } x = (n + 1)(2n + 1)/6 - (n + 1)^2/4 = (n^2 - 1)/12$$

So $\quad \text{cov}(x, y)/(\text{var } x \,.\, \text{var } y)^{\frac{1}{2}} = \text{cov}(x, y)/\text{var } x$

$$= 1 - 6(\sum_i d_i^2)/(n^3 - n) \quad . \quad . \quad . \quad (6.9.1)$$

This is *Spearman's coefficient of rank correlation*, R. If $\sum_i d_i^2 = 0$, $R = 1$, and there is perfect correlation by rank (since $d_i = 0$ for all i, and, so, for all i, $x_i = y_i$).

What happens, however, if the two rankings are exactly the reverse of one another? This is the most unfavourable case and, consequently, $\sum_i d_i^2$ is a maximum, while, since for all i, $x_i + y_i$ will be equal to $n + 1$, $\sum_i (x_i + y_i)^2 = n(n + 1)^2$. We have, then, $2\sum_i x_i y_i = n(n + 1)^2 - 2n(n + 1)(2n + 1)/6$ or $\sum_i x_i y_i = n(n + 1)(n + 2)/6$. Cov (x, y) is $-(n^2 - 1)/12$ and var (x) is $+(n^2 - 1)/12$. $\therefore R = -1$. Thus R varies between the two limits ± 1.

Worked Example 1: *The figures in the following table give the number of criminal convictions (in thousands) and the numbers unemployed (in millions) for the years* 1924–33. *Find the coefficient of rank-correlation.*

Year	1924	1925	1926	1927	1928	1929	1930	1931	1932	1933
Number convicted of crime .	7·88	8·12	7·86	7·25	7·44	7·22	8·28	8·83	10·54	9·46
Number of unemployed . .	1·26	1·24	1·43	1·19	1·33	1·34	2·5	2·67	2·78	2·26

Treatment: We rank the data, thus:

Year	1924	1925	1926	1927	1928	1929	1930	1931	1932	1933
Number convicted	6	5	7	9	8	10	4	3	1	2
Number unemployed . .	8	9	5	10	7	6	3	2	1	4
d_i^2 . . .	4	16	4	1	1	16	1	1	0	4

We have $\sum_i d_i^2 = 48$, and, since $n = 10$, $n^3 - n = 990$. Consequently,

$$R = 1 - 6 \times \tfrac{48}{990} = 0{\cdot}709$$

Exercise : *Find r, the product-moment correlation coefficient, for the above data.*

Worked Example 2 : *Two judges in a baby-competition rank the* 12 *entries as follows :*

X .	1	2	3	4	5	6	7	8	9	10	11	12
Y .	12	9	6	10	3	5	4	7	8	2	11	1

What degree of agreement is there between the judges ?

Treatment : Here we have no objective information about the babies, but the coefficient of rank correlation will tell us something about the judges. We have

$$\sum_i d_i^2 = 416, \; n^3 - n = 1{,}716$$

Thus, $R = -0{\cdot}455$, indicating that the judges have fairly strongly divergent likes and dislikes where babies are concerned !

6.10. Kendall's Coefficient. A second coefficient of rank correlation has been suggested by M. G. Kendall. Consider the rankings in Example 2 above. If we take the first number of the second ranking, 12, with each *succeeding* number, we shall have 11 number-pairs. To each pair, (a, b), say, allot the score 1 if $a < b$, and the score -1 if $a > b$. Thus for the 11 pairs (a, b), where $a = 12$, the total score is -11. Now consider the 10 pairs (a, b), where $a = 9$, viz., (9, 6), (9, 10), (9, 3), etc. The total score for this set is $-1 + 1 - 1 - 1 - 1 - 1 - 1 - 1 + 1 - 1 = -6$. Continuing in this way, we obtain the 11 following scores, -11, -6, -1, -6, 3, 0, 1, 0, -1, 0, -1, totalling -22. Had the numbers been in their natural order, as in the upper ranking, the total score would have been $11 + 10 + 9 + 8 + 7 + 6 + 5 + 4 + 3 + 2 + 1 = 66$.

The Kendall rank correlation coefficient, τ, is the ratio of the actual to the maximum score, i.e., in this case,

$$\tau = -\tfrac{22}{66} = -\tfrac{1}{3}$$

The Spearman coefficient, R, for the same data was $-0{\cdot}451$.

Generally, if there are n *individuals in the ranking, the Kendall coefficient is*

$$\tau = 2S/n(n - 1) \quad . \quad . \quad . \quad (6.10.1)$$

where S *is the actual score calculated according to the method used above.*

A shorter method of calculating S is:

> In the second ranking, the figure 1 has 0 numbers to its right and 11 to its left. Allot the score $0 - 11 = -11$ and cross out the 1. 2 has 1 number to its right and 9 numbers to its left: the score, therefore, allotted is $1 - 9 = 8$; cross out 2. 3 has 5 numbers to its right and 4 to its left; score is $5 - 4 = 1$; cross out 3. Continue in this way, obtaining the set of scores: $-11, -8, 1, -2, -1, 2, -1, -2, 1, 0, -1$, the total of which is $S = -22$.

Alternatively, we may set down the two rankings, one of which is in natural order, one above the other, and join 1 to 1, 2 to 2, 3 to 3 and so on. Then if we count the number of intersections (care must be taken not to allow any two such intersections to coincide), N, say, S will be given by

$$S = n(n - 1)/2 - 2N$$

and, therefore,

$$\tau = 2S/n(n - 1) = 1 - 4N/n(n - 1) \quad . \quad (6.10.2)$$

Like Spearman's R, Kendall's τ is $+1$ when the correspondence between the rankings is perfect, and -1 only if one is the inverse of the other. When n is large τ is about $2R/3$.

Worked Example: *Show that the values of* τ *between the natural order* 1, 2, . . . 10 *and the following rankings are* $-0{\cdot}24$ *and* $0{\cdot}60$:

7, 10, 4, 1, 6, 8, 9, 5, 2, 3
10, 1, 2, 3, 4, 5, 6, 7, 8, 9

Find also τ *between the two rankings as they stand.* (*Modified from M. G. Kendall,* Advanced Theory of Statistics, *Vol. I, p.* 437.)

Treatment: (1) Consider the first ranking. Using the short method of calculating S, we have

$$S = (6 - 3) + (1 - 7) + (0 - 7) + (4 - 2) + (0 - 5) + (2 - 2) + (3 - 0) + (1 - 1) + (0 - 1) = -11$$

Hence $$\tau = -11/45 = \underline{-0{\cdot}24}.$$

(2) Using the alternative short method for the second ranking we have:

1, 2, 3, 4, 5, 6, 7, 8, 9, 10
10, 1, 2, 3, 4, 5, 6, 7, 8, 9

and, obviously, $N = 9$, the number of inversions of the natural order. Thus

$$\tau = 1 - 4 \times 9/90 = 3/5 = \underline{0 \cdot 60}$$

(3) To find τ between the two rankings, rearrange both so that one is in the natural order. Here it is easier to put the second in that order:

10, 4, 1, 6, 8, 9, 5, 2, 3, 7
1, 2, 3, 4, 5, 6, 7, 8, 9, 10

Then $$S = -5 \text{ and } \tau = -\tfrac{5}{45} = \underline{-\tfrac{1}{9}}.$$

Exercise: *Show that R between the natural order* 1, 2, . . . 10 *and the above two rankings has the values* $-0 \cdot 37$ *and* $0 \cdot 45$ *respectively and that between the two rankings as they stand* $R = -0 \cdot 19$.

6.11. Coefficient of Concordance. Frequently we need to investigate the degree of concordance between more than two rankings. Suppose, for example, we have the following 3 rankings:

X	1	2	3	4	5	6	7	8	9	10
Y	7	10	4	1	6	8	9	5	2	3
Z	9	6	10	3	5	4	7	8	2	1

Summing the columns, we have the sums

17 18 17 8 16 18 23 21 13 14

Had there been perfect concordance, we should have had

3 6 9 12 15 18 21 24 27 30

and the *variance of these numbers would then have been a maximum.* But when, as in the present case, there is little concordance, the variance is small. It is reasonable, therefore, to take *the ratio of the variance of the actual sums to the variance in the case of perfect concordance as a measure of rank-concordance.*

The mean of each ranking is $(n + 1)/2$ in the general case; therefore, if there are m rankings, the mean of the sums will be $m(n + 1)/2$. With perfect concordance, these sums will be $m, 2m, 3m, \ldots nm$ and their variance, then,

$$m^2(1^2 + 2^2 + 3^2 + \ldots + n^2)/n - m^2(n + 1)^2/4 = m^2(n^2 - 1)/12$$

Let S be the sum of the squared deviations of the actual sums from their mean, $m(n + 1)/2$. We define the *coefficient of concordance*, W, between the rankings, by

$$W \equiv (S/n)/m^2(n^2 - 1)/12 = 12S/m^2n(n^2 - 1) \quad . \quad (6.11.1)$$

Clearly, W varies between 0 and 1.

In the case of the three rankings given, $m = 3$, $n = 10$ and

$$W = 12 \times 158{\cdot}5/9 \times 990 = 0{\cdot}2134$$

It may be shown (see Kendall, *Advanced Theory of Statistics*, vol. 1, p. 411) that if $R_{av.}$ denote the average of Spearman's R between *all possible pairs of rankings*,

$$R_{av.} = (mW - 1)/(m - 1) \quad . \quad . \quad (6.11.2)$$

Exercise : *Verify that* (6.11.2) *holds in the case of the three rankings given at the beginning of this section.*

6.12. Polynomial Regression. So far we have limited our discussion of regression to bivariate distributions where the regression curves were straight lines. Such distributions are, however, the exception rather than the rule, although they are important exceptions. If, using the notation of 6.6, we plot $\bar{y}_i$ against x_i (or $\bar{x}_j$ against y_j), the line about which these points tend to cluster most closely is usually curved rather than straight. When this is the case, the coefficient of correlation, r, which, it will be recalled, is a measure of the extent to which any relationship between the variates tends towards linearity, is no longer a suitable measure of correlation.

The simplest type of non-linear equation is that in which one of the variates is a *polynomial* function of the other, viz.,

$$y = a_0 + a_1x + a_2x^2 + \ldots + a_rx^r + \ldots + a_kx^k$$
$$= \sum_{r=0}^{k} a_rx^r \quad . \quad (6.12.1)$$

where the coefficients a_r, ($r = 0, 1, 2, \ldots k$), are not all zero. If the regression equation of y on x (or x on y) is of this form, we have *polynomial regression*.

Once we have decided upon the degree, k, of the polynomial, we again use the *Method of Least Squares* to determine the coefficients, a_r, ($r = 0, 1, 2, \ldots k$).

Referring to Table 6.2.2, let $\bar{y}_i$ be the actual mean of the x_i-array, and let $\bar{Y}_i$ be the calculated, or predicted, value when $x = x_i$ is substituted in (6.12.1). (If the data are not grouped and only one value of y corresponds to a given x, that value of y is, of course, itself the mean.)

The sum of the squared residuals, S^2, is then given by:

$$S^2 = \sum_i f_{i.}(\bar{y}_i - \overline{Y}_i)^2 = \sum_i f_{i.}(\bar{y}_i - \sum_r a_i x_i^r)^2 \quad . \quad (6.12.2)$$

S^2 is thus a function of the $k + 1$ quantities, $a_r, (r = 0, 1, \ldots k)$. To find the values of these quantities which minimise S^2, we differentiate S^2 partially with respect to each of these quantities and equate each partial derivative, $\partial S^2/\partial a_r$, to zero. This gives us $K + 1$ simultaneous equations in the a's, *the normal equations*, $\partial S^2/\partial a_r = 0$ $(r = 0, 1, \ldots k)$, from which the required coefficients may be determined.

The following example illustrates the method when $k = 2$.

Worked Example : *The profits, £y, of a certain company in the xth year of its life are given by* :

x .	1	2	3	4	5
y .	1,250	1,400	1,650	1,950	2,300

Find the parabolic regression of y on x.

(*Weatherburn.*)

Treatment : Put $u = x - 3$; $v = (y - 1{,}650)/50$. Then—

x.	u.	u^2.	u^3.	u^4.	y.	v.	vu.	vu^2.
1	−2	4	−8	16	1,250	− 8	16	−32
2	−1	1	−1	1	1,400	− 5	5	− 5
3	0	0	0	0	1,650	−13	0	−37
4	1	1	1	1	1,950	6	6	6
5	2	4	8	16	2,300	13	26	52
	0	10	0	34	—	6	53	21

For parabolic regression of v on u, $v = a + bu + cu^2$ and, so, $S^2 = \sum_i (a + bu_i + cu_i^2 - v_i)^2$.

$$\therefore \quad \partial S^2/\partial a = 2 \sum_i (a + bu_i + cu_i^2 - v_i)$$

$$= 2(na + b \sum_i u_i + c \sum_i u_i^2 - \sum_i v_i)$$

$$\partial S^2/\partial b = 2 \sum_i (a + bu_i + cu_i^2 - v_i)u_i$$
$$= 2(a \sum_i u_i + b \sum_i u_i^2 + c \sum_i u_i^3 - \sum_i v_i u_i)$$
$$\partial S^2/\partial c = 2 \sum_i (a + bu_i + cu_i^2 - v_i)u_i^2$$
$$= 2(a \sum_i u_i^2 + b \sum_i u_i^3 + c \sum_i u_i^4 - \sum_i v_i u_i^2)$$

In the present example, the normal equations $\partial S^2/\partial a$, $\partial S^2/\partial b$, $\partial S^2/\partial c = 0$, are

$$5a + 10c - 6 = 0; \quad 10b - 53 = 0; \quad 10a + 34c - 21 = 0$$

giving $a = -0{\cdot}086,\ b = 5{\cdot}3,\ c = 0{\cdot}643.$

The regression equation of v on u is, therefore,

$$v = -0{\cdot}086 + 5{\cdot}3u + 0{\cdot}643u^2.$$

Changing back to our old variates, the required regression equation is

$$\underline{y = 1{,}140 + 72x + 32{\cdot}15x^2}$$

6.13. Least Squares and Moments. If we differentiate (6.12.2) partially with respect to a_r, we have

$$\partial S^2/\partial a_r = \sum_i f_{i.}(\bar{y}_i - \sum_r a_r x_i^r) \,.\, (-2x_i^r)$$

and, equating to zero,

$$\sum_i f_{i.} x_i^r \bar{y}_i = \sum_i f_{i.} x_i^r \overline{Y}_i, \text{ for all } r,$$

showing that—

> **The process of fitting a polynomial curve of degree k to a set of data by the method of Least Squares is equivalent to equating the moments of order 0, 1, 2 . . . k of the polynomial to those of the data.**

6.14. Correlation Ratios. The correlation table being (6.2.2), let the regression equation of y on x be $y = y(x)$. Then $\overline{Y}_i = y(x_i)$. If, then, S_y^2 is the standard error of estimate of y from this equation, i.e., the mean square deviation of the y's from the regression curve,

$$NS_y^2 = \sum_i \sum_j f_{ij}(y_j - \overline{Y}_i)^2 = \sum_i \sum_j f_{ij}(y_j - \bar{y}_i + \bar{y}_i - \overline{Y}_i)^2$$
$$= \sum_i \sum_j f_{ij}(y_j - \bar{y}_i)^2 + 2 \sum_i \sum_j f_{ij}(y_j - \bar{y}_i)(\bar{y}_i - \overline{Y}_i)$$
$$+ \sum_i \sum_j f_{ij}(\bar{y}_i - \overline{Y}_i)^2.$$

Let $n_i = f_{i\cdot} \equiv \sum_j f_{ij}$, the total frequency in the x_ith array, and $s_{y,i}^2$, the variance of the y's in the same array. Then, since $\sum_j f_{ij}(y_j - \bar{y}_i) = 0$,

$$NS_y^2 = \sum_i n_i s^2_{y,i} + \sum_i n_i(\bar{y}_i - \bar{Y}_i)^2 \quad . \quad (6.14.1)$$

It follows that if all the means of the x-arrays lie on $y = y(x)$, i.e., $(\bar{y}_i - \bar{Y}_i) = 0$, for all i, S_y^2 is the mean value of the variance of y in each x-array, taken over all such arrays. Consequently, if all the variances are equal, each is equal to S_y^2.

> **When this is the case, the regression of y on x is said to be *homoscedastic* (equally scattered).**

If the regression is also linear, $S_y^2 = s_y^2\,(1 - r^2)$ and so the standard deviation of each array is $s_y\,(1 - r^2)^{\frac{1}{2}}$.

Now let $S_y'^2$ be the mean square deviation of the y's *from the mean of their respective arrays*. Then

$$NS_y'^2 = \sum_i \sum_j f_{ij}(y_j - \bar{y}_i)^2 = \sum_i \sum_j f_{ij}y_j^2 - 2\sum_i \sum_j f_{ij}y_j\bar{y}_i + \sum_i \sum_j f_{ij}\bar{y}_i^2$$

$$= \sum_i \sum_j f_{ij}y_j^2 - 2\sum_i [\bar{y}_i(\sum_j f_{ij}y_j)] + \sum_i \sum_j f_{ij}\bar{y}_i^2$$

But $\sum_j f_{ij}y_j = \bar{y}_i \sum_j f_{ij}$, and, therefore,

$$NS_y'^2 = \sum_i \sum_j f_{ij}y_j^2 - \sum_i \sum_j f_{ij}\bar{y}_i^2$$

$$= Nm_{02}' - \sum_i n_i\bar{y}_i^2 = Ns_y^2 + N\bar{y}^2 - \sum_i n_i\bar{y}_i^2$$

$$= Ns_y^2 - (\sum_i n_i\bar{y}_i^2 - N\bar{y}^2)$$

But $\bar{y}$ is the mean of the array-means, $\bar{y}_i$; therefore the expression in brackets is N times the *variance of the means of the arrays*, which we shall denote by $s_{\bar{y}}^2$. So

$$S_y'^2 = s_y^2 - s_{\bar{y}}^2 \quad . \quad . \quad . \quad . \quad (6.14.2)$$

By analogy with (6.7.2), we write this

$$S_y'^2 = s_y^2(1 - e_{yx}^2) \quad . \quad . \quad . \quad (6.14.3)$$

where

$$e_{yx} = s_{\bar{y}}/s_y \quad . \quad . \quad . \quad . \quad . \quad . \quad (6.14.4)$$

and is called the *correlation ratio of y on x*. Likewise $e_{xy} = s_{\bar{x}}/s_x$, is the *correlation ratio of x on y*. Since both $S_y'^2$ and

s_y^2 are positive, (6.14.3) shows that $e_{yx}^2 \leqslant 1$. Moreover, since the mean-square deviation of a set of quantities from their mean is a minimum,

$$0 \leqslant S_y'^2 \leqslant S_y^2 \quad \text{or} \quad 0 \leqslant 1 - e_{yx}^2 \leqslant 1 - r^2,$$
$$\text{i.e., } r^2 \leqslant e_{yx}^2 \leqslant 1$$

or

$$0 \leqslant e_{yx}^2 - r^2 \leqslant 1 - r^2. \quad . \quad . \quad (6.14.5)$$

Since we regard r as a measure of the degree to which any association between the variates tends towards linearity and since the residual dispersion, $1 - r^2$, is 0 when $r^2 = 1$, and 1 when $r = 0$, *a non-zero value of* $e_{yx}^2 - r^2$ *may be regarded tentatively as a measure of the degree to which the regression departs from linearity.* (But see 10.10.)

That e_{yx} is a *correlation* measure will be appreciated by noting that, when $e_{yx}^2 = 1$, $S_y'^2 = 0$, and, so, all the points (x_i, y_j) lie on the curve of means, the regression curve, $y = y(x)$, i.e., there is an exact functional relationship between the variates.

6.15. Worked Example.

Calculate the correlation ratio e_{yx} for the data of 6.8.

Treatment :

(1) $$e_{yx}^2 = s_{\bar{y}}^2/s_y^2 = (\sum_i n_i\bar{y}_i^2 - N\bar{y}^2)/Ns_y^2 \quad . \quad (6.15.1)$$

Let $T_i(y)$ be the sum of the y's in the x_ith array. Then $T_i(y) = n_i\bar{y}_i$ and $\sum_i T_i(y) = N\bar{y}$. If $T(y)$ be the sum of the y's in the distribution, $T(y) = \sum_i T_i(y)$. Then $N\bar{y}^2 = [T(y)]^2/N$ and $\sum_i n_i\bar{y}_i^2 = \sum_i \left(\frac{[T_i(y)]^2}{n_i}\right)$.

Consequently

$$e_{yx}^2 = \frac{1}{Ns_y^2}\left[\sum_i \left(\frac{[T_i(y)]^2}{n_i}\right) - \frac{[T(y)]^2}{N}\right] \quad . \quad (6.15.2)$$

From the definition, $e_{yx}^2 = s_{\bar{y}}^2/s_y^2$, we see that, since deviation from the mean is unchanged by change of origin, e_{yx}^2 is unchanged thereby. Furthermore, since both numerator and denominator involve only squares, they are changed in the same ratio by any change of unit employed. Hence e_{yx}^2 is unchanged by change of unit and origin, and we may, therefore, work with the variables X and Y in our table of 6.8(2). From that table, then, we see that $T(y)$ is the total of row F, and $\sum_i \left(\frac{[T_i(y)]^2}{n_i}\right)$ the sum of those quantities each of which is the square of a term in row F divided by the corresponding term in row E.

(2) We have then : $T(y)$ = sum of row $F = 177$ and $N = 1{,}000$, giving $[T(y)]^2/N = 31{\cdot}329$. Also

$$\sum_i \left(\frac{[T_i(y)]^2}{n_i}\right) = \frac{37^2}{26} + \frac{113^2}{97} + \frac{161^2}{226} + \frac{11^2}{244} + \frac{120^2}{189} + \frac{184^2}{137} + $$
$$+ \frac{112^2}{55} + \frac{66^2}{21} + \frac{17^2}{5}$$

$$= 1{,}117 \text{ (to 4 significant figures).}$$

Thus $$e_{yx}^2 = \frac{1{,}117 - 31}{1{,}000 \times 2{\cdot}308} \qquad (\because \quad s_y^2 = 2{\cdot}308 \text{ from } 6{\cdot}8\ (3))$$

$$= 0{\cdot}471$$

or $$\underline{e_{yx} = 0{\cdot}686}, \text{ approximately.}$$

Since $e_{yx}^2 - r^2 = 0{\cdot}009$, the departure from linearity is small.

6.16. Multivariate Regression. When we have more than two correlated variates, two major problems present themselves :

(1) we may wish to examine the influence on one of the variates of the others of the set—this is the problem of *multivariate regression*; or
(2) we may be interested in assessing the interdependence of two of the variates, after eliminating the influence of all the others—this is the problem of *partial correlation*.

Here we confine ourselves to the case of three variates, x_1, x_2, x_3, measured from their means, with variances s_1^2, s_2^2, s_3^2 respectively.

Since the variates *are* measured from their means, let the regression equations be

$$x_1 = b_{12\cdot3}x_2 + b_{13\cdot2}x_3 \quad . \quad . \quad . \quad (6.16.1)$$
$$x_2 = b_{23\cdot1}x_3 + b_{21\cdot3}x_1 \quad . \quad . \quad . \quad (6.16.2)$$
$$x_3 = b_{31\cdot2}x_1 + b_{32\cdot1}x_2 \quad . \quad . \quad . \quad (6.16.3)$$

We shall determine the b's by the method of Least Squares. Consider (6.16.1). The sum of the squared deviations of observed values of x_1 from the estimated values is given by

$$S^2 = \Sigma\,(x_1 - b_{12\cdot3}x_2 - b_{13\cdot2}x_3)^2 \quad . \quad (6.16.4)$$

The normal equations are :

$$b_{12\cdot3}\,\Sigma\,x_2^2 + b_{13\cdot2}\,\Sigma\,x_2x_3 = \Sigma\,x_1x_2 \quad . \quad (6.16.5)$$
$$b_{12\cdot3}\,\Sigma\,x_2x_3 + b_{13\cdot2}\,\Sigma\,x_3^2 = \Sigma\,x_1x_3 \quad . \quad (6.16.6)$$

Solving these, we have

$$b_{12\cdot 3} = \frac{s_1}{s_2}\left[\frac{r_{12} - r_{13}r_{23}}{1 - r_{23}^2}\right] \quad . \quad . \quad . \quad (6.16.7)$$

$$b_{13\cdot 2} = \frac{s_1}{s_3}\left[\frac{r_{13} - r_{12}r_{32}}{1 - r_{23}^2}\right] \quad . \quad . \quad (6.16.8)$$

Here r_{12}, r_{23}, r_{31} are *total correlations* : r_{12}, for instance, is the correlation between x_1 and x_2, formed, by ignoring the values of x_3, in the usual manner.

The coefficients $b_{12\cdot 3}$ and $b_{13\cdot 2}$ are called *partial regression coefficients*. Whereas $r_{ij} = r_{ji}$, $b_{ij.k}$ is not in general equal to $b_{ji.k}$.

The reader familiar with determinant notation [1] will realise that we may simplify these expressions. Let R denote the determinant

$$\begin{vmatrix} r_{11} & r_{12} & r_{13} \\ r_{21} & r_{22} & r_{23} \\ r_{31} & r_{32} & r_{33} \end{vmatrix} \quad \begin{array}{ll} \text{where } r_{11} = r_{22} = r_{33} = 1 \\ \text{and} \quad r_{ij} = r_{ji} \text{ for } i, j = 1, 2, 3, \text{ but } i \neq j. \end{array}$$

Then, if R_{ij} denotes the cofactor of r_{ij} in R, we have

$$R_{11} = 1 - r_{23}^2; \quad - R_{12} = r_{12} - r_{13}r_{23}; \quad - R_{13} = r_{13} - r_{12}r_{32}.$$

also

$$\left.\begin{array}{l} r_{11}R_{11} + r_{12}R_{12} + r_{13}R_{13} = R \\ r_{21}R_{11} + r_{22}R_{12} + r_{23}R_{13} = 0 \\ r_{31}R_{11} + r_{32}R_{12} + r_{33}R_{13} = 0 \end{array}\right\} \text{or} \left\{\begin{array}{l} R_{11} + r_{12}R_{12} + r_{13}R_{13} = R \\ r_{21}R_{11} + R_{12} + r_{23}R_{13} = 0 \\ r_{13}R_{11} + r_{23}R_{12} + R_{13} = 0 \end{array}\right\} \quad (6.16.9)$$

The regression equations become :

(1) Regression of x_1 on x_2 and x_3 :

$$\frac{R_{11}}{s_1}x_1 + \frac{R_{12}}{s_2}x_2 + \frac{R_{13}}{s_3}x_3 = 0 \quad . \quad (6.16.10(a))$$

(2) Regression of x_2 on x_3 and x_1 :

$$\frac{R_{22}}{s_2}x_2 + \frac{R_{23}}{s_3}x_3 + \frac{R_{21}}{s_1}x_1 = 0 \quad . \quad (6.16.10(b))$$

(3) Regression of x_3 on x_1 and x_2 :

$$\frac{R_{33}}{s_3}x_3 + \frac{R_{31}}{s_1}x_1 + \frac{R_{32}}{s_2}x_2 = 0 \quad . \quad (6.16.10(c))$$

In the space of the three variates, these equations are represented by planes. These *regression planes* should not be

[1] See Mathematical Note at end of Chapter.

confused with the *regression lines* : the regression line of x_1 on x_2 being $x_1 = (r_{12}s_1/s_2)x_2$, for instance.

6.17. Multiple Correlation.

DEFINITION : The coefficient of multiple correlation of x_1 with x_2 and x_3, denoted by $r_{1\cdot 23}$, is the coefficient of product-moment correlation of x_1 and its estimate from the regression equation of x_1 on x_2 and x_3.

That this is a natural definition is clear if we recall that if x_1 lies everywhere on the regression plane, there is an exact functional relationship between the three variates.

From the definition, $r_{1\cdot 23} = \dfrac{\text{cov}\,(x_1, b_{12\cdot 3}x_2 + b_{13\cdot 2}x_3)}{[\text{var}\,x_1 \,.\, \text{var}\,(b_{12\cdot 3}x_2 + b_{13\cdot 2}x_3)]^{\frac{1}{2}}}$.

(i) $\text{cov}\,(x_1, b_{12\cdot 3}x_2 + b_{13\cdot 2}x_3)$

$$= \mathcal{E}(b_{12\cdot 3}x_1x_2 + b_{13\cdot 2}x_1x_3), \text{ since } \bar{x}_1 = \bar{x}_2 = \bar{x}_3 = 0$$
$$= b_{12\cdot 3}\mathcal{E}(x_1x_2) + b_{13\cdot 2}\mathcal{E}(x_1x_3)$$
$$= b_{12\cdot 3}\,\text{cov}(x_1x_2) + b_{13\cdot 2}\,\text{cov}\,(x_1x_3)$$
$$= -\frac{s_1}{s_2}\frac{R_{12}}{R_{11}} r_{12}s_1s_2 - \frac{s_1}{s_3}\frac{R_{13}}{R_{11}} r_{13}s_1s_3$$
$$= -\frac{s_1^2}{R_{11}}[r_{12}R_{12} + r_{13}R_{13}]$$

Now, using the first equation of (6.16.9),

$$\text{cov}\,(x_1, b_{12\cdot 3}x_2 + b_{13\cdot 2}x_3) = -\frac{s_1^2}{R_{11}}[R - r_{11}R_{11}]$$
$$= s_1^2[1 - R/R_{11}], \quad \because \quad r_{11} = 1.$$

(ii) $\text{var}\,(x_1) = s_1^2$.
(iii) $\text{var}\,(b_{12\cdot 3}x_2 + b_{13\cdot 2}x_3)$

$$= b_{12\cdot 3}^2s_2^2 + b_{13\cdot 2}^2s_3^2 + 2b_{12\cdot 3}b_{13\cdot 2}r_{23}s_2s_3 \text{ (see 7.7.4)}$$
$$= \frac{s_1^2}{R_{11}^2}[R_{12}^2 + R_{13}^2 + 2R_{12}R_{13}r_{23}]$$
$$= \frac{s_1^2}{R_{11}^2}[R_{12}(R_{12} + r_{23}R_{13}) + R_{13}(R_{13} + r_{23}R_{12})]$$

Using the second and third equations of (6.16.9),

$$\text{var}\,(b_{12\cdot 3}x_2 + b_{13\cdot 2}x_3) = \frac{s_1^2}{R_{11}^2}[- R_{12}R_{11}r_{12} - R_{13}R_{11}r_{13}]$$
$$= -\frac{s_1^2}{R_{11}}[r_{12}R_{12} + r_{13}R_{13}] = s_1^2[1 - R/R_{11}].$$

Consequently,

$$r_{1\cdot 23} = [1 - R/R_{11}]^{\frac{1}{2}} = \left[\frac{r_{12}^2 + r_{13}^2 - 2r_{12}r_{23}r_{31}}{1 - r_{23}^2}\right]^{\frac{1}{2}}. \quad (6.17.1)$$

Likewise

$$r_{2\cdot 31} = [1 - R/R_{22}]^{\frac{1}{2}} \text{ and } r_{3\cdot 12} = [1 - R/R_{33}]^{\frac{1}{2}}$$

6.18. Worked Example.

Calculate the multiple correlation coefficient of x_1 on x_2 and x_3, $r_{1\cdot 23}$, from the following data :

x_1.	x_2.	x_3.
5	2	21
3	4	21
2	2	15
4	2	17
3	3	20
1	2	13
8	4	32

Find also the regression equation of x_1 on x_2 and x_3.

Treatment :

x_1	$X_1 = x_1 - 4$	X_1^2	x_2	$X_2 = x_2 - 3$	X_2^2	x_3	$X_3 = x_3 - 20$	X_3^2	X_1X_2	X_2X_3	X_3X_1
5	+1	1	2	−1	1	21	+ 1	1	−1	− 1	+ 1
3	−1	1	4	+1	1	21	+ 1	1	−1	+ 1	− 1
2	−2	4	2	−1	1	15	− 5	25	+2	+ 5	+10
4	0	0	2	−1	1	17	− 3	9	0	+ 3	0
3	−1	1	3	0	0	20	0	0	0	0	0
1	−3	9	2	−1	1	13	− 7	49	+3	+ 7	+21
8	+4	16	4	+1	1	32	+12	144	+4	+12	+48
	−2	32		−2	6		− 1	229	+7	+27	+79

$\bar{X}_1 = -\frac{2}{7} = -0{\cdot}286$; $\bar{X}_2 = -\frac{2}{7} = -0{\cdot}286$; $\bar{X}_3 = -\frac{1}{7} = -0{\cdot}143$. $\frac{1}{7}\Sigma X_1^2 = 4{\cdot}571$; $\frac{1}{7}\Sigma X_2^2 = 0{\cdot}857$; $\frac{1}{7}\Sigma X_3^2 = 32{\cdot}714$; $\frac{1}{7}\Sigma X_1X_2 = \frac{7}{7} = 1$; $\frac{1}{7}\Sigma X_2X_3 = \frac{27}{7} = 3{\cdot}857$; $\frac{1}{7}\Sigma X_3X_1 = \frac{79}{7} = 11{\cdot}286$.

$$\underline{\text{cov}\,(x_1x_2)} = \tfrac{1}{7}\Sigma X_1X_2 - \bar{X}_1\bar{X}_2 = 1 - (-0{\cdot}286)(-0{\cdot}286)$$
$$= 1 - 0{\cdot}082 = \underline{0{\cdot}918}$$

$$\underline{\text{cov}\,(x_2x_3)} = \tfrac{1}{7}\Sigma X_2X_3 - \bar{X}_2\bar{X}_3 = 3{\cdot}857 - (-0{\cdot}286)(-0{\cdot}143)$$
$$= 3{\cdot}857 - 0{\cdot}041 = \underline{3{\cdot}816}$$

$$\underline{\text{cov}\,(x_3x_1)} = \tfrac{1}{7}\Sigma X_3X_1 - \bar{X}_3\bar{X}_1 = 11{\cdot}286 - (-0{\cdot}286)(-0{\cdot}143)$$
$$= 11{\cdot}286 - 0{\cdot}041 = \underline{11{\cdot}245}$$

$\underline{\text{var}(x_1)} = \frac{1}{7}\Sigma X_1^2 - \bar{X}_1^2 = 4{\cdot}571 - (-0{\cdot}286)^2$
$= 4{\cdot}571 - 0{\cdot}082 = \underline{4{\cdot}489}$

$\underline{\text{var}(x_2)} = \frac{1}{7}\Sigma X_2^2 - \bar{X}_2^2 = 0{\cdot}857 - (-0{\cdot}286)^2$
$= 0{\cdot}857 - 0{\cdot}082 = \underline{0{\cdot}775}$

$\underline{\text{var}(x_3)} = \frac{1}{7}\Sigma X_3^2 - \bar{X}_3^2 = 32{\cdot}714 - (-0{\cdot}143)^2$
$= 32{\cdot}714 - 0{\cdot}020 = \underline{32{\cdot}694}$

$$\underline{r_{12}} = \frac{0{\cdot}918}{[4{\cdot}489 \times 0{\cdot}775]^{\frac{1}{2}}} = 0{\cdot}492;\ r_{23} = \frac{3{\cdot}816}{[0{\cdot}775 \times 32{\cdot}694]^{\frac{1}{2}}}$$
$$= \underline{0{\cdot}758};\ r_{31} = \frac{11{\cdot}245}{[32{\cdot}694 \times 4{\cdot}489]^{\frac{1}{2}}} = \underline{0{\cdot}927}$$

$$R = \begin{vmatrix} 1 & 0{\cdot}492 & 0{\cdot}927 \\ 0{\cdot}492 & 1 & 0{\cdot}758 \\ 0{\cdot}927 & 0{\cdot}758 & 1 \end{vmatrix} = 0{\cdot}0584$$

$\underline{R_{11}} = [1 - (0{\cdot}758)^2] = \underline{0{\cdot}4254};\ \underline{R_{12}} = -[0{\cdot}492 - 0{\cdot}758 \times 0{\cdot}927]$
$= -\underline{0{\cdot}05533};\ \underline{R_{13}} = [0{\cdot}492 \times 0{\cdot}758 - 0{\cdot}927] = -\underline{0{\cdot}5541}$

$$\therefore\ \underline{r_{1\cdot23}} = \left[1 - \frac{R}{R_{11}}\right]^{\frac{1}{2}} = \left[1 - \frac{0{\cdot}0584}{0{\cdot}4254}\right]^{\frac{1}{2}} = \underline{0{\cdot}98}$$

Regression equation of x_1 on x_2 and x_3 is (6.16.10(*a*)):—

$$\frac{R_{11}}{s_1}(x_1 - \bar{x}_1) + \frac{R_{12}}{s_2}(x_2 - \bar{x}_2) + \frac{R_{13}}{s_3}(x_3 - \bar{x}_3) = 0,$$

where $\bar{x}_1 = \bar{X} + 4 = 3{\cdot}714$, $\bar{x}_2 = \bar{X}_2 + 3 = 2{\cdot}714$, $\bar{x}_3 = \bar{X}_3 + 20 = 19{\cdot}857$, and $s_1 = (4{\cdot}489)^{\frac{1}{2}} = 2{\cdot}11873$, $s_2 = (0{\cdot}775)^{\frac{1}{2}} = 0{\cdot}88034$, $s_3 = (32{\cdot}694)^{\frac{1}{2}} = 5{\cdot}71787$.

Hence the required regression equation is

$$0{\cdot}20072(x_1 - 3{\cdot}714) + 0{\cdot}24024(x_2 - 2{\cdot}714) - 0{\cdot}09708(x_3 - 19{\cdot}857) = 0$$

or $$\underline{20{\cdot}1x_1 + 24{\cdot}0x_2 - 9{\cdot}7x_3 + 53{\cdot}0 = 0}$$

Exercise: *Calculate $r_{2\cdot31}$ and $r_{3\cdot12}$ and find the other two regression equations.*

6.19. Partial Correlation. In many situations where we have three or more associated variates, it is useful to obtain some measure of the correlation between two of them when the influence of the others has been eliminated.

Suppose we have the three variates, x_1, x_2, x_3, with regression equations (6.16.1), (6.16.2) and (6.16.3). Let x_3 be held constant, then at this value of x_3, the two partial regression lines of x_1 on x_2 and of x_2 on x_1 will have regression coefficients $b_{12\cdot3}$ and $b_{21\cdot3}$. In line with (6.6.14), we therefore define the *partial correlation of* x_1 and x_2 to be given by

$$r_{12\cdot3}{}^2 = (b_{12\cdot3} \times b_{21\cdot3}) \quad . \quad . \quad . \quad . \quad . \quad (6.19.1)$$

Likewise

$$r_{23\cdot1}^2 = (b_{23\cdot1} \times b_{32\cdot1})$$

and $$r_{31\cdot2}^2 = (b_{31\cdot2} \times b_{13\cdot2}).$$

It follows that

$$r_{12\cdot3}^2 = -\frac{s_1 R_{12}}{s_2 R_{11}} \times -\frac{s_2 R_{21}}{s_1 R_{22}} = \frac{R_{12}^2}{R_{11}R_{22}}$$

$$= \frac{(r_{12} - r_{13}r_{23})^2}{(1 - r_{23}^2)(1 - r_{31}^2)}$$

i.e., $$\underline{r_{12\cdot3} = \frac{r_{12} - r_{13}r_{23}}{[(1 - r_{23}^2)(1 - r_{31}^2)]^{\frac{1}{2}}}} \quad . \quad . \quad . \quad (6.19.2)$$

In practice it is seldom found that $r_{12\cdot3}$ is independent of x_3, and we therefore regard the value of $r_{12\cdot3}$ given by (6.19.2) as a rough average over the varying values of x_3.

Using the data of 6.18, we have

$$\underline{r_{12\cdot3}} = \frac{0{\cdot}05533}{[0{\cdot}4254 \times 0{\cdot}1407]^{\frac{1}{2}}} = \underline{0{\cdot}226}.$$

Mathematical Note to Chapter Six

If a, b, c, d are any four numbers we denote the quantity $ad - bc$ by $\begin{vmatrix} a & b \\ c & d \end{vmatrix}$. Thus $\begin{vmatrix} 1 & 3 \\ 5 & 7 \end{vmatrix} = 1 \times 7 - 3 \times 5 = -8$. Such a function of its four elements is called a determinant of order 2, having 2×2 elements. A determinant of order three has 3×3 elements and is written

$$\begin{vmatrix} a_{11} & a_{12} & a_{13} \\ a_{21} & a_{22} & a_{23} \\ a_{31} & a_{32} & a_{33} \end{vmatrix},$$

the suffixes of an element indicating the row and column it occupies in the determinant.

Suppose we select any element, a_{21} say, and rule out the row and column in which it occurs. We are left with the 4 elements $\begin{vmatrix} a_{12} & a_{13} \\ a_{32} & a_{33} \end{vmatrix}$. The determinant of these four numbers multiplied by $(-1)^{2+1} = -1$ is called the *cofactor* of a_{21} in the determinant. The cofactor of a_{33} is

$$(-1)^{3+3} \begin{vmatrix} a_{11} & a_{12} \\ a_{21} & a_{22} \end{vmatrix} = + \begin{vmatrix} a_{11} & a_{12} \\ a_{21} & a_{22} \end{vmatrix}$$

In general, we denote the cofactor of an element a_{ij} by A_{ij}.

The value, Δ, of the determinant

$$\begin{vmatrix} a_{11} & a_{12} & a_{13} \\ a_{21} & a_{22} & a_{23} \\ a_{31} & a_{32} & a_{33} \end{vmatrix}$$

may be obtained by forming the sum of the products of the elements of any row (or column) and their respective cofactors. Thus

$$\begin{aligned} \Delta = a_{11}A_{11} + a_{12}A_{12} + a_{13}A_{13} &= a_{21}A_{21} + a_{22}A_{22} + a_{23}A_{23} \\ &= a_{31}A_{31} + a_{32}A_{32} + a_{33}A_{33} \\ = a_{11}A_{11} + a_{21}A_{21} + a_{31}A_{31} &= a_{12}A_{12} + a_{22}A_{22} + a_{32}A_{32} \\ &= a_{13}A_{13} + a_{23}A_{23} + a_{33}A_{33}. \end{aligned}$$

For instance $\begin{vmatrix} 1 & -2 & 3 \\ 7 & 4 & -1 \\ 2 & -3 & 2 \end{vmatrix}$

$$= 1 \begin{vmatrix} 4 & -1 \\ -3 & 2 \end{vmatrix} + (-1) \times (-2) \begin{vmatrix} 7 & -1 \\ 2 & 2 \end{vmatrix} + 3 \begin{vmatrix} 7 & 4 \\ 2 & -3 \end{vmatrix}$$

$$= (8 - 3) + 2(14 + 2) + 3(-21 - 8) = -50.$$

Suppose now the elements of any row (or column) are proportional to those of another row (or column). Say, for example, we have

$$\begin{vmatrix} a_{11} & a_{12} & a_{13} \\ \lambda a_{11} & \lambda a_{12} & \lambda a_{13} \\ a_{31} & a_{32} & a_{33} \end{vmatrix} = \begin{aligned} &a_{11}\lambda a_{12}a_{33} - a_{11}\lambda a_{13}a_{32} - a_{12}\lambda a_{11}a_{33} \\ &+ a_{12}\lambda a_{13}a_{31} + a_{13}\lambda a_{11}a_{32} - a_{13}\lambda a_{12}a_{31} = 0 \end{aligned}$$

In fact, if any two rows (or columns) of a determinant are identical or their elements are proportional, the value of the determinant is zero.

Now let us write

$$\begin{vmatrix} a_{11} & a_{12} & a_{13} \\ a_{11} & a_{12} & a_{13} \\ a_{31} & a_{32} & a_{33} \end{vmatrix} = a_{11}A_{21} + a_{12}A_{22} + a_{13}A_{23}$$

Then, clearly, $a_{11}A_{21} + a_{12}A_{22} + a_{13}A_{23} = 0$.

In fact, if we form the sum of the products of the elements of any row (or column) and the cofactors of the corresponding elements of another row (or column), that sum is zero.

(The reader will find a useful introduction to determinants in C. A. B. Smith's *Biomathematics* (Griffin); a more detailed discussion is to be found in Professor A. C. Aitken's *Determinants and Matrices* (Oliver & Boyd).)

EXERCISES ON CHAPTER SIX

1. Calculate the means of the following values of x and y:

x . .	0·25	1·00	2·25	4·00	6·25
y . .	0·12	0·90	2·13	3·84	6·07

The corresponding values of x and y satisfy approximately the equation $y = mx + c$. By the method of least squares obtain the best values of the constants m, c, assuming that there is error in the y values only.

2. Daily Newspapers (London and Provincial) 1930–40:

Year	1930	1931	1932	1933	1934	1935
Number . .	169	164	156	157	147	148
Average circulation (millions) . .	17·9	17·6	17·9	18·2	18·0	18·2
Year	**1936**	**1937**	**1938**	**1939**	**1940**	
Number . .	148	145	142	141	131	
Average circulation (millions) . .	18·5	19·1	19·2	19·5	18·9	

Fit a straight line to each of these series by the method of least squares, represent graphically and comment on the fit. (L.U.)

3. Calculate the coefficient of correlation between the continuous variables x and y from the data of the following table:

y.	x.							Total.
	−4 to −3.	−3 to −2.	−2 to −1.	−1 to 0.	0 to 1.	1 to 2.	2 to 3.	
−3 to −2	150	40	20	10	—	—	—	220
−2 to −1	20	60	90	20	10	—	—	200
−1 to 0	10	40	60	50	20	—	—	180
0 to 1	—	30	36	42	20	16	6	150
1 to 2	10	16	30	20	16	6	2	100
2 to 3	24	38	48	34	6	—	—	150
Total	214	224	284	176	72	22	8	1,000

(I.A.)

4. Calculate the correlation coefficient for the following U.S. data :

Index of income payments	114	137	172	211	230	239
Index of retail food prices	97	105	124	139	136	139

(L.U.)

5. An ordinary pack of 52 cards is dealt to four whist players. If one player has r hearts, what is the average number held by his partner? *Deduce* that the correlation coefficient between the number of hearts in the two hands is $-\frac{1}{3}$. (R.S.S.)

6. In the table below, verify that the means of the x-arrays are collinear, and also those of the y-arrays, and deduce that the correlation coefficient is $-0{\cdot}535$.

y \ x	0	1	2	3	4
0				4	3
1			18	36	9
2		12	54	36	3
3	1	12	18	4	

(R.S.S.)

7. The ranks of the same 15 students in Mathematics and Latin were as follows, the two numbers within brackets denoting the ranks of the same student : (1, 10), (2, 7), (3, 2), (4, 6), (5, 4), (6, 8), (7, 3), (8, 1), (9, 11), (10, 15), (11, 9), (12, 5), (13, 14), (14, 12), (15, 13). Show that the rank correlation coefficient is 0·51.

(Weatherburn.)

8. From the table below compute the correlation ratio of y on x and the correlation coefficient :

Values of x

	0·5–1·5.	1·5–2·5.	2·5–3·5.	3·5–4·5.	4·5–5·5.	Total.
Number of cases	20	30	35	25	15	125
Mean y .	11·3	12·7	14·5	16·5	19·1	—

The standard deviation of y is 3·1. (*Hint* : Use (6.15.1).)

(L.U.)

9. The three variates x_1, x_2, x_3 are measured from their means. $s_1 = 1$; $s_2 = 1{\cdot}3$; $s_3 = 1{\cdot}9$; $r_{12} = 0{\cdot}370$; $r_{13} = -0{\cdot}641$; $r_{23} = -0{\cdot}736$. Calculate $r_{13\cdot2}$. If $x_4 = x_1 + x_2$, obtain r_{42}, r_{43} and $r_{43\cdot2}$. Verify that the two partial correlation coefficients are equal and explain this result. (L.U.)

Solutions

1. $m = 0{\cdot}988(4)$; $c = -0{\cdot}105$. 3. $r = 0{\cdot}334$.
4. 0·972. 8. $e_{yx} = 0{\cdot}77(4)$; $r = 0{\cdot}76(4)$.
9. $r_{13\cdot2} = -0{\cdot}586$; $r_{42} = 0{\cdot}874$; $r_{43} = 0{\cdot}836$; $r_{43\cdot2} = -0{\cdot}586$.

CHAPTER SEVEN

SAMPLE AND POPULATION

I: SOME FUNDAMENTALS OF SAMPLING THEORY

7.1. Inferences and Significance. So far we have been concerned with problems of *descriptive statistics*: we have concentrated on describing distributions, summarising their main properties mathematically and establishing certain general principles exemplified by them. We have not as yet *used* these summaries and general principles for other purposes. This we must now start to do. For one of the fundamental problems of statistics is:

> How, and with what accuracy, may we draw inferences about the nature of a population when we have only the evidence of samples of that population to go on?

Suppose, for example, that we wish to find whether among males in the British Isles belonging to some specified age-group there is any correlation between height and weight. In practice, we cannot weigh and measure every individual belonging to this "population". We therefore resort to sampling. Common sense tells us, first, that, other things being equal, the larger the sample, the better any estimate we base on our examination of that sample; and, secondly, that, whatever the size of the sample, that sample must be a *representative* one.

Assuming, for the time being, that we have settled on the size of the sample or samples we shall take, how do we make sure that the sample will be representative, a *random* sample? This is our first problem.

Suppose, however, that we are satisfied that our method of sampling is of a kind to ensure random samples: we take our samples, measure the height and weight of each individual in a sample, and calculate a value for r, the correlation coefficient, based on the sample size, N. Immediately a host of new doubts and misgivings arise:

> How do we know that the value obtained for r is really *significant*? Could it not have arisen by chance? Can we be reasonably sure that, although the variate-values obtained from a sample show a certain degree of correla-

tion, in the population as a whole the variates are correlated?

Suppose we obtain from a second sample of N a different value for r; or suppose that with a different value of N we obtain yet another value for r. Which, if any, of these values shall we use as the best estimate of ρ, the correlation-coefficient in the population?

Clearly, unless we can establish some general rules of guidance on such matters, all our descriptive analysis will be of little use. This is one of the main tasks of that branch of statistics usually termed *Sampling Theory*.

Before starting a more detailed discussion, let us set down what appear to be a few of the main types of problem with which the necessity of making statistical inference—inference from sample to population based on probabilities—confronts us:

(*a*) There are those problems involved in the concept of *randomness* and in devising methods of obtaining random samples.

(*b*) There are those problems which arise from the variation, from sample to sample of the same population, of the various sample statistics—problems concerned with the *distribution of sample statistics*.

(*c*) There are those problems connected with *how to estimate population parameters from sample statistics* and with the degree of trustworthiness of such estimates.

And, lastly,

(*d*) There are those problems which arise when we seek to test a hypothesis about a population or set of populations in the light of evidence afforded by sampling, *problems*, broadly, of *significance*.

7.2. What Do We Mean by " Random "? Unfortunately it is not possible here to enter into a detailed discussion of the difficulties involved in the concept of *randomness*. The " dictionary definition " of *random sample* is usually something along the following lines:

> A sample obtained by selection of items of a population is a *random sample* from that population if each item in the population has an equal chance of being selected.

Like most dictionary definitions, this one is not really very satisfactory, for, as the reader will realise, it has the air of trying desperately to disguise something that looks suspiciously like circularity. Nevertheless, we must reconcile ourselves, here at least, to using it. It has, however, this virtue, that it brings out the fact that the adjective *random* applies to the *method of selection* rather than to any characteristic of the sample detected after it has been drawn. In this connection, two other, related, points must be made :

(1) What we are out to get when we sample a population is information about that particular population in respect of some specified characteristic, or set of characteristics, of the items of that population. When sampling, we should keep asking ourselves, " What precisely are we trying to find out about what population ? "
(2) A method that ensures random selection from one population need not necessarily do so when used to sample another population.

What are the main types of population we may sample ?

In the first place, there are those *populations which actually exist and are finite*. Because all measurement entails approximation, the distribution of any variate in such a population is necessarily discrete. There are two ways of sampling such a population : after selecting an item, we may either replace it or we may not. *Sampling without replacement* will eventually exhaust a finite population and automatically, after each selection, the probability of any item being selected is altered. *Sampling with replacement*, however, can never exhaust even a finite population, and is thus equivalent to sampling from a hypothetical infinite population. If the probability of any item in the population being chosen is constant throughout the sampling process, we call the sampling *simple*. Thus, with a stable population, sampling with replacement is simple sampling. It may happen, however, that a population is so large that even sampling without replacement does not materially alter the probability of an item being selected. In such a case, sampling without replacement approximates to simple sampling.

The second type of population we are likely to encounter are *theoretical or conceptual populations*. The difference between an actual population and a conceptual one is illustrated when we compare a truck-load of granite chips with, say, the population of all real numbers between 0 and 1. Conceptual populations may be finite or infinite, but any infinite population is necessarily conceptual; so is any population in which the variate is continuous. Apart from their intrinsic interest, conceptual populations are important because they can be used as models of actual populations or arise in the solution of problems concerned with actual populations.

Finally, there are " populations " such as that of " all possible throws of a die " or that of " all possible measurements of this steel rod ". These are certainly not existing populations like a truck-load of granite chips, nor are they anything like as definite as the population of " all real numbers between 0 and 1 ", which is, mathematically, precise. There are many difficulties with such " populations ". Can we, for instance, regard the result of six throws of an actual die as a random *sample* of some hypothetical population of " all possible throws " ? And, since there is no selection, no choice, can they be regarded as constituting a *random* sample ? And in what way do we conceive essentially imaginary members of such a " population " as having the same probability of being selected as those members which, in Kendall's phrase, " assume the mantle of reality " ? Perhaps all we can say at the moment is that such " populations " receive their ultimate justification in the empirical fact that some events do happen *as if* they are random samples of such " populations ".

7.3. Random Sampling. We come then to the very much more practical question of how to draw random samples from given populations for specific purposes. Certain general principles should be borne in mind.

To begin with, *successful sampling demands specialised knowledge of the type of population to be sampled.* For example, successful sampling of the varieties of birds visiting a given 10 acres of common land during a certain period of the year requires that the sampling scheme be drawn up with the assistance of ornithologists intimately acquainted with the habits of possible visitors.

On the other hand, *the method of selection must be independent of the property or variate in which we are interested.* If we wish to sample a truck-load of granite chips, just arrived in the siding, for chip-size, it would be fatal to assume that, since the chips have been thoroughly shaken up on the journey, any shovelful will provide us with a random sample. A moment's reflection will convince us that there will have been at least a tendency for the more massive chips to gravitate towards the bottom of the truck, while the lighter and smaller tend to come to the top. However, had we been interested in sampling a given number of churns of milk for fat content, an adequate sampling scheme would have been to select a number of the churns at random and, then, having thoroughly stirred their contents, to ladle out a given quantity from each. But how can we select a number of churns at random? Can we rely on "haphazard" human choice? The answer is "No". Indeed, *we should seek to eliminate the human factor as far as possible.* For experience tells us that human choice is certainly not random in accordance with the definition we have here adopted. Even in cases where, at first sight, bias would seem hardly likely, as, for instance, in choosing the final digit in a set of four digit numbers, bias is most definitely operative. So to eliminate this factor, we resort to a number of methods, of which but two can be mentioned here.

7.4. Ticket Sampling. The first method is *ticket sampling*. Let us assume that we have a finite population of N items. We construct a model of this population as follows:

> On N similar cards we write down the relevant features of each member of the population, shuffle the cards thoroughly and draw n cards, say, representing a sample of n from the actual population.

This is a fairly reliable method, but, if the population is large, involves much work preparing the model. Moreover, to ensure that shuffling is really thorough is by no means as simple as it sounds.

7.5. Random Sampling Numbers. The second method is the method of using random sampling numbers. Given a finite population, we assign to each item of this population an ordinal number 1, 2, 3, . . . N. This set of numbers is virtually a conceptual model of the actual population.

Suppose we wish to draw a sample of n. We use a table of random numbers. Among the best known are:

- L. H. C. Tippett, *Tracts for Computers*, No. 15, giving 10,400 four-figure numbers, composed of 41,600 digits.
- M. G. Kendall and B. Babington Smith, *Tracts for Computers*, No. 24, giving 100,000 digits grouped in twos and fours and in 100 separate thousands.
- R. A. Fisher and F. Yates, *Statistical Tables for Biological, Agricultural and Medical Research*, giving 15,000 digits arranged in twos.
- *A Million Random Digits*, published by the Rand Corporation, Santa Monica, California, giving five-figure numbers (see Table 7.1).

We do not "pick out" numbers haphazardly from such tables as these. Indeed, it is essential not to do so, for it is extremely likely that if this is done the bias of number-preference, which we seek to eliminate by using such tables, will operate once more. Instead, having stated the table of numbers used and having indicated which section is taken, we should work systematically through that section. An example will make the procedure clear.

Example : *Draw a random sample of* 20 *from the " population " in Table* 5.1. *Calculate the mean of the sample and compare it with the population mean* (*see* 5.6, *Example* 1, *where the mean is found to be* 67·852 *in.*).

Treatment : referring to the table, we number the items as follows :

Height (in.).	Frequency.	Sampling Number.
59 and under	23	1–23
60–	169	24–192
61–	439	193–631
62–	1,030	632–1,161
63–	2,116	1,162–3,777
64–	3,947	3,778–7,724
65–	5,965	7,725–13,689
66–	8,012	13,690–21,701
67–	9,089	21,702–30,790
68–	8,763	30,791–39,553
69–	7,132	39,554–46,685
70–	5,314	46,686–51,999
71–	3,320	52,000–55,319
72–	1,884	55,320–57,203
73–	876	57,204–58,079
74–	383	58,080–58,462
75–	153	58,463–58,615
76–	63	58,616–58,678
77 and over	25	58,679–58,703
	58,703	—

We now read off from Table 7.1 20 successive five-figure numbers less than 58,704, ignoring those greater than 58,703. We thus obtain :

23780 28391 05940 55583 45325 05490 11186 15367 11370
42789 29511 55968 17264 37119 08853 44155 44236 10089
44373 21149

Our sample of 20 is consequently made up as follows :

2 items from the 64– class; 4 items from the 65– class;
3 items from the 66– class; 3 items from the 67– class;
1 item from the 68– class; 5 items from the 69– class;
2 items from the 72– class.

Taking the mid-value of the classes as those of 5.6, e.g., the mid-value of the 65– class to be 65·375 in., the mean value of the sample is immediately found to be 1351·5/20 = 67·575 in., as compared with 67·852 in., the population mean.

Exercise : *It is desired to obtain random samples from the following : (i) a truck-load of granite chips; (ii) a forest of mixed hardwood and softwood; (iii) the population of London; (iv) all the cattle in Oxfordshire; (v) the varieties of birds visiting a given* 10 *acres of common land; (vi) plants in a very large area of the Scottish Highlands.*

Explain the principles which would guide you in collecting such samples. (L.U.)

TABLE 7.1. *Random Numbers*

(From *A Million Random Digits*, published for the Rand Corporation by the Free Press (Glencoe, Illinois), previously published in the *Journal of the American Statistical Association*, Vol. 48, No. 264, December 1953.)

23780	28391	05940	55583	81256	45325	05490	65974	11186	15357
88240	92457	89200	94696	11370	42789	69758	79701	29511	55968
97523	17264	82840	59556	37119	08853	59083	95137	76538	44155
80274	79932	44236	10089	44373	82805	21149	03425	17594	31427
64971	49055	95091	08367	28381	03606	46497	28626	87297	36568
67286	28749	81905	15038	38338	65670	72111	91884	66762	11428
14262	09513	25728	52539	86806	57375	85062	89178	08791	39342
39483	62469	30935	79270	91986	51206	65749	11885	49789	97081
70908	21506	16269	54558	18395	69944	65036	63213	56631	88862
94963	22581	17882	83558	31960	99286	45236	47427	74321	67351

NOTE : This table gives 500 random digits, grouped for convenience, in five-digit numbers. Suppose six random numbers less than 161 are required, read off successive groups of three successive digits, rejecting those greater than 160. The result is :

(237)	(802)	(839)	105	(940)	(555)	(838)	125	(645)	(325)	054
(906)	(597)	(411)	(186)	153	(578)	(824)	092	(457)	(892)	009

The numbers in brackets are those greater than 160 and are rejected. The six random numbers less than 161 so obtained are therefore :

105 125 54 153 92 and 9

7.6. The Distribution of Sample Statistics. In the example of the previous section, we saw that our sample mean differed somewhat from the mean of the population. A different sample of 20 would have yielded a different value, also differing from the population mean. Were we to take a large number of samples of 20 we should have what in fact would be a frequency distribution of the mean of so many samples of 20.

Suppose we drew every possible sample of 20 from the population of 58,703. This would give us, for sampling with replacement, the enormous number of $58{,}703^{20}/20!$ such samples. (How?) If we drew the relative frequency polygon for this distribution, it would approximate closely to a continuous probability curve, with its own mean, variance and moments of higher order. Likewise, other sample statistics, the sample variance, for instance, also have their distributions for samples of a given size. So the question arises:

> What do we know about the distribution of sample statistics when: (*a*) the population sampled is not specified, and (*b*) the population is specified?

7.7. The Distribution of the Sample Mean. We begin by recalling our definition of a *random sample* (7.2) and then, to make it of practical, mathematical use, reformulate it as follows:

> **Definition: Random Sample. If x_i, ($i = 1, 2, 3, \ldots n$) is a set of n statistically independent variates, each distributed with the same probability density $\phi(x)$ and if the joint probability density of the set is given by $f(x_1, x_2, \ldots x_n) = \phi(x_1) \cdot \phi(x_2) \ldots \phi(x_n)$, then the set x_i, ($i = 1, 2, 3, \ldots n$) is a random sample of n from a population whose probability density is $\phi(x)$.**

Now suppose from the n variates x_i, with means $\mu_1'(x_i)$, we form a new variate

$$X \equiv a_1x_1 + a_2x_2 + \ldots + a_ix_i + \ldots + a_nx_n = \sum_{i=1}^{n} a_ix_i \quad (7.7.1)$$

where the a's are arbitrary constants, not all zero. We have

$$\mathcal{E}(X) = \mathcal{E}\left(\sum_{i=1}^{n} a_ix_i\right) = \sum_{i=1}^{n} a_i\mathcal{E}(x_i)$$

or

$$\mu_1'(X) = \sum_{i=1}^{n} a_i\mu_1'(x_i) \quad . \quad . \quad . \quad . \quad . \quad (7.7.2)$$

If we put $a_i = 1/n$, for all i, and subject the x_i to the condition that they all have the same probability density, we have

$$\mathcal{E}(x_1) = \mathcal{E}(x_2) = \ldots = \mathcal{E}(x_n) = \mathcal{E}(x) = \mu,$$

and X becomes $(x_1 + x_2 + \ldots + x_n)/n$, the mean of a sample of n from a population $\phi(x)$ and mean μ. So (7.7.2) becomes

$$\mathcal{E}(\bar{x}) = \frac{1}{n}\sum_{i=1}^{n} \mathcal{E}(x_i) = \frac{1}{n} \cdot n\mathcal{E}(x) = \mu \quad . \qquad (7.7.3)$$

Thus

> **the mean value of the mean of all possible samples of n is the mean of the population sampled:** or
>
> **the mean of the sampling distribution of $\bar{x}$ is the population mean.**

If $n = 1$, that this is so is obvious, for, taking all possible samples of 1, the distribution of the sample mean is identical with the distribution of the individual items in the population. (7.7.3) is also the justification of the common-sense view that the average of a number of measurements of the " length " of a rod, say, is a better estimate of the " length " of the rod than any one measurement.

What of the variance of $\bar{x}$? We write μ_i for the mean of x_i, μ_X for that of X, and σ_i^2 and σ_X^2 for the variances of x_i and X, respectively. Also let ρ_{ij} be the coefficient of the correlation between x_i and x_j $(i \neq j)$, assuming such correlation to exist.

Then

$$(X - \mu_X)^2 = \left(\sum_{i=1}^{n} a_i(x_i - \mu_i)\right)^2, \quad \text{or, if} \quad i \neq j,$$

$$= \sum_{i=1}^{n} a_i^2(x_i - \mu_i)^2 + \sum_{i=1}^{n}\sum_{j=1}^{n} a_i a_j (x_i - \mu_i)(x_j - \mu_j)$$

So

$$\mathcal{E}[(X - \mu_X)^2] = \sum_{i=1}^{n} a_i^2 \mathcal{E}[(x_i - \mu_i)^2] + \sum_{i=1}^{n}\sum_{j=1}^{n} a_i a_j \mathcal{E}[(x_i - \mu_i)(x_j - \mu_j)]$$

But

$$\mathcal{E}[(x_i - \mu_i)^2] = \mathcal{E}(x_i^2 - 2\mu_i x_i + \mu_i^2) = \mathcal{E}(x_i^2) - \mu_i^2 = \sigma_i^2$$

Also, when $i \neq j$,

$$\begin{aligned}\mathcal{E}[(x_i - \mu_i)(x_j - \mu_j)] &= \mathcal{E}(x_i x_j - \mu_i x_j - \mu_j x_i + \mu_i \mu_j) \\ &= \mathcal{E}(x_i x_j) - \mu_i \mu_j \\ &= \text{cov}\,(x_i x_j) = \sigma_i \sigma_j \rho_{ij}\end{aligned}$$

Hence

$$\sigma_X^2 = \sum_{i=1}^{n} a_i^2 \sigma_i^2 + \sum_{i=1}^{n}\sum_{j=1}^{n} a_i a_j \sigma_i \sigma_j \rho_{ij}, \ (i \neq j) \qquad (7.7.4)$$

This is an important formula in its own right. If, however, the variates x_i are independent, then $\rho_{ij} = 0$, for all i, j, and

$$\sigma_X{}^2 = a_1{}^2\sigma_1{}^2 + a_2{}^2\sigma_2{}^2 + \ldots + a_n{}^2\sigma_n{}^2 \equiv \sum_{i=1}^{n} a_i{}^2\sigma_i{}^2 \qquad (7.7.4\ (a))$$

Again putting $a_i = 1/n$, for all i, and subjecting the x's to the condition that they all have the same probability density $\phi(x)$, so that $X = \bar{x}$, the mean of a sample of n from $\phi(x)$, and $\sigma_1{}^2 = \sigma_2{}^2 = \ldots = \sigma_n{}^2 = \sigma^2$, say, we have, since x_i and $x_j (i \neq j)$ are independent,

$$\boldsymbol{\sigma_X{}^2 = \sigma_{\bar{x}}{}^2 = \sigma^2/n \quad \text{or} \quad \sigma_{\bar{x}}{}^2 = \frac{\sigma}{\sqrt{n}}} \quad . \quad (7.7.5)$$

Thus :

> **The variance of the distribution of the sample mean is 1/nth that of the variance of the parent population, n being the size of the sample.**

In other words, the larger the sample, the more closely the sample means cluster about the population mean value.

The standard deviation of the sampling distribution of $\bar{x}$ is usually called the *Standard Error of the Mean*, and, in general, the standard deviation of the sampling distribution of any statistic is called the Standard Error of that statistic.

The above results hold for *any* population, no matter how the variate is distributed. However, it is known that, whatever the population sampled, as the sample size increases, the distribution of $\bar{x}$ tends towards normality; while, even for relatively small values of n, there is evidence that the $\bar{x}$-distribution is approximately normal.

7.8. The Distribution of $\bar{x}$ when the Population Sampled is Normal. Consider a normal population defined by

$$\phi(x) \equiv \frac{1}{\sigma\sqrt{2\pi}} \exp\left[-(x - \mu)^2/2\sigma^2\right].$$

Here, we recall, μ is the population mean and σ^2, the population variance.

The mean-moment generating function for a normal distribution of variance σ^2 is $M_m(t) \equiv \exp(\frac{1}{2}\sigma^2t^2)$, (5.4.2), and the function generating the moments about the origin is

$$M(t) \equiv M_m(t) \exp(\mu t) = \exp(\mu t + \tfrac{1}{2}\sigma^2t^2).$$

Now, remembering that the m.g.f. for any distribution is $M(t) \equiv \mathcal{E}(\exp xt)$, the m.g.f. of the mean, $\bar{x}$, of the n independent variates x_i, ($i = 1, 2, 3, \ldots n$), each with probability function $\phi(x)$, is

$$\mathcal{E}(\exp \bar{x}t) = \mathcal{E}(\exp \sum_{i=1}^{n} x_i t/n) = \mathcal{E}\left(\prod_{i=1}^{n} \exp x_i t/n\right)$$
$$= \prod_{i=1}^{n} [\mathcal{E}(\exp x_i t/n)]$$

But, since $(x_1, x_2, \ldots x_n)$ is a sample from $\phi(x)$,

$$\mathcal{E}(\exp \bar{x}t) = (\mathcal{E}(\exp xt/n))^n = (M(t/n))^n$$
$$= \exp\{n(\mu t/n + \tfrac{1}{2}\sigma^2 t^2/n^2)\},$$

i.e., the m.g.f. for $\bar{x}$ is

$$\exp(\mu t + \tfrac{1}{2}(\sigma^2/n)t^2) \quad . \quad . \quad . \quad . \quad (7.8.1)$$

But this is the m.g.f. of a normal population with mean μ and variance σ^2/n. Hence—

The mean of samples of n from a normal population (μ, σ) *is itself normally distributed about* μ *as mean with standard deviation (error)* $\sigma/\sqrt{n}$.

This is in agreement with (7.7.3) and (7.7.5), but adds the important information that the distribution of $\bar{x}$, when the population sampled is normal, is itself normal. Actually this is a particular case of a more general theorem :

If $x_1, x_2, \ldots x_n$ *are n independent variates normally distributed about a common mean (which may be taken at zero), with variances* $\sigma_1^2, \sigma_2^2, \ldots \sigma_n^2$, *then any linear function of these n variates is itself normally distributed.*

The proof is simple : Let $X = \sum_{i=1}^{n} a_i x_i$. The m.m.g.f. of x_i, $M_i(t)$ is $\exp(\tfrac{1}{2}\sigma_i^2 t^2)$ and therefore

$$M_X(t) = \mathcal{E}(\exp Xt) = \mathcal{E}\left(\exp\left(\sum_{i=1}^{n} a_i x_i t\right)\right) = \mathcal{E}\left(\prod_{i=1}^{n} (\exp a_i x_i t)\right).$$

But the x's are independent, and, so,

$$M_X(t) = \prod_{i=1}^{n} \mathcal{E}(\exp a_i x_i t) = \prod_{i=1}^{n} \mathcal{E}(\exp x_i(a_i t))$$
$$= \prod_{i=1}^{n} M_i(a_i t) = \exp\left[\tfrac{1}{2}\left(\sum_{i=1}^{n} a_i^2\sigma_i^2\right)t^2\right]$$

which is the m.g.f. of a normal distribution with variance

$$\sigma_X^2 = \sum_{i=1}^{n} a_i^2\sigma_i^2 \quad . \quad . \quad . \quad . \quad (7.8.2)$$

Consequently,

(i) if $n = 2$ and $a_1 = a_2 = 1$, the distribution of the sum, $x_1 + x_2$, of the two normal variates x_1, x_2, is normal about the common mean with variance $\sigma_1{}^2 + \sigma_2{}^2$; and
(ii) if $n = 2$ and $a_1 = 1$, $a_2 = -1$, the distribution of the difference, $x_1 - x_2$, of the two normal variates, x_1, x_2, is normal about the common mean with variance $\sigma_1{}^2 + \sigma_2{}^2$.

Now in many of the problems we encounter, n is large, and so we may assume that $\bar{x}$, the mean of a sample of n from an infinite population of mean μ and variance σ^2, is approximately normally distributed about μ as mean with variance σ^2/n, although we do not know that the population sampled is normal. This being the case *the variate* $t = (\bar{x} - \mu/(\sigma/\sqrt{n})$ *will be approximately normally distributed about zero with unit variance.* In other words:

The probability that the sample mean, $\bar{x}$, will differ *numerically* from the population mean, μ, by less than an amount d (measured in units of the standard error of the sample mean) is given approximately by

$$P(|\bar{x} - \mu| \leqslant d) = 2\int_0^d \phi(t)dt$$

where $$\phi(t) = \frac{1}{\sqrt{2\pi}} \exp\left(-\tfrac{1}{2}t^2\right).$$

It must be emphasised, however, that here we are sampling a *population whose variance is assumed known.* When this is not the case, the problem is complicated somewhat and will be dealt with later.

7.9. Worked Examples.

1. *The net weight of "half-pound" boxes of chocolates has a mean of* 0·51 *lb. and a standard deviation of* 0·02 *lb. The chocolates are despatched from manufacturer to wholesaler in consignments of* 2,500 *boxes. What proportion of these consignments can be expected to weigh more than* 1,276 *lb. net? What proportion will weigh between* 1,273 *and* 1,277 *lb. net?*

Treatment: We are here drawing samples of 2,500 from an assumed infinite population. The mean net weight of boxes in a consignment weighing 1,276 lb. will be 1,276/2,500 lb. = 0·5104 lb.

The standard error of the mean net weight for samples of 2,500 will be $0{\cdot}02/\sqrt{2{,}500} = 0{\cdot}0004$ lb. Thus in this case $t = 0{\cdot}0004/0{\cdot}0004 = 1$. The probability that the sample mean will deviate from the population mean by more than this amount is $P(t > 1) = 0{\cdot}5 - P(0 < t \leqslant 1)$, for this is a "one-tail" problem. $P(t \leqslant 1) = 0{\cdot}3413$. Therefore $P(t > 1) = 0{\cdot}1587$. *Therefore just under* 16% *of the consignments of* 2,500 *boxes will weigh more than* 1,276 lb.

If a consignment weighs 1,273 lb., the mean weight of a box in that consignment is 0·5092. The deviation from the mean is then − 0·0008, or, in standardised units, − 2. If the consignment weighs 1,277 lb., the corresponding mean weight is 0·5108 lb., a deviation from the population mean of + 2 standard errors. The probability that a consignment will weigh between these two limits is then—this being a "two-tail" problem—

$$P(-2 \leqslant t \leqslant 2) = 2P(0 < t \leqslant 2) = 2 \times 0{\cdot}4772 = 0{\cdot}9544$$

In other words, *just over* 95% *of the batches of* 2,500 *boxes will lie between the given net weights.*

2. *The "guaranteed" average life of a certain type of electric light bulb is* 1,000 *hours with a standard deviation of* 125 *hours. It is decided to sample the output so as to ensure that* 90% *of the bulbs do not fall short of the guaranteed average by more than* 2·5%. *What must be the minimum sample size?*

Treatment: Let n be the size of a sample that the conditions may be fulfilled. Then the standard error of the mean is $125/\sqrt{n}$. Also the deviation from the 1,000-hour mean must not be more than 25 hours, or, in standardised units, not more than $25/(125/\sqrt{n}) = \sqrt{n}/5$. This is a "one-tail" problem, for we do not worry about those bulbs whose life is longer than the guaranteed average.

$$P(t > n^{\frac{1}{2}}/5) = 0{\cdot}1 \quad \text{and, so,} \quad P(0 < t \leqslant n^{\frac{1}{2}}/5) = 0{\cdot}4$$

Using Table 5·4, we find that $t = 1{\cdot}281$. Therefore, $n^{\frac{1}{2}}/5 = 1{\cdot}281$ or $n = 40{\cdot}96$. Consequently, *the required minimum sample size is* **41**.

3. *The means of simple samples of* 1,000 *and* 2,000 *are* 67·5 *and* 68·0 *respectively. Can the samples be regarded as drawn from a single population of standard deviation* 2·5?

Treatment: Just as the sample mean has its own distribution, so, too, does the difference between the means of two samples of a given size. If x_1 and x_2 are two independent variates distributed about mean μ_1, μ_2 with variances σ_1^2, σ_2^2, respectively, let $X = x_1 - x_2$. Then $\bar{X} = \mu_1 - \mu_2$, and, by 7.7.4 (*a*), $\sigma_x^2 = \sigma_1^2 + \sigma_2^2$. Now set up the hypothesis that two samples of n_1 and n_2 are drawn from a single population (μ, σ). Then, if $\bar{x}_1$ and $\bar{x}_2$ are the means of these two samples, $\bar{X}$ is distributed about zero mean with variance $\sigma_{\bar{X}}^2 = \sigma^2/n_1 + \sigma^2/n_2$. And, since $\bar{x}_1$ and $\bar{x}_2$ are approximately normally distributed, so is $\bar{X}$.

In our example, $\bar{X} = 0{\cdot}5$ and $\sigma_{\bar{X}}^2 = (2{\cdot}5)^2\ (1/1{,}000 + 1/2{,}000) = 0{\cdot}009375$ or $\sigma_{\bar{X}} = 0{\cdot}0968$. Thus the *observed* $\bar{X}$ *is more than* 5 *times the standard error of its distribution* calculated on the hypothesis that the samples are from the same population with standard deviation

2.5. This, on the assumption that $\bar{X}$ is approximately normally distributed, is most unlikely. We therefore reject the hypothesis that the samples are from a single population of standard deviation 2.5.

7.10. Sampling Distribution of the Mean when Sampling is without Replacement from a Finite Population. Let the population sampled consist of N items. Let the sample size be n. The number of samples of n that can be drawn without replacement from N is $\binom{N}{n}$. In these samples any one value of the variate, x_i, say, figures $\binom{N-1}{n-1}$ times, for if x_i is chosen, there are but $\binom{N-1}{n-1}$ ways of forming samples of n. Let the population mean be zero. Then $\sum_{i=1}^{N} x_i = 0$. If m_j is the mean of the jth sample, let m be the mean value of all possible values of m_j. Denoting the sum of the items in the jth sample by $\left(\sum_{i=1}^{n} x_i\right)_j$, we have

$$nm_j = \left(\sum_{i=1}^{n} x_i\right)_j \quad \text{and} \quad \binom{N}{n} m = \sum_{j=1}^{\binom{N}{n}} m_j$$

Consequently,

$$\sum_{j=1}^{\binom{N}{n}} \left(\sum_{i=1}^{n} x_i\right)_j = \binom{N-1}{n-1} \sum_{i=1}^{N} x_i,$$

since each x_i occurs $\binom{N-1}{n-1}$ times and so $n \sum_{j=1}^{\binom{N}{n}} m_j = 0$, i.e., $m = 0$. Thus *the mean of the means of all possible samples is the mean of the parent population.*

If σ^2 is the variance of the population, we have, taking the population mean as origin, $N\sigma^2 = \sum_{i=1}^{N} x_i^2$.

Moreover, if σ_m^2 is the variance of the sample mean,

$$\binom{N}{n} \sigma_m^2 = \sum_{j=1}^{\binom{N}{n}} m_j^2 = \frac{1}{n^2} \sum_{j=1}^{\binom{N}{n}} \left(\sum_{i=1}^{n} x_i\right)^2$$

$$= \frac{1}{n^2}\left[\binom{N-1}{n-1} \sum_{i=1}^{N} x_i^2 + \binom{N-2}{n-2} \sum_i \sum_j x_i x_j\right], \; (i \neq j)$$

But $$\left(\sum_{i=1}^{N} x_i\right)^2 = \sum_{i=1}^{N} x_i^2 + \sum_i \sum_j (x_i x_j),\ (i \neq j),$$

and, since $$\sum_{i=1}^{N} x_i = 0,\ \sum_i \sum_j (x_i x_j) = -\sum_{i=1}^{N} x_i^2.$$

$$\therefore \sum_{j=1}^{\binom{N}{n}} m_j^2 = \frac{1}{n^2}\left[\binom{N-1}{n-1} - \binom{N-2}{n-2}\right]\sum_{i=1}^{N} x_i^2$$

$$= \frac{\sigma^2}{n} \cdot \frac{N-n}{N-1} \cdot \frac{N!}{n!\,(N-n)!}$$

or $$\sigma_m^2 = \frac{\sigma^2}{n} \cdot \frac{N-n}{N-1} \quad . \quad . \quad . \quad (7.10.1)$$

If we let $N \to \infty$, $\sigma_m^2 \to \sigma^2/n$, showing that when a population is very large, sampling without replacement approximates to simple sampling.

7.11. Distribution of the Sample Variance. Let s^2 be the variance of a sample of n and let $\bar{x}$ be the sample mean. Then

$$s^2 = \frac{1}{n}\sum_{i=1}^{n} (x_i - \bar{x})^2 = \frac{1}{n}\sum_{i=1}^{n} x_i^2 - \bar{x}^2 = \frac{1}{n}\sum_{i=1}^{n} x_i^2 - \left(\sum_{i=1}^{n} x_i/n\right)^2$$

$$= \frac{1}{n}\sum_{i=1}^{n} x_i^2 - \frac{1}{n^2}\sum_{i=1}^{n} x_i^2 - \frac{1}{n^2}\sum_i \sum_j (x_i x_j),\ (i \neq j)$$

$$= \frac{n-1}{n^2}\sum_{i=1} x_i^2 - \frac{1}{n^2}\sum_i \sum_j (x_i x_j),\ (i \neq j)$$

Consequently

$$\mathcal{E}(s^2) = \frac{n-1}{n^2}\mathcal{E}\left(\sum_{i=1}^{n} x_i^2\right) - \frac{1}{n^2}\mathcal{E}\left[\sum_i \sum_j (x_i x_j)\right],\ (i \neq j)$$

But there are n ways of chosing x_i from n values and, once x_i is chosen, there are $(n - 1)$ ways of chosing x_j so that $x_j \neq x_i$. Also, since x_i and x_j are independent

$$\mathcal{E}\left(\sum_i \sum_j (x_i x_j)\right) = \sum_i \sum_j [\mathcal{E}(x_i x_j)] = \sum_i \sum_j [\mathcal{E}(x_i) \cdot \mathcal{E}(x_j)]$$

$$= \sum_i \sum_j (\mathcal{E}(x))^2 = 0$$

since $\mathcal{E}(x) \equiv \mu_1' = 0$. Therefore

$$\mathcal{E}(s^2) = \frac{n-1}{n^2} \cdot n\,\mu_2' = \frac{n-1}{n}\mu_2 = \frac{n-1}{n}\sigma^2 \quad . \quad (7.11.1)$$

μ_1', μ_2', and $\mu_2 \equiv \sigma^2$, being population parameters.

Thus *the mean value of the variance of all possible samples of n is $(n-1)/n$ times the variance of the parent population*; and, as we should expect, $\mathcal{E}(s^2) \to \sigma^2$, as the sample size increases indefinitely.

Thus if we draw a single sample of n from a population and calculate the variance, s^2, of that sample, we shall have

$$\mathcal{E}(ns^2/(n-1)) \equiv \mathcal{E}((x_i - \bar{x})^2/(n-1)) = \sigma^2 \quad . \quad (7.11.2)$$

In other words:

If we calculate $\sum_i (x_i - \bar{x})^2/(n-1)$, instead of the usual $\sum_i (x_i - \bar{x})^2/n$, we have an *unbiased* estimate of the population variance, σ^2.

Of course, the actual figure calculated from the data of a single sample will, in general, differ from the actual value of σ^2. But, if we continue sampling and calculating $ns^2/(n-1)$, we shall obtain a set of values, the mean value of which will tend to the actual value of σ^2 as the number, N, of samples of n drawn increases. A function of x and n which in this way yields, as its values, *unbiased estimates* of a population parameter is called an *unbiased estimator* of that parameter. Thus if θ is a population parameter and $\hat{\theta}$ (read "theta cap") is an estimator of θ, $\hat{\theta}$ is an unbiased estimator if $\mathcal{E}(\hat{\theta}) = \theta$. $m_1' \equiv \sum_i x_i/n$ is an unbiased estimator of μ, the population mean, since $\mathcal{E}(m_1') = \mu$; on the other hand, $s^2 \equiv \sum_i (x_i - \bar{x})^2/n$ is a biased estimator of σ^2. For this reason, some writers define the variance of a sample to be $\sum_i f_i(x_i - \bar{x})^2/(n-1)$, $\sum_i f_i = n$; with this definition, the sample variance is an unbiased estimate of the population variance. Although we have not adopted this definition here, we are introduced by it to an important notion—that of *the degrees of freedom of a sample.*

Let $\bar{x}$ be the mean of a sample of n. Then $n\bar{x} = \sum_i x_i$, and, *for a given $\bar{x}$*, there are only $n - 1$ independent x's, for when we have selected $n - 1$ items of the sample, the nth is necessarily determined. $\sum_i x_i = n\bar{x}$ is a linear *equation of constraint* on the sample.

If there are $p(< n$, of course) linear equations of constraint on the sample, the number of degrees of freedom of the sample is reduced by p.

We must now ascertain the *standard error of the sample*

variance. Once again we confine our attention to the case when the population sampled is normal with zero mean and variance σ^2.

What is the probability that a sample $(x_1, x_2, \ldots x_n)$ from such a population is such that its mean lies between $\bar{x} \pm \frac{1}{2}d\bar{x}$ and a standard deviation lying between $s \pm \frac{1}{2}ds$?

Since the n x's are independent yet are drawn from the same population, the probability that the n values of x shall lie simultaneously between

$$x_1 \pm \tfrac{1}{2}dx_1,\ x_2 \pm \tfrac{1}{2}dx_2,\ \ldots\ x_n \pm \tfrac{1}{2}dx_n \text{ is}$$

$$dp = \frac{1}{(2\pi\sigma^2)^{\frac{1}{2}n}} \exp\left(-(x_1^2 + x_2^2 + \ldots + x_n^2)/2\sigma^2\right)dx_1dx_2 \ldots dx_n \tag{7.11.3}$$

Now think of $(x_1, x_2, \ldots x_n)$ as the co-ordinates of a point P in a *space of n-dimensions.* Then $dx_1dx_2 \ldots dx_n$ is an element of volume in that space. Call it dv. Then dp is the probability that the point P shall lie within this volume element. If now we choose this volume element dv in such a way that any point P, lying within it, represents a sample of n with mean lying between $\bar{x} \pm \frac{1}{2}d\bar{x}$ and a standard deviation between $s \pm \frac{1}{2}ds$, dp will be the probability that our sample has a mean and standard deviation lying between these limits. Our problem therefore is to find an appropriate dv. Now we have the two equations,

$$\sum_{i=1}^{n} x_i = n\bar{x} \text{ and } \sum_{i=1}^{n} (x_i - \bar{x})^2 = ns^2.$$

Each of these equations represents a locus in our n-dimensional space. If n were equal to 3, the equation $\sum_{i=1}^{n} x_i = n\bar{x}$ may be written $(x_1 - \bar{x}) + (x_2 - \bar{x}) + (x_3 - \bar{x}) = 0$ and represents a plane through the point $(\bar{x}, \bar{x}, \bar{x})$. Moreover, the length of the perpendicular from the origin on to this plane is $3\bar{x}/3^{\frac{1}{2}} = \bar{x} \,.\, 3^{\frac{1}{2}}$ and, so, the perpendicular distance between this plane and the parallel plane through $(\bar{x} + d\bar{x}, \bar{x} + d\bar{x}, \bar{x} + d\bar{x})$ is $d\bar{x} \,.\, 3^{\frac{1}{2}}$. In the n-dimensional case, the equation $\sum_{i=1}^{n} x_i = n\bar{x}$ represents a "hyperplane", as it is called, and the "distance" between this "plane" and the "parallel plane" is $d\bar{x} \,.\, n^{\frac{1}{2}}$.

Again, if $n = 3$, the equation $\sum_{i=1}^{n} (x_i - \bar{x})^2 = ns^2$ becomes

$(x_1 - \bar{x})^2 + (x_2 - \bar{x})^2 + (x_3 - \bar{x})^2 = 3s^2$, and thus represents a sphere, with centre $(\bar{x}, \bar{x}, \bar{x})$ and radius $s \,.\, 3^{\frac{1}{2}}$. The plane $\sum_{i=1}^{3} x_i = 3\bar{x}$ passes through the centre of this sphere. The section will therefore be a circle of radius $s \,.\, 3^{\frac{1}{2}}$, whose area is proportional to s^2. If s increases from $s - \frac{1}{2}ds$ to $s + \frac{1}{2}ds$, the increase in the area of section is proportional to $d(s^2)$. So the volume, dv, enclosed by the two neighbouring spheres and the two neighbouring planes will be proportional to $d\bar{x} \,.\, d(s^2)$. In the n-dimensional case, instead of a sphere, we have a " hyper-sphere " of " radius " $s \,.\, n^{\frac{1}{2}}$ and this " hypersphere " is cut by our " hyperplane " in a section which now has a " volume " proportional to s^{n-1}. So, in this case, dv is proportional to $d\bar{x} \,.\, d(s^{n-1}) = ks^{n-2}dsd\bar{x}$, say. Consequently, the probability that our sample of n will lie within this volume is given by

$$dp = \frac{K}{(2\pi\sigma^2)^{n/2}} \exp\left\{- \frac{1}{2\sigma^2} \sum_{i=1}^{n} x_i^2\right\} s^{n-2}dsd\bar{x} \quad . \qquad (7.11.3(a))$$

But the equation $\sum_{i=1}^{n} (x_i - \bar{x})^2 = ns^2$ may be written $\sum_{i=1}^{n} x_i^2 = n(s^2 + \bar{x}^2)$ and, therefore,

$$dp = k_1 \exp(-n\bar{x}^2/2\sigma^2)d\bar{x} \times$$
$$\times\, k_2 \exp(-ns^2/2\sigma^2)(s^2)^{(n-3)/2}d(s^2) \quad . \qquad (7.11.4)$$

where k_1 and k_2 are constants.[1]

---

[1] *Determination of* k_1: Since

$$\int_{-\infty}^{+\infty} k_1 \exp(-n\bar{x}^2/2\sigma^2)d\bar{x} = 1$$

we have immediately (5.4(e) footnote) $k_1 = (2\pi\sigma^2/n)^{-\frac{1}{2}}$.

Determination of k_2: s^2 varies from 0 to ∞ ; therefore

$$\int_0^{\infty} k_2 \exp(-ns^2/2\sigma^2)(s^2)^{(n-3)/2}d(s^2) = 1$$

Put $ns^2/2\sigma^2 = x$; then

$$k_2 \int_0^{\infty} (2\sigma^2/n)^{(n-1)/2} \exp(-x)x^{(n-1)/2-1}dx = 1$$

But since, by definition (see Mathematical Note to Chapter Three),

$$\int_0^{\infty} \exp(-x)x^{(n-1)/2-1}dx = \Gamma((n-1)/2)$$

$$k_2 = (n/2\sigma^2)^{(n-1)/2}/\Gamma((n-1)/2).$$

We see immediately that, when the population sampled is normal :

(i) **the mean $\bar{x}$ and the variance s^2 of a sample of n are distributed independently ;**
(ii) **the sample mean is distributed normally about the population mean—taken here at the origin—with variance σ^2/n ; and**
(iii) **the sample variance s^2 is not normally distributed.**

The moment-generating function for the s^2-distribution is $M(t) \equiv \mathcal{E}(\exp ts^2)$. Thus

$$M(t) = k_2 \int_0^\infty \exp(-ns^2/2\sigma^2)\exp(ts^2)(s^2)^{(n-3)/2}d(s^2)$$

$$= k_2 \int_0^\infty \exp\left[-\frac{ns^2}{2\sigma^2}\left(1 - \frac{2\sigma^2 t}{n}\right)\right](s^2)^{\frac{n-3}{2}}\,d(s^2)$$

Put $\dfrac{ns^2}{2\sigma^2}\left(1 - \dfrac{2\sigma^2 t}{n}\right) = X^2$ and $k_2 = \left(\dfrac{n}{2\sigma^2}\right)^{\frac{n-1}{2}} \Big/ \Gamma\left(\dfrac{n-1}{2}\right)$;

we have

$$M(t) = \left[1 - \frac{2\sigma^2 t}{n}\right]^{-\left(\frac{n-1}{2}\right)} \Big/ \Gamma\left(\frac{n-1}{2}\right) \times$$

$$\times \int_0^\infty \exp(-X^2)(X^2)^{\left(\frac{n-1}{2}\right)-1}d(X^2)$$

But, by 3.A.3.,

$$\int_0^\infty \exp(-X^2)\,.\,(X^2)^{\left(\frac{n-1}{2}\right)-1}d(X^2) = \Gamma\left(\frac{n-1}{2}\right)$$

$$\therefore\ M(t) = \left[1 - \frac{2\sigma^2 t}{n}\right]^{-\left(\frac{n-1}{2}\right)} \quad . \quad . \quad (7.11.5)$$

The coefficient of t in the expansion of this function is the first moment of s^2 about the origin : $(n - 1)\sigma^2/n$, as already established. The coefficient of $t^2/2\,!$ is the second moment of s^2 about the origin: $(n^2 - 1)\sigma^4/n^2$. Hence

$$\text{var}\,(s^2) = (n^2 - 1)\sigma^4/n^2 - (n - 1)^2\sigma^4/n^2 = 2(n - 1)\sigma^4/n^2$$

For large samples, therefore, var $(s^2) \simeq 2\sigma^4/n$. In other words, *the standard error of the sample variance for a normal parent population is approximately* $\sigma^2\sqrt{\frac{2}{n}}$ *for large samples.*

7.12. Worked Example.

If s_1^2 and s_2^2 are the variances in two independent samples of the same size taken from a common normal population, determine the distribution of $s_1^2 + s_2^2$. (L.U.)

Treatment: The moment-generating function of s^2 for samples of n from a normal population $(0, \sigma)$ is (7.11.5)

$$M(t) \equiv (1 - 2\sigma^2 t/n)^{-(n-1)/2}$$

Hence $$\mathcal{E}(\exp ts_1^2) = \mathcal{E}(\exp ts_2^2) = M(t)$$

But, since the samples are independent,

$$\mathcal{E}(\exp t(s_1^2 + s_2^2)) = \mathcal{E}[(\exp ts_1^2)(\exp ts_2^2)] \equiv [M(t)]^2$$

Hence the m.g.f. for the sum of the two sample variances is

$$(1 - 2\sigma^2 t/n)^{-(n-1)}.$$

Expanding this in powers of t, we find that the mean value of $s_1^2 + s_2^2$ is $2(n - 1)\sigma^2/n$—the coefficient of $t/1\,!$—and var $(s_1^2 + s_2^2) = 4n(n - 1)\sigma^4/n^2 - 4(n - 1)^2\sigma^4/n^2 = 4(n - 1)\sigma^4/n^2$, which, for large n, is approximately equal to $4\sigma^4/n$.

The probability differential for $s_1^2 + s_2^2$ is

$$dp = \frac{(n/2\sigma^2)^{n-1}}{(n-1)} \exp(-n(s_1^2 + s_2^2)/2\sigma^2)(s_1^2 + s_2^2)^{n-2} d(s_1^2 + s_2^2)$$

EXERCISES ON CHAPTER SEVEN

1. Using the table of random numbers given in the text, draw a random sample of 35 from the " population " in Table 5.1. Calculate the sample mean and compare it with the result obtained in 7.5.

2. A bowl contains a very large number of black and white balls. The probability of drawing a black ball in a single draw is p and that of drawing a white ball, therefore, $1 - p$. A sample of m balls is drawn at random, and the number of black balls in the sample is counted and marked as the score for that draw. A second sample of m balls is drawn, and the number of white balls in this sample is the corresponding score. What is the expected combined score, and show that the variance of the combined score is $2mp(1 - p)$.

3. Out of a batch of 1,000 lb. of chestnuts from a large shipment, it is found that there are 200 lb. of bad nuts. Estimate the limits between which the percentage of bad nuts in the shipment is almost certain to lie.

4. A sample of 400 items is drawn from a normal population whose mean is 5 and whose variance 4. If the sample mean is 4·45, can the sample be regarded as a truly random sample?

5. A sample of 400 items has a mean of 1·13; a sample of 900 items has a mean of 1·01. Can the samples be regarded as having been drawn at random from a common population of standard deviation 0·1?

6. A random variate x is known to have the distribution

$$p(x) = c(1 + x/a)^{m-1} \exp(-mx/a), \quad -a \leqslant x < \infty$$

Find the constant c and the first four moments of x. Derive the linear relation between β_1 and β_2 of this distribution. (L.U)

7. Pairs of values of two variables x and y are given. The variances of x, y and $(x - y)$ are σ_x^2, σ_y^2 and $\sigma_{(x-y)}^2$ respectively. Show that the coefficient of correlation between x and y is

$$\frac{\sigma_x^2 + \sigma_y^2 - \sigma_{(x-y)}^2}{2\sigma_x\sigma_y}.$$

(L.U.)

8. If $u = ax + by$ and $v = bx - ay$, where x and y represent deviations from respective means, and if the correlation coefficient between x and y is ρ, but u and v are uncorrelated, show that

$$\sigma_n\sigma_v = (a^2 + b^2)\sigma_x\sigma_y\sqrt{1 - \rho^2}$$

(L.U.)

Solutions

2. Expected score is m.

3. Probability p of 1 lb. of bad nuts is $\frac{200}{1000} = 0{\cdot}2$. Assume this is constant throughout the batch, $q = 0{\cdot}8$. Mean is np and variance is npq. For the *proportion* of bad nuts we divide the variate by n and hence the variance by n^2, giving variance $= pq/n$. The standard error of the proportion of bad nuts is $\sqrt{\frac{pq}{n}} = \sqrt{\frac{0{\cdot}2 \times 0{\cdot}8}{1000}}$ $= 0{\cdot}1264$. The probability that a normal variate will differ from its mean value by more than three times its standard error is 0·0027. We can be practically sure that no deviation will be greater than this. Required limits are therefore—for the % of bad nuts—$100(0{\cdot}2 \pm 3 \times 0{\cdot}01264) = 23{\cdot}8\%$ and $16{\cdot}2\%$.

4. No, deviation of sample mean from population mean $> 4 \times S.E$ of mean for sample of size given.

5. Difference between means is nearly twenty that of $S.E$ of difference of means.

6. *Hint:* $\int_{-a}^{\infty} p(x)dx = 1$. Transform by using substitution $1 + x/a = t/m$. $c = m^m e^{-m}/a\Gamma(m)$; mean-moment generating function is $e^{-at}\left[1 - \frac{at}{m}\right]^{-m}$; $\mu'_1 = a$; $\mu_2/2! = a^2/2m$; $\mu_3/3! = a^3/3m^2$; $\mu_4/4! = a^4(m + 2)/8m^2$; $2\beta_2 - 3\beta_1 = 6$.

CHAPTER EIGHT

SAMPLE AND POPULATION
II : t, z, AND F

8.1. The *t*-distribution. We have seen that if $\bar{x}$ is the mean of a sample of n from a normal population (μ, σ) the variate

$$t \equiv (\bar{x} - \mu)/\sigma/\sqrt{n}$$

is normally distributed about zero mean with unit variance. *But what if the variance of the parent population is unknown* and we wish to test whether a given sample can be considered to be a random sample from that population ? The best we can do is to use an unbiased estimate of σ based on our sample of n, i.e., $s\{n/(n-1)\}^{\frac{1}{2}}$, s being the sample variance. But if we do this, we cannot assume that

$$t \equiv (\bar{x} - \mu)(n-1)^{\frac{1}{2}}/s \quad . \quad . \quad . \quad (8.1.1)$$

is a normal variate. In fact, it is not. What is the distribution of this t (called *Student's t*) ?

Let the population mean be taken as origin, then

$$t \equiv (n-1)^{\frac{1}{2}}\bar{x}/s \quad . \quad . \quad . \quad (8.1.1(a))$$

Since we may write $t \equiv (n-1)^{\frac{1}{2}}\{(\bar{x}/\sigma)/(s/\sigma)\}$, t, and, therefore, the t-distribution, is independent of the population variance—a most convenient consequence which contributes greatly to the importance of the distribution. *If we hold s constant* we have $sdt = (n-1)^{\frac{1}{2}}d\bar{x}$. Now $\bar{x}$ is normally distributed about zero with variance n^{-1} (since t is independent of σ, we may take $\sigma = 1$) and, as we showed in the last chapter, $\bar{x}$ and s^2 are statistically independent, when the parent population is normal. Thus

$$dp(\bar{x}) = (n/2\pi)^{\frac{1}{2}} \exp(-n\bar{x}^2/2)d\bar{x}$$

Consequently, the *probability differential of t for a constant s^2* may be obtained from $dp(\bar{x})$ by using 8.1.1(a) and the relation $sdt = (n-1)^{\frac{1}{2}}d\bar{x}$; we have

$$dp(t, \text{constant } s^2) = [n/2\pi(n-1)]^{\frac{1}{2}}s \exp[-ns^2t^2/2(n-1)]dt \quad (8.1.2)$$

If now we multiply this by the probability differential of s^2 and integrate with respect to s^2 from 0 to ∞, we obtain the *probability differential of t for all* s^2. By (7.11.4),

$$dp(s^2) = \frac{(n/2)^{(n-1)/2}}{\Gamma[(n-1)/2]} \exp(-ns^2/2)(s^2)^{(n-3)/2} d(s^2)$$

$$\therefore\ dp(t) = dt\int_0^\infty [n/2\pi(n-1)]^{\frac{1}{2}} \exp[-ns^2t^2/2(n-1)]\, s \times$$
$$\times \frac{(n/2)^{(n-1)/2}}{\Gamma[(n-1)/2]} \exp(-ns^2/2)(s^2)^{(n-3)/2} d(s^2)$$
$$= \frac{(n/2)^{(n-1)/2}[n/2\pi(n-1)]^{\frac{1}{2}}}{\Gamma[(n-1)/2]} \times$$
$$\times\ dt\int_0^\infty (s^2)^{(n-2)/2} \exp[-ns^2\{1 + t^2/(n-1\}/2]d(s^2)$$

Putting $s^2 = 2v/n[1 + t^2/(n-1)]$, we have

$$dp(t) = \frac{(n/2)^{(n-1)/2}[n/2\pi(n-1)]^{\frac{1}{2}}}{\Gamma[(n-1)/2]}$$
$$\times\ (2/n)^{n/2}[1 + t^2/(n-1)]^{-n/2} dt \int_0^\infty v^{(n/2)-1} \exp(-v)dv$$

$$= \frac{\Gamma(n/2)}{\sqrt{\pi}(n-1)^{\frac{1}{2}}\Gamma[(n-1)/2]} \cdot [1 + t^2(n-1)]^{-n/2} dt$$

$$\left(\text{since} \int_0^\infty v^{(n/2)-1} \exp(-v)dv = \Gamma(n/2)\right)$$

$$= \frac{\Gamma(n/2)}{\Gamma(\frac{1}{2})\Gamma[(n-1)/2]} \cdot \frac{1}{\sqrt{n-1}} [1 + t^2/(n-1)]^{-n/2} dt$$

$$(\text{since } \sqrt{\pi} = \Gamma(\tfrac{1}{2}))$$

$$\text{or } dp(t) = \frac{1}{B\left(\frac{n-1}{2}, \frac{1}{2}\right)} \cdot \frac{1}{\sqrt{n-1}}[1 + t^2/(n-1)]^{-n/2} dt \qquad (8.1.3)$$

We see at once that t is not normally distributed. If, for instance, $n = 2$, we have $dp(t) = (1/\pi)(1 + t^2)^{-1}$, which defines what is known as the Cauchy distribution, a distribution departing very considerably from normality, the variance, for example, being infinite. However, using Stirling's approximation (5.2.7), it can be shown, as the reader should verify for himself, that $B[(n-1)/2,\ 1/2] \,.\, (n-1)^{\frac{1}{2}}$ tends to $\sqrt{2\pi}$ as $n \longrightarrow \infty$; at the same time, since $[1 + t^2/(n-1)]^{-n/2}$ may be written $[(1 + t^2/(n-1)]^{-\frac{1}{2}(n-1)} \times (1 + t^2/(n-1))]^{-\frac{1}{2}}$, while

$(1 + x/m)^m \longrightarrow \exp x$ as $m \longrightarrow \infty$, $(1 + t^2/(n-1))^{-\frac{1}{2}(n-1)} \longrightarrow \exp(-t^2/2)$.

Thus *the t-distribution approaches normality* $\left(\frac{1}{\sqrt{2\pi}}\exp(-t^2/2)\right)$ *as n increases.*

It is customary to put $\nu = (n - 1)$, the number of *degrees of freedom* of the sample, and to write the probability function of t for ν degrees of freedom thus

$$F_\nu(t) = \frac{1}{\nu^{\frac{1}{2}}B(\nu/2, 1/2)} \cdot (1 + t^2/\nu)^{-(\nu+1)/2} \qquad (8.1.4)$$

In his *Statistical Methods for Research Workers,* Sir R. A. Fisher gives a table of the values of $|t|$ for given ν which will be exceeded, in random sampling, with certain probabilities (P). Fisher's P is related to $F_\nu(t)$ by $P = 1 - 2\int_0^\infty F_\nu(t)dt$.

8.2. Worked Example.

A random sample of 16 *values from a normal population is found to have a mean of* 41·5 *and a standard deviation of* 2·795. *On this information is there any reason to reject the hypothesis that the population mean is* 43 ?

Treatment: $t = 1{\cdot}5 \times 15^{\frac{1}{2}}/2{\cdot}795 = 2{\cdot}078$ for 15 degrees of freedom. Entering Table 8.1 at $\nu = 15$, we find that the probability of $t > 1{\cdot}75$ is 0·10 and of $t > 2{\cdot}13$ is 0·05. Thus the probability that the population mean is 43 is over 0·05. On the information provided by the sample there is then no reason for rejecting the hypothesis.

8.3. Confidence Limits. Suppose, in the above example, we had wanted to find, from the sample data, the limits within which the population mean will lie with a probability of 0·95. We call these limits the 95% *confidence limits* of the population mean for the sample in question. To find these limits, we put

$$|t| = \frac{|41{\cdot}5 - \mu|}{2{\cdot}795} \times 15^{\frac{1}{2}}$$

Entering Table 8.1 at $\nu = 15$, we find that the value of $|t|$ which will be exceeded with a probability of 0·05 is 2·13. Hence

$$\frac{|41{\cdot}5 - \mu|}{2{\cdot}795} \times 15^{\frac{1}{2}} < 2{\cdot}13$$

or

$$\underline{39{\cdot}9 < \mu < 43{\cdot}1}$$

Exercise : *Show that the* 98% *confidence limits are* 39·62 *and* 43·38.

TABLE 8.1. *Values of | t | for Degrees of Freedom Exceeded with Probability P in Random Sampling*

(Abridged, by permission of the author, Sir R. A. Fisher, and the publishers, Messrs. Oliver and Boyd, from *Statistical Methods for Research Workers.*)

ν. \ P.	0·50	0·10	0·05	0·02	0·01
1	1·000	6·34	12·71	31·82	63·66
2	0·816	2·92	4·30	6·96	9·92
3	0·765	2·35	3·18	4·54	5·84
4	0·741	2·13	2·78	3·75	4·60
5	0·727	2·02	2·57	3·36	4·03
6	0·718	1·94	2·45	3·14	3·71
7	0·711	1·90	2·36	3·00	3·50
8	0·706	1·86	2·31	2·90	3·36
9	0·703	1·83	2·26	2·82	3·25
10	0·700	1·81	2·23	2·76	3·17
11	0·697	1·80	2·20	2·72	3·11
12	0·695	1·78	2·18	2·68	3·06
13	0·694	1·77	2·16	2·65	3·01
14	0·692	1·76	2·14	2·62	2·98
15	0·691	1·75	2·13	2·60	2·95
16	0·690	1·75	2·12	2·58	2·92
17	0·689	1·74	2·11	2·57	2·90
18	0·688	1·73	2·10	2·55	2·88
19	0·688	1·73	2·09	2·54	2·86
20	0·687	1·72	2·09	2·53	2·84
25	0·684	1·71	2·06	2·48	2·79
30	0·683	1·70	2·04	2·46	2·75
35	0·682	1·69	2·03	2·44	2·72
40	0·681	1·68	2·02	2·42	2·71
45	0·680	1·68	2·02	2·41	2·69
50	0·679	1·68	2·01	2·40	2·68
60	0·678	1·67	2·00	2·39	2·66
∞	0·674	1·64	1·96	2·33	2·58

In general, for a sample of n with mean $\bar{x}$ and variance s^2,

$$|t| = \frac{|\bar{x} - \mu|}{s} \cdot \nu^{\frac{1}{2}}$$

And if t_P is the value of t with a probability P of being exceeded for ν degrees of freedom, then the $(1 - P)100\%$ confidence limits for μ are:

$$\bar{x} - st_P/\nu^{\frac{1}{2}} < \mu < \bar{x} + st_P/\nu^{\frac{1}{2}} \quad . \quad . \quad . \quad (8.3.1)$$

8.4. Other Applications of the *t*-distribution. It has been shown by Sir R. A. Fisher that:

> **If *t* is a variate which is a fraction, the numerator of which is a normally distributed statistic and the denominator the square root of an independently distributed and unbiased estimate of the variance of the numerator with ν degrees of freedom, then *t* is distributed with probability function $F_\nu(t)$.**

Problem: *Given two independent samples of n_1 and n_2 values with means $\bar{x}$ and $\bar{X}$, how can we test whether they are drawn from the same normal population?*

We begin by setting up the hypothesis that the samples are from the same population. Let x_i, $(i = 1, 2, \ldots n_1)$, and X_j, $(j = 1, 2, \ldots n_2)$, be the two samples. Then $\bar{x} = \sum_{i=1}^{n_1} x_i/n_1$ and $\bar{X} = \sum_{j=1}^{n_2} X_j/n_2$, while the sample variances are respectively

$$s_1^2 = \sum_{i=1}^{n_1} (x_i - \bar{x})^2/n_1 \text{ and } s_2^2 = \sum_{j=1}^{n_2} (X_j - \bar{X})^2/n_2$$

These give unbiased estimates of the population variance,

$$n_1 s_1^2/(n_1 - 1) \text{ and } n_2 s_2^2/(n_2 - 1).$$

Now since

$$\mathcal{E}(n_1 s_1^2 + n_2 s_2^2) = (n_1 - 1)\sigma^2 + (n_2 - 1)\sigma^2 = (n_1 + n_2 - 2)\sigma^2$$

$$\hat{\sigma}^2 \equiv (n_1 s_1^2 + n_2 s_2^2)/(n_1 + n_2 - 2) \quad . \quad . \quad (8.4.1)$$

gives an unbiased estimate of σ^2 based on the two samples, with $\nu = n_1 + n_2 - 2$ degrees of freedom.

If our hypothesis is true—if, that is, our samples are from the same normal population, $\bar{x}$ and $\bar{X}$ are normally distributed about μ, the population mean, with variances σ^2/n_1 and σ^2/n_2 respectively. Therefore (7.9 Example 3), since the samples are independent, the difference, $\bar{x} - \bar{X}$, of their means is normally distributed with variance $\sigma^2(1/n_1 + 1/n_2)$. It follows that $\hat{\sigma}^2(1/n_1 + 1/n_2)$ is an unbiased estimate of the variance of the normally distributed statistic $\bar{x} - \bar{X}$, and therefore, in accordance with the opening statement of this section,

$$\frac{\bar{x} - \bar{X}}{\hat{\sigma}} [n_1 n_2/(n_1 + n)_2]^{\frac{1}{2}} \quad . \quad . \quad . \quad (8.4.2)$$

is distributed like t with $\nu = n_1 + n_2 - 2$ degrees of freedom.

8.5. Worked Example.

1. *Ten soldiers visit the rifle range two weeks running. The first week their scores were*

67, 24, 57, 55, 63, 54, 56, 68, 33, 43

The second week they score, in the same order:

70, 38, 58, 58, 56, 67, 68, 77, 42, 38

Is there any significant improvement? How would the test be affected if the scores were not shown in the same order each time? (A.I.S.)

Treatment:

1st week score (x).	2nd week score (X).	$X - x$	$(X - x)^2$	x^2	X^2
67	70	3	9	4,489	4,900
24	38	14	196	576	1,444
57	58	1	1	3,249	3,364
55	58	3	9	3,025	3,364
63	56	−7	49	3,969	3,136
54	67	13	169	2,916	4,489
56	68	12	144	3,136	4,624
68	77	9	81	4,624	5,929
33	42	9	81	1,089	1,764
43	38	−5	25	1,849	1,444
520 ($10\bar{x}$)	572 ($10\bar{X}$)	52	764	28,922	34,458

(1) We assume there is no significant improvement, that, consequently, both X and x are drawn from the same normal population and that, therefore, $X - x$ is normally distributed about zero. Then, regarding the 10 values of $X - x$ as our sample, we have

$$s^2 \equiv \text{var}\,(X - x) = \Sigma\,(X - x)^2/n - (\bar{X} - \bar{x})^2$$
$$= 76{\cdot}4 - 27{\cdot}04 = 49{\cdot}36;$$

and, therefore, $s = 7{\cdot}026$. Hence

$$t \equiv (\bar{X} - \bar{x})(n - 1)^{\frac{1}{2}}/s = 5{\cdot}2 \times 3/7{\cdot}026 = 2{\cdot}22$$

Entering Table 8.1 at $\nu = 9$ we find that the probability with which $t = 2{\cdot}26$ is exceeded is $0{\cdot}05$, while the probability with which $t = 1{\cdot}83$ is exceeded is $0{\cdot}10$. Therefore the result, while significant at the 10% level, is not significant at the 5% level. We conclude, therefore, that *there is some small evidence of improvement.*

(2) Had the scores not been given in the same order, we should have had to rely on the difference between the mean scores. We

again suppose that there has been no significant improvement and use the variate

$$t = \frac{\bar{X} - \bar{x}}{\hat{\sigma}} \cdot (n_x n_X/(n_x + n_X))^{\frac{1}{2}},$$

where $\hat{\sigma}^2 = (n_x s_x{}^2 + n_X s_X{}^2)/(n_x + n_X - 2)$.

In the present case $n_x = n_X = 10$, and we have

$$10s_x{}^2 = \Sigma x^2 - 10\bar{x}^2 \text{ and } 10s_X{}^2 = \Sigma X^2 - 10\bar{X}^2.$$

$$\therefore \quad 10(s_x{}^2 + s_X{}^2) = \Sigma x^2 + \Sigma X^2 - 10(\bar{x}^2 + \bar{X}^2)$$

$$= 28{,}922 + 34{,}458 - 10(52^2 + 57{\cdot}2^2) = 3{,}622.$$

$$\therefore \quad \hat{\sigma}^2 = 10(s_x{}^2 + s_X{}^2)/18 = 201{\cdot}2 \text{ or } \hat{\sigma} = 14{\cdot}18.$$

Consequently, $t = \frac{5{\cdot}2}{14{\cdot}18} \times (100/20)^{\frac{1}{2}} = 0{\cdot}82$ for $\nu = 18$ d.f.

Entering Table 8.1 at $\nu = 18$, we find that there is a 0·5 probability that t will exceed 0·688 and a probability of 0·10 that t will exceed 1·73. Consequently, the result is not significant at the 10% level and *there is no reason to reject the hypothesis that there has been no significant improvement.*

2. *In an ordnance factory two different methods of shell-filling are compared. The average and standard deviation of weights in a sample of* 96 *shells filled by one process are* 1·26 *lb. and* 0·013 *lb., and a sample of* 72 *shells filled by the second process gave a mean of* 1·28 *lb. and a standard deviation of* 0·011 *lb. Is the difference in weights significant?* (Brookes and Dick.)

Treatment: Assuming that there is no significance in the difference of weights,

$$\hat{\sigma}^2 = \frac{96 \times (0{\cdot}013)^2 + 72 \times (0{\cdot}011)^2}{96 + 72 - 2}$$

or $\hat{\sigma} = 0{\cdot}0125$;

$$|\bar{x} - \bar{X}| = 0{\cdot}02 \text{ and } (n_x n_X/(n_x + n_X))^{\frac{1}{2}} = (96 \times 72/168)^{\frac{1}{2}} = 6{\cdot}43.$$

$$\therefore \ |t| = 0{\cdot}020 \times 6{\cdot}43/0{\cdot}0125 = 10{\cdot}29 \text{ for 166 degrees of freedom.}$$

Since ν is so large in this case, we may assume that t is normally distributed about zero mean with unit variance. Then $|t| > 10$ standard deviations and is, therefore, highly unlikely by chance alone. The difference in the weights is, then, highly significant.

8.6. The Variance-ratio, *F*. We now discuss a test of significance of the difference between the variances of two samples from the same population. Actually, if the sample variances are such that the two samples cannot have been drawn from the same population, it is useless to apply the t-test to ascertain whether the difference between the means is significant, for we assume in establishing that test that the samples are in fact from the same population. Thus, the present problem is logically the more fundamental.

Problem : *A standard cell, whose voltage is known to be* 1·10 *volts, was used to test the accuracy of two voltmeters, A and B. Ten independent readings of the voltage of the cell were taken with each voltmeter. The results were :*

A .	1·11	1·15	1·14	1·10	1·09	1·11	1·12	1·15	1·13	1·14
B .	1·12	1·06	1·02	1·08	1·11	1·05	1·06	1·03	1·05	1·08

Is there evidence of bias in either voltmeter, and is there any evidence that one voltmeter is more consistent than the other?

(R.S.S.)

We already know how to tackle the first part of the problem (see at the end of this section), but what about the second part? The consistency of either meter will be measured by the variance of the population of all possible readings of the voltmeter, and this variance will be estimated from the ten sample readings given. Thus we have to devise a test to compare the two estimates. This has been done by Sir R. A. Fisher, whose test is :

If u^2 and v^2 are unbiased estimates of a population variance based on $n_1 - 1$ and $n_2 - 1$ degrees of freedom respectively (where n_1 and n_2 are the respective sample sizes), then by calculating $z \equiv \frac{1}{2} \log_e (u^2/v^2)$ and using the appropriate tables given in *Statistical Methods for Research Workers*, we can decide whether the value of this *variance ratio*, u^2/v^2, is likely to result from random sampling from the same population.

Let x_i, $(i = 1, 2, 3, \ldots n_1)$, and X_j, $(j = 1, 2, 3, \ldots n_2)$, be two independent samples with means $\bar{x}$ and $\bar{X}$ respectively. Unbiased estimates of the population variance are :

$$u^2 = n_1 s_1^2/(n_1 - 1), \text{ and } v^2 = n_2 s_2^2/(n_2 - 1),$$

where s_1^2 and s_2^2 are the respective sample variances. If $\nu_1 \equiv n_1 - 1$, $\nu_2 \equiv n_2 - 1$,

$$s_1^2 = \nu_1 u^2/(\nu_1 + 1) \quad \text{and} \quad s_2^2 = \nu_2 v^2/(\nu_2 + 1) \quad . \quad (8.6.1)$$

Now the sample variance, s^2, has the probability differential (7.11.4)

$$dp(s^2) = \frac{(n/2\sigma^2)^{\frac{n-1}{2}}}{\Gamma\left(\frac{n-1}{2}\right)} \exp\left(-ns^2/2\sigma^2\right)(s^2)^{\frac{n-3}{2}} d(s^2)$$

Substituting from (8.6.1), the probability differential of u^2 is

$$dp(u^2) = [(\nu_1/2\sigma^2)^{\nu_1/2}/\Gamma(\nu_1/2)](u^2)^{\frac{\nu_1-2}{2}} \exp(-\nu_1 u^2/2\sigma^2)d(u^2) \quad (8.6.2)$$

But u and v are independent; therefore the joint probability differential of u^2 and v^2 is

$$dp(u^2, v^2) = \frac{(\nu_1/2\sigma^2)^{\nu_1/2} \cdot (\nu_2/2\sigma^2)^{\nu_2/2}}{\Gamma(\nu_1/2) \cdot \Gamma(\nu_2/2)} (u^2)^{\frac{\nu_1-2}{2}} \cdot (v^2)^{\frac{\nu_2-2}{2}} \times$$
$$\times \exp[-(\nu_1 u^2 + \nu_2 v^2)/2\sigma^2]d(u^2)d(v^2) \quad . \quad (8.6.3)$$

Now let

$$z \equiv \log_e(u/v) = \tfrac{1}{2}\log_e(u^2/v^2) \quad . \quad . \quad (8.6.5)$$

Then $u^2 = v^2 \exp(2z)$, and, *for a given v*, $d(u^2) = 2v^2 \exp(2z)dz$. Therefore

$$dp(v^2, z) = \frac{2(\nu_1/2\sigma^2)^{\nu_1/2}(\nu_2/2\sigma^2)^{\nu_2/2}}{\Gamma(\nu_1/2)\Gamma(\nu_2/2)} \exp(\nu_1 z) \times$$
$$\times \exp[-(\nu_1 e^{2z} + \nu_2)v^2/2\sigma^2](v^2)^{\frac{\nu_1+\nu_2-2}{2}} d(v^2)dz \quad . \quad (8.6.6)$$

To find the probability differential of z, we integrate this with respect to v^2 between 0 and ∞, obtaining

$$dp(z) = \frac{2(\nu_1/2\sigma^2)^{\nu_1/2}(\nu_1/2\sigma^2)^{\nu_2/2}}{\Gamma(\nu_1/2)\Gamma(\nu_2/2)} \times$$
$$\times \exp(\nu_1 z)dz \times \int_0^\infty \exp[-(\nu_1 e^{2z} + \nu_2)v^2/2\sigma^2](v^2)^{\frac{\nu_1+\nu_2-2}{2}} d(v^2)$$

Recalling that

$$\Gamma(n) = \int_0^\infty x^{n-1}\exp(-x)dx, \quad \text{we put} \quad x = \frac{1}{2\sigma^2}(\nu_1 e^{2z} + \nu_2)v^2.$$

Then $$dp(z) = 2\nu_1^{\nu_1/2}\nu_2^{\nu_2/2} \frac{\Gamma\left(\frac{\nu_1+\nu_2}{2}\right)}{\Gamma(\nu_1/2)\Gamma(\nu_2/2)} \cdot \frac{\exp(\nu_1 z)}{(\nu_1 e^{2z} + \nu_2)^{\frac{\nu_1+\nu_2}{2}}} \cdot dz$$

or $$dp(z) = \frac{2\nu_1^{\nu_1/2}\nu_2^{\nu_2/2}}{B(\nu_1/2, \nu_2/2)} \cdot \frac{\exp(\nu_1 z)}{(\nu_1 e^{2z} + \nu_2)^{\frac{\nu_1+\nu_2}{2}}} dz \quad . \quad (8.6.7)$$

This defines Fisher's z-distribution, which, it should be noted, is independent of the variance of the parent population.

How do we use it?

The probability, $P(z \leqslant Z)$, that z will be not greater than some given value Z for ν_1, ν_2 degrees of freedom is $\int_0^Z dp(z)$. Then $P(z > Z) = 1 - P(z \leqslant Z) = 1 - \int_0^Z dp(z)$. In his book Fisher gives tables setting down the values of Z exceeded with probabilities 0·05 and 0·01 for given ν_1 and ν_2. He calls these values, $Z_{0\cdot05}$ and $Z_{0\cdot01}$, the "*5% and 1% points" of z.*

To obviate the necessity of using logarithms, Snedecor (*Statistical Methods*, Collegiate Press, Inc., Ames, Iowa) tabulated the 5% and 1% points of the variance ratio, u^2/v^2, which he denotes by F, in honour of Fisher, instead of $z = \frac{1}{2}\log_e F$. Substituting $F = u^2/v^2$, where u^2 *is the larger of the two estimates of the population variance*, or $F = \exp(2z)$, in (8.6.7), we have

$$dp(F) = \frac{\nu_1^{\nu_1/2}\nu_2^{\nu_2/2}}{B(\nu_1/2, \nu_2/2)} \cdot \frac{F^{(\nu_1-2)/2}}{(\nu_1 F + \nu_2)^{\frac{\nu_1+\nu_2}{2}}} dF \quad (8.6.8)$$

[1]

In the F-table, Table 8.6, the d.f. ν_1, of the larger estimate, give the column required, and ν_2, the d.f. of the smaller estimate, the row required. At the intersection of the appropriate column and row we find two figures: the *upper figure* is that value of F exceeded with a probability of 0·05, the 5% point; the *lower figure* is that value exceeded with a probability of 0·01, *the* 1% *point*.

We may now return to the problem at the beginning of this section.

---

[1] Writing

$$x = \nu_1 F/(\nu_1 F + \nu_2) \quad \text{or} \quad F = \nu_2 x/\nu_1(1 - x)$$

we have

$$dp(x) = \frac{1}{B(\nu_1/2, \nu_2/2)} x^{(\nu_1-2)/2}(1-x)^{(\nu_2-2)/2} dx$$

Hence $$P(x \leqslant X) = \frac{1}{B(\nu_1/2, \nu_2/2)} \int_0^X x^{(\nu_1-2)/2}(1-x)^{(\nu_2-2)/2} dx$$

and the integral is $B_X(\nu_1/2, \nu_2/2)$. Thus $P(x \leqslant X)$ is the Incomplete B-function Ratio, $I_X(\nu_1/2, \nu_2/2)$ and can be found from the appropriate tables (see *Mathematical Note to Chapter Three*, D).

TABLE 8.6. *5% and 1% Points for the Distribution of the Variance Ratio, F*

(Adapted, by permission of the author and publishers, from Table 10.5.3 of *Statistical Methods* by G. W. Snedecor (5th Edition, 1956, pp. 246–249).

ν_2 \ ν_1	1	2	3	4	5	6	8	12	24	∞
1	161	200	216	225	230	234	239	244	249	254
	4052	4999	5403	5625	5764	5859	5981	6106	6234	6366
2	18·51	19·00	19·16	19·25	19·30	19·33	19·37	19·41	19·45	19·50
	98·49	99·01	99·17	99·25	99·30	99·33	99·36	99·42	99·46	99·50
3	10·13	9·55	9·28	9·12	9·01	8·94	8·84	8·74	8·64	8·53
	34·12	30·81	29·46	28·71	28·24	27·91	27·49	27·05	26·60	26·12
4	7·71	6·94	6·59	6·39	6·26	6·16	6·04	5·91	5·77	5·63
	21·20	18·00	16·69	15·98	15·52	15·21	14·80	14·37	13·93	13·46
5	6·61	5·79	5·41	5·19	5·05	4·95	4·82	4·70	4·53	4·36
	16·26	13·27	12·06	11·39	10·97	10·67	10·27	9·89	9·47	9·02
6	5·99	5·14	4·76	4·53	4·39	4·28	4·15	4·00	3·84	3·67
	13·74	10·92	9·78	9·15	8·75	8·47	8·10	7·79	7·31	6·88
7	5·59	4·74	4·35	4·12	3·97	3·87	3·73	3·57	3·41	3·23
	12·25	9·55	8·45	7·85	7·46	7·19	6·84	6·47	6·07	5·65
8	5·32	4·46	4·07	3·84	3·69	3·58	3·44	3·28	3·12	2·93
	11·26	8·65	7·59	7·01	6·63	6·37	6·03	5·67	5·28	4·86
9	5·12	4·26	3·86	3·63	3·48	3·37	3·23	3·07	2·90	2·71
	10·56	8·02	6·99	6·42	6·06	5·80	5·47	5·11	4·73	4·31
10	4·96	4·10	3·71	3·48	3·33	3·22	3·07	2·91	2·74	2·54
	10·04	7·56	6·55	5·99	5·64	5·39	5·06	4·71	4·33	4·31
11	4·84	3·98	3·59	3·36	3·20	3·09	2·95	2·79	2·61	2·40
	9·65	7·20	6·22	5·67	5·32	5·07	4·74	4·40	4·02	3·60
12	4·75	3·88	3·49	3·26	3·11	3·00	2·85	2·69	2·50	2·30
	9·33	6·93	5·95	5·41	5·06	4·82	4·50	4·16	3·78	3·36
13	4·67	3·80	3·41	3·18	3·02	2·92	2·77	2·60	2·42	2·21
	9·07	6·70	5·74	5·20	4·86	4·62	4·30	3·96	3·59	3·16
14	4·60	3·74	3·34	3·11	2·96	2·85	2·70	2·53	2·35	2·13
	8·86	6·51	5·56	5·03	4·69	4·46	4·14	3·80	3·43	3·00
15	4·54	3·68	3·29	3·06	2·90	2·79	2·64	2·48	2·29	2·07
	8·68	6·36	5·42	4·89	4·56	4·32	4·00	3·67	3·29	2·87
16	4·49	3·63	3·24	3·01	2·85	2·74	2·59	2·42	2·24	2·01
	8·53	6·23	5·29	4·77	4·44	4·20	3·89	3·55	3·18	2·75
17	4·45	3·59	3·20	2·96	2·81	2·70	2·55	2·38	2·19	1·96
	8·40	6·11	5·18	4·67	4·34	4·10	3·79	3·45	3·08	2·65
18	4·41	3·55	3·16	2·93	2·77	2·66	2·51	2·34	2·15	1·92
	8·28	6·01	5·09	4·58	4·25	4·01	3·71	3·37	3·00	2·57
19	4·38	3·52	3·13	2·90	2·74	2·63	2·48	2·31	2·11	1·88
	8·18	5·93	5·01	4·50	4·17	3·94	3·63	3·30	2·92	2·49

TABLE 8.6. *Continued*

ν_2 \ ν_1	1	2	3	4	5	6	8	12	24	∞
20	4·35 8·10	3·49 5·85	3·10 4·94	2·87 4·43	2·71 4·10	2·60 3·87	2·45 3·56	2·28 3·23	2·08 2·86	1·84 2·42
21	4·32 8·02	3·47 5·78	3·07 4·87	2·84 4·37	2·68 4·04	2·57 3·81	2·42 3·51	2·25 3·17	2·05 2·80	1·81 2·36
22	4·30 7·94	3·44 5·72	3·05 4·82	2·82 4·31	2·66 3·99	2·55 3·76	2·40 3·45	2·23 3·12	2·03 2·75	1·78 2·31
23	4·28 7·88	3·42 5·66	3·03 4·76	2·80 4·26	2·64 3·94	2·53 3·71	2·38 3·41	2·20 3·07	2·00 2·70	1·76 2·26
24	4·26 7·82	3·40 5·61	3·01 4·72	2·78 4·22	2·62 3·90	2·51 3·67	2·36 3·36	2·18 3·03	1·98 2·66	1·73 2·21
30	4·17 7·56	3·32 5·39	2·92 4·51	2·69 4·02	2·53 3·70	2·42 3·47	2·27 3·17	2·09 2·84	1·89 2·47	1·62 2·01
40	4·08 7·31	3·23 5·18	2·84 4·31	2·61 3·83	2·45 3·51	2·34 3·29	2·18 2·99	2·00 2·66	1·79 2·29	1·51 1·80
60	4·00 7·08	3·15 4·98	2·76 4·13	2·52 3·65	2·37 3·34	2·25 3·12	2·10 2·82	1·92 2·50	1·70 2·12	1·39 1·60
120	3·92 6·85	3·07 4·79	2·68 3·95	2·45 3·48	2·29 3·17	2·17 2·96	2·02 2·66	1·83 2·34	1·61 1·95	1·25 1·38
∞	3·84 6·64	2·99 4·60	2·60 3·78	2·37 3·32	2·21 3·02	2·09 2·80	1·94 2·51	1·75 2·18	1·52 1·79	1·00 1·00

NOTE TO TABLE 8.6

(1) To find the 5% and 1% points for values of ν_1 or ν_2 not given in the above table, when $\nu_1 > 8$ and $\nu_2 > 24$ we proceed as illustrated below:

(*a*) To find the 5% point of F when $\nu_1 = 200$, $\nu_2 = 18$, enter the Table at $\nu_2 = 18$. The 5% point for $\nu_1 = 24$ is 2·15; the 5% point for $\nu_1 = \infty$ is 1·92. Divide 24/24 = 1; divide 24/∞ = 0; divide 24/200 = 0·12. The difference between the two given 5% points is 0·23. 0·12 of this difference, 0·12 × 0·23 = 0·0276. We add this to 1·92, obtaining 1·95, correct to two decimal places.

(*b*) To find the 1% point of F when $\nu_1 = 11$, $\nu_2 = 21$, enter the Table at $\nu_2 = 21$. The 1% point when $\nu_1 = 8$ is 3·51 and when $\nu_1 = 12$ is 3·17. 24/8 = 3; 24/12 = 2; 24/11 = 2·18. The difference between the two known 1% points is 3·51 − 3·17 = 0·34. 0·18 × 0·34 = 0·06. Hence the required 1% point is 3·17 + 0·06 = 3·23.

(*c*) To find the 5% point of F when $\nu_1 = 4$, $\nu_2 = 55$, enter the Table at $\nu_1 = 4$. The 5% point for $\nu_2 = 40$ is 2·61; the 5% point for $\nu_2 = 60$ is 2·52. 120/40 = 3; 120/60 = 2; 120/55 = 2·18. 2·61 − 2·52 = 0·09. 0·18 × 0·09 = 0·016. The required 5% point is 2·52 + 0·016 = 2·54 correct to two decimal places.

(*d*) To find the 1% point of F when $\nu_1 = 12$, $\nu_2 = 500$, enter the Table at $\nu_1 = 12$. The 1% for $\nu_2 = 120$ is 2·34; the 1% point for $\nu_2 = \infty$ is 2·18. 120/120 = 1; 120/∞ = 0; 120/500 = 0·24. 2·34 − 2·18 = 0·16. 0·24 × 0·16 = 0·038. The required 1% point is 2·18 + 0·038 = 2·22, correct to two decimal places.

(2) If we make the substitution $F = t^2$ in (8.6.8), simultaneously putting $\nu_1 = 1$ and $\nu_2 = \nu$, we find that the probability differential of F transforms into that for t. Thus we may use the F-tables to find the 5% and 1% points of t. They are, in fact, the square roots of the 5% and 1% points of F for $\nu_1 = 1$. (See also 10.3).

We tabulate the working as follows :

Reading of voltmeter A (x).	($x - 1\cdot10$).	($x - 1\cdot10)^2$.
1·11	0·01	0·0001
1·15	0·05	0·0025
1·14	0·04	0·0016
1·10	—	—
1·09	−0·01	0·0001
1·11	0·01	0·0001
1·12	0·02	0·0004
1·15	0·05	0·0025
1·13	0·03	0·0009
1·14	0·04	0·0016
	0·24	0·0098

$$\bar{x} = 1\cdot10 + 0\cdot24/10$$
$$= \underline{1\cdot124}$$
$$s_x^2 = \Sigma (x - 1\cdot10)^2/10 - (\bar{x} - 1\cdot10)^2$$
$$= \underline{0\cdot000404}$$
$$\therefore \quad s_x = \underline{0\cdot0201}$$

Reading of voltmeter B (X).	($X - 1\cdot10$).	($X - 1\cdot10)^2$.
1·12	0·02	0·0004
1·06	−0·04	0·0016
1·02	−0·08	0·0064
1·08	−0·02	0·0004
1·11	0·01	0·0001
1·05	−0·05	0·0025
1·06	−0·04	0·0016
1·03	−0·07	0·0049
1·05	−0·05	0·0025
1·08	−0·02	0·0004
	−0·34	0·0208

$$\bar{X} = 1\cdot10 - 0\cdot034$$
$$= \underline{1\cdot066}$$
$$s_X^2 = 0\cdot00208 - (0\cdot034)^2$$
$$= \underline{0\cdot000924}$$
$$\therefore \quad s_X = \underline{0\cdot0304}$$

For voltmeter A: $|t| = 0{\cdot}024 \times 9^{\frac{1}{2}}/0{\cdot}0201 = \underline{3{\cdot}58}$. Entering Table 8.1 at $\nu = 9$ we find that the value of t exceeded with a probability of 0·01 is 3·25. The result is therefore significant at the 1% level. Since the value of t here is positive, *the voltmeter A definitely reads high.*

For voltmeter B: $|t| = 0{\cdot}0340 \times 9^{\frac{1}{2}}/0{\cdot}0304 = 3{\cdot}36$. Once again the value of t is significant at the 1% level and we conclude that, since t is here negative, *the voltmeter reads low.*

To test whether there is evidence that one voltmeter is more consistent than the other, we set up the null hypothesis that there is no difference in consistency. In other words, we assume that the samples are from populations of the same variance.

$F = u^2/v^2$, where $u^2 > v^2$ and u^2 and v^2 are unbiased estimates of the population variance based on, in this case, the same number of degrees of freedom, 9. Since the samples are of equal size, we have

$$F = s_X{}^2/s_x{}^2 = 0{\cdot}000924/0{\cdot}000404 = \underline{2{\cdot}29}.$$

Entering Table 8.6 at $\nu_2 = 9$, we read that the 5% point of F for $\nu_1 = 8$ is 3·23, while that for $\nu_1 = 12$ is 3·07. $24/8 = 3$; $24/12 = 2$; $24/9 = 1{\cdot}67$. $3{\cdot}23 - 3{\cdot}07 = 0{\cdot}16$. $0{\cdot}16 \times 0{\cdot}67 = 0{\cdot}107$. Therefore the 5% point of F for $\nu_1 = \nu_2 = 9$ is $3{\cdot}177 = 3{\cdot}18$, correct to two decimal places. The value of F obtained, 2·29, is, therefore, not significant at the 5% level, and *we have no reason to reject the hypothesis that there is no difference in consistency between the two voltmeters.*

EXERCISES ON CHAPTER EIGHT

1. A sample of 14 eggs of a particular species of wild bird collected in a given area is found to have a mean length of 0·89 cm. and a standard deviation of 0·154 cm. Is this compatible with the hypothesis that the mean length of the eggs of this bird is 0·99 cm.?

2. A group of 8 psychology students were tested for their ability to remember certain material, and their scores (number of items remembered) were as follows:

A	B	C	D	E	F	G	H
19	14	13	16	19	18	16	17

They were then given special training purporting to improve memory and were retested after a month. Scores then:

A	B	C	D	E	F	G	H
26	20	17	21	23	24	21	18

A control group of 7 students was tested and retested after a month, but was given no special training. Scores in two tests:

21	19	16	22	18	20	19
21	23	16	24	17	17	16

Compare the change in the two groups by calculating t and test whether there is significant evidence to show the value of the special training. Do you consider that the experiment was properly designed? (R.S.S.)

3. A sample of 6 values from an unknown normal population: 20, 25, 24, 28, 22, 26. Another sample of 5 values: 21, 24, 27, 26, 25. Show that there is no good reason to suppose that the samples are not from the same population.

4. Two marksmen, P and Q, on 25 targets each, obtained the scores tabulated below. Ascertain whether one marksman may be regarded as the more consistent shot.

Score . .		93	94	95	96	97	98	99	100	Total
Frequency	P	2	1	4	0	5	5	2	6	25
	Q	0	2	2	3	3	8	5	2	25

(I.A.)

5. Latter has given the following data for the length in mm.s of cuckoo's eggs which were found in nests belonging to the hedge-sparrow (A), reed-warbler (B) and wren (C):

Host.

A 22·0, 23·9, 20·9, 23·8, 25·0, 24·0, 21·7, 23·8, 22·8, 23·1, 23·1, 23·5, 23·0, 23·0

B 23·2, 22·0, 22·2, 21·2, 21·6, 21·6, 21·9, 22·0, 22·9, 22·8

C 19·8, 22·1, 21·5, 20·9, 22·0, 21·0, 22·3, 21·0, 20·3, 20·9, 22·0, 20·0, 20·8, 21·2, 21·0

Is there any evidence from these data that the cuckoo can adapt the size of its egg to the size of the nest of the host?

Solutions

1. Not significant at 0·02 level.

2. Evidence of improvement in test group highly significant; that of control group highly insignificant. Initial scores in control group too high for control to be useful.

4. F not significant at 0·05 point, i.e., although there is evidence that Q is more consistent this could arise from random variation alone.

CHAPTER NINE

ANALYSIS OF VARIANCE

9.1. The Problem Stated. The test of significance of the variance-ratio, F, described in the previous chapter encourages us to embark on a much wider investigation, that of the analysis of variance. This important statistical technique has been defined by its originator, Sir R. A. Fisher, as

> " The separation of the variance ascribable to one group of causes from the variance ascribable to other groups " (*Statistical Methods for Research Workers*, Eleventh Edition, 1950, p. 211).

Suppose that from a large herd of cows we pick fifty animals at random and record the milk-yield of each over a given period. These fifty amounts (in gallons, say) are a sample of fifty values of our variate. Now the herd may consist, perhaps, of five different breeds—Ayrshire, Jersey, etc.—and we want to find an answer to the following problem, using the evidence provided by our sample :

> Does milk-yield vary with the breed of cow? Or, in other words, are milk-yield and breed connected?

As a first step towards answering this question, it would be reasonable to divide our sample into five sub-samples or classes, according to breed. Then if we could split up the total variance of our sample into two components—that due to variation between the mean milk-yields of different breeds and that due to variation of yield within breeds, we could subject these two components to further scrutiny.

To do this *we first set up the null hypothesis that the factor according to which we classify the population and, therefore, the sample values of the variate, has no effect on the value of the variate*, i.e., in our present case that breed (the factor of classification) does not influence milk-yield. If, indeed, this is the case, each class into which we divide our sample will itself be a random sample from one and the same population. Consequently any unbiased estimates we may make of the population variance on the basis of these sub-samples should be compatible and, on the further assumption that the population sampled is normal, these estimates should not differ significantly when subjected to a variance-ratio test. However, should they be found to differ significantly, we should have to conclude that our sub-samples are not random samples from one homogeneous population, but are in fact drawn from several different populations brought into being as it were by our method of classification. We should have to conclude, in short, that our null hypothesis was untenable and that milk-yield and breed *are* connected.

In practice, of course, the problem is seldom as simple as this and may involve more than one criterion of classification. We may, for instance, have to analyse, not merely the influence of breed on milk-yield, but also that of different varieties of feeding-stuffs. This would present us with a problem of analysis of variance with two criteria of classification. Problems arising from three or more criteria are also common. Although the general principle underlying the treatment of all such problems is the same, each presents its own particular problems.

9.2. One Criterion of Classification. Consider a random sample of N values of a given variate x. Let us classify these N values into m classes according to some criterion of classification and let the ith class have n_i members. Then $\sum_{i=1}^{m} n_i = N$. Also, let the jth member of the ith class be x_{ij}. The sample values may then be set out as follows :

Class 1. .	x_{11}	x_{12}	. . .	x_{1j}	. . .	x_{1n_1}
Class 2. .	x_{21}	x_{22}	. . .	x_{2j}	. . .	x_{2n_2}
. . .	. . .	. . .	. . .	. . .	. . .	. . .
Class i .	x_{i1}	x_{i2}	. . .	x_{ij}	. . .	x_{in_i}
. . .	. . .	. . .	. . .	. . .	. . .	. . .
Class m .	x_{m1}	x_{m2}	. . .	x_{mj}	. . .	x_{mn_m}

It is frequently the case that, for all i, $n_i = n$, i.e., each class has n members and, consequently, $N = mn$.

Let the mean of the ith class be $\bar{x}_{i.}$ and the general mean of the N values be $\bar{x}_{..}$ Then, for all i,

$$\sum_{j=1}^{n_i} (x_{ij} - \bar{x}_{i.}) = 0 \quad . \quad . \quad . \quad (9.2.1)$$

Consequently,

$$\sum_{j=1}^{n_i} (x_{ij} - \bar{x}_{..})^2 = \sum_{j=1}^{n_i} (x_{ij} - \bar{x}_{i.} + \bar{x}_{i.} - \bar{x}_{..})^2$$

$$= \sum_{j=1}^{n_i} (x_{ij} - \bar{x}_{i.})^2 + n_i(\bar{x}_{i.} - \bar{x}_{..})^2 + 2(\bar{x}_{i.} - \bar{x}_{..}) \sum_{j=1}^{n_i} (x_{ij} - \bar{x}_{i.})$$

$$= \sum_{j=1}^{n_i} (x_{ij} - \bar{x}_{i.})^2 + n_i(\bar{x}_{i.} - \bar{x}_{..})^2, \text{ (in virtue of (9.2.1))}$$

Hence

$$\sum_{i=1}^{m} \sum_{j=1}^{n_i} (x_{ij} - \bar{x}_{..})^2 = \sum_{i=1}^{m} n_i(\bar{x}_{i.} - \bar{x}_{..})^2 + \sum_{i=1}^{m} \sum_{j=1}^{n_i} (x_{ij} - \bar{x}_{i.})^2 \quad (9.2.2)$$

The left-hand member of this equation is the total sum of the squared deviations of the sample values of the variate from the general mean; it is a measure of the "total variation". The right-hand side of the equation shows that this "total variation" may be resolved into two components:

one, measured by the first term on the right-hand side, is the variation which would have resulted had there been no variation within the classes; this is easily seen by putting $x_{ij} = \bar{x}_{i.}$ for all i; it is therefore the *variation between classes*;

the other, measured by the second term on the right-hand side, is the residual *variation within classes*, after the variation between classes has been separated out from the total variation.

In short,

TOTAL VARIATION = VARIATION BETWEEN CLASSES + VARIATION WITHIN CLASSES

Assuming that the classifying factor does not influence variate-values, each class into which the sample is divided by this factor will be a random sample from the parent population. Taking expected values of the terms in (9.2.2):

$$\mathcal{E}\left(\sum_{i=1}^{m} \sum_{j=1}^{n_i} (x_{ij} - \bar{x}_{..})^2\right) = (N - 1)\sigma^2,$$

where σ^2 is the variance of the parent population. Also

$$\mathcal{E}\left(\sum_{i=1}^{m} \sum_{j=1}^{n_i} (x_{ij} - \bar{x}_{i.})^2\right) = \sum_{i=1}^{m}\left[\mathcal{E}\left(\sum_{j=1}^{n_i} (x_{ij} - \bar{x}_{i.})^2\right)\right]$$

$$= \sum_{i=1}^{m} (n_i - 1)\sigma^2 = (N - m)\sigma^2.$$

Consequently,

$$\mathcal{E}\left(\sum_{i=1}^{m} n_i(\bar{x}_{i\cdot} - \bar{x}_{\cdot\cdot})^2\right) = (N-1)\sigma^2 - (N-m)\sigma^2 = (m-1)\sigma^2$$

Thus, providing our null hypothesis stands, (9.2.2) leads us to two unbiased estimates of σ^2, viz.,

$$\sum_{i=1}^{m} n_i(\bar{x}_{i\cdot} - \bar{x}_{\cdot\cdot})^2/(m-1),$$

based on $m - 1$ degrees of freedom, and

$$\sum_{i=1}^{m}\sum_{j=1}^{n_i}(x_{ij} - \bar{x}_{i\cdot})^2/(N-m),$$

based on $N - m$ degrees of freedom.

So far all we have said has been true for any population. *We now impose the restriction that the population sampled be normal.* With this restriction, the two unbiased estimates are also independent, and all the conditions for applying either Fisher's z-test or Snedecor's version of that test are fulfilled.

We now draw up the following analysis of variance table :

Analysis of Variance for One Criterion of Classification

Source of variation.	Sum of squares.	Degrees of freedom.	Estimate of variance.
Between classes	$\sum_{i=1}^{m} n_i(\bar{x}_{i\cdot} - \bar{x}_{\cdot\cdot})^2$	$m - 1$	$\sum_{i=1}^{m} n_i(\bar{x}_{i\cdot} - \bar{x}_{\cdot\cdot})^2/(m-1)$
Within classes	$\sum_{i=1}^{m}\sum_{j=1}^{n_i}(x_{ij} - \bar{x}_{i\cdot})^2$	$N - m$	$\sum_{i=1}^{m}\sum_{j=1}^{n_i}(x_{ij} - \bar{x}_{i\cdot})^2/(N-m)$
TOTAL	$\sum_{i=1}^{m}\sum_{j=1}^{n_i}(x_{ij} - \bar{x}_{\cdot\cdot})^2$	$N - 1$	—

Since, from the conditions of the problem, both N and m are greater than 1, the estimate of σ^2 from the variation within classes must, of necessity, be based upon more degrees of freedom than that of σ^2 from the variation between classes.

It is reasonable, therefore, to take the estimate of σ^2 from the variation within classes as the more reliable estimate, even if the null hypothesis is untenable. If, then, the other estimate of σ^2, that from the variation between classes, is smaller than this, but not considerably so, we may straightaway conclude that there is no evidence upon which to reject the hypothesis. If, however, it is greater, we may test whether it is significantly greater by means of a variance-ratio test.

9.3. Worked Example.

Six machines produce steel wire. The following data give the diameters at ten positions along the wire for each machine. Examine whether the machine means can be regarded as constant.

Machine.	Diameters in thousandths of an inch.									
A	12	13	13	16	16	14	15	15	16	17
B	12	14	14	16	16	18	17	19	20	18
C	14	21	17	14	19	18	17	17	16	15
D	23	27	25	21	26	24	27	24	20	21
E	12	14	13	16	13	17	16	15	15	14
F	13	18	13	16	17	15	15	16	16	17

(Paradine and Rivett)

Treatment: (1) We set up the hypothesis that the machine means are constant.

(2) We note that :

(*a*) since the variance of a set of values is independent of the origin, a *shift of origin does not affect variance-calculations.* We may therefore choose any convenient origin which will reduce the arithmetic involved. We take our new origin at $x = 20$;

(*b*) since we are concerned here only with the ratio of two variances, *any change of scale will not affect the value of this ratio.* This also contributes to reducing the arithmetic, but in the present example is unnecessary.

(3) We may further reduce the work of calculation as follows :

Let $$T = \sum_i \sum_j x_{ij} \quad \text{and} \quad T_i = \sum_j x_{ij}.$$

Then (*a*) $$\sum_i \sum_j (x_{ij} - \bar{x})^2 = \sum_i \sum_j x_{ij}^2 - N\bar{x}^2 = \sum_i \sum_j x_{ij}^2 - T^2/N$$

(*b*) $$\sum_i \sum_j (x_{ij} - \bar{x}_i)^2 = \sum_i \left(\sum_j (x_{ij} - \bar{x}_i)^2\right) = \sum_i \left(\sum_j x_{ij}^2 - T_i^2/n_i\right) = \sum_i \sum_j x_{ij}^2 - \sum_i (T_i^2/n_i)$$

(*c*) $$\sum_i n_i(\bar{x}_i - \bar{x})^2 = \sum_i (T_i^2/n_i) - T^2/N$$

(4) In our example, $n_i = 10$, for all i, and $m = 6$. Therefore $N = nm = 60$. We set up the following table :

Machines ($m = 6$).	Positions ($n = 10$)										T_i	T_i^2/n_i	$\Sigma_j x_{ij}^2$
	1.	2.	3.	4.	5.	6.	7.	8.	9.	10.			
A	12	13	13	16	16	14	15	15	16	17	−53	280·9	305
	−8	−7	−7	−4	−4	−6	−5	−5	−4	−3			
	64	49	49	16	16	36	25	25	16	9			
B	12	14	14	16	16	18	17	19	20	18	−36	129·6	186
	−8	−6	−6	−4	−4	−2	−3	−1	0	−2			
	64	36	36	16	16	4	9	1	0	4			
C	14	21	17	14	19	18	17	17	16	15	−32	102·4	146
	−6	1	−3	−6	−1	−2	−3	−3	−4	−5			
	36	1	9	36	1	4	9	9	16	25			
D	23	27	25	21	26	24	27	24	20	21	+38	144·4	202
	3	7	5	1	6	4	7	4	0	1			
	9	49	25	1	36	16	49	16	0	1			
E	12	14	13	16	13	17	16	15	15	14	−55	302·5	325
	−8	−6	−7	−4	−7	−3	−4	−5	−5	−6			
	64	36	49	16	49	9	16	25	25	36			
F	13	18	13	16	17	15	15	16	16	17	−44	193·6	218
	−7	−2	−7	−4	−3	−5	−5	−4	−4	−3			
	49	4	49	16	9	25	25	16	16	9			
	$T^2/N = 182^2/60 = 552{\cdot}07$										$T = -182$	$\Sigma_i T_i^2/n_i = 1153{\cdot}4$	$\Sigma_i \Sigma_j x_{ij}^2 = 1382$

The analysis of variance table is, accordingly—

Source of variation.	Sum of squares.	Degrees of freedom.	Estimate of variance.	F.
Between machines	1,153·4 − 552·1 = 601·3	5	120·3	28·6
Within machines	1,382·0 − 1,153·4 = 228·6	6 × 9 = 54	4·2	—
TOTAL	829·8	59	—	—

Entering Table 8.6 at $\nu_1 = 5$, $\nu_2 = 54$, we find that this value of F is significant at the 1% point. We, therefore, reject the hypothesis that there is no difference between the machine-means. In other words, *there is a significant variation, from machine to machine, of the diameter of the wire produced.*

9.4. Two Criteria of Classification. Now let us consider the case where there are two criteria of classification. Suppose, for instance, we classify our cows not only according to breed but also according to the variety of fodder given them. To examine where milk-yield varies significantly with breed and with diet, we must analyse the variation in yield into three components, that due to breed, that due to variety of fodder, and, finally, the residual variation, due to unspecified or unknown causes, assumed to be normal.

Let our sample be of N values of x, the variate, such that $N = nm$, and let us classify it according to some factor A into m classes, and, according to another factor B, into n classes. Let the sample variate-value in the ith A-class and jth B-class be x_{ij}. The reader should verify, using the method of the last section, that

$$\sum_{i=1}^{m}\sum_{j=1}^{n}(x_{ij} - \bar{x}_{..})^2 = \sum_{i=1}^{m} n(\bar{x}_{i.} - \bar{x}_{..})^2 + \sum_{j=1}^{n} m(\bar{x}_{.j} - \bar{x}_{..})^2 + \\ + \sum_{i=1}^{m}\sum_{j=1}^{n}(x_{ij} - \bar{x}_{i.} - \bar{x}_{.j} + \bar{x}_{..})^2 \quad (9.4.1)$$

The first term on the right-hand side of this equation is the sum of the squared deviations from the general mean if all variation within the A-classes is eliminated, i.e., if each item in an A-class is replaced by the mean value of that class; the second term is the sum of squared deviations from the general mean if all variation within B-classes is eliminated; while the third term, the residual term, measures the variation in x remaining after the variation due to that between A-classes and that between B-classes has been separated out; once again we assume it to be normal and due to unspecified or unknown causes.

Since it has been shown (A. T. Craig, " On the Difference between Two Sample Variates ", *National Mathematical Magazine*, vol. II, (1937), pp. 259–262) that the three terms on the right are independent, we have

$$\left.\begin{aligned} &\mathcal{E}\left(\sum_{i=1}^{m}\sum_{j=1}^{n}(x_{ij} - \bar{x}_{..})^2\right) = (mn - 1)\sigma^2; \\ &\mathcal{E}\left(\sum_{i=1}^{m} n(\bar{x}_{i.} - \bar{x}_{..})^2\right) = (m - 1)\sigma^2; \\ &\mathcal{E}\left(\sum_{j=1}^{m} m(\bar{x}_{.j} - \bar{x}_{..})^2\right) = (n - 1)\sigma^2; \\ &\text{and} \\ &\mathcal{E}\left(\sum_{i=1}^{m}\sum_{j=1}^{n}(x_{ij} - \bar{x}_{i.} - \bar{x}_{.j} + \bar{x}_{..})^2\right) \\ &\qquad = (mn - 1)\sigma^2 - (n - 1)\sigma^2 - (m - 1)\sigma^2 \\ &\qquad = (m - 1)(n - 1)\sigma^2. \end{aligned}\right\} \quad (10.4.2)$$

Here σ^2 is, of course, the variance of the parent population, assumed homogeneous with respect to the factors of classification, A and B.

The analysis of variance table is, therefore :

Analysis of Variance for Two Criteria of Classification

Source of variation.	Sum of squares.	Degrees of freedom.	Estimate of variance.
Between A-classes	$\sum_{i=1}^{m} n(\bar{x}_{i\cdot} - \bar{x}_{\cdot\cdot})^2$	$m - 1$	$\sum_{i=1}^{m} n(\bar{x}_{i\cdot} - \bar{x}_{\cdot\cdot})^2/(m - 1)$
Between B-classes	$\sum_{j=1}^{n} m(\bar{x}_{\cdot j} - \bar{x}_{\cdot\cdot})^2$	$n - 1$	$\sum_{j=1}^{n} m(\bar{x}_{\cdot j} - \bar{x}_{\cdot\cdot})^2/(n - 1)$
Residual (A × B)	$\sum_{i=1}^{m} \sum_{j=1}^{n} (x_{ij} - \bar{x}_{i\cdot} - \bar{x}_{\cdot j} + \bar{x}_{\cdot\cdot})^2$	$(m - 1)(n - 1)$	$\sum_{i=1}^{m} \sum_{j=1}^{n} (x_{ij} - \bar{x}_{i\cdot} - \bar{x}_{\cdot j} + \bar{x}_{\cdot\cdot}^2)/(m - 1)(n - 1)$
TOTAL	$\sum_{i=1}^{m} \sum_{j=1}^{n} (x_{ij} - \bar{x}_{\cdot\cdot})^2$	$mn - 1$	—

Let us call the three resulting estimates of σ^2, Q_A, Q_B and $Q_{A \times B}$ respectively. The test procedure is, then, as follows :

(*a*) Test $Q_A/Q_{A \times B}$ for $m - 1$ and $(m - 1)(n - 1)$ degrees of freedom using the F-table; and

(*b*) test $Q_B/Q_{A \times B}$ for $n - 1$ and $(m - 1)(n - 1)$ degrees of freedom using the F-table.

9.5. Three Criteria of Classification. We now assume that we have $N = lmn$ sample values of a given normal variate, classified according to three criteria, A, B, C, into l groups of m rows and n columns. Let x_{ijk} be the value of the variate in the jth row and kth column of the ith group (see Table 9.5). i takes the values 1, 2, 3, . . . l; j, the values 1, 2, 3, . . . m; and k, the values 1, 2, 3, . . . n.

We shall use the following notation :

$\bar{x}_{\cdot\cdot\cdot}$ = general mean;

$\bar{x}_{ij\cdot} = \left(\sum_{k=1}^{n} x_{ijk}\right)/n$ = mean of values in ith group, jth row

$$\bar{x}_{i.k} = \left(\sum_{j=1}^{m} x_{ijk}\right) / m = \quad ,, \quad ,, \quad ,, \quad i\text{th group}, k\text{th column};$$

$$\bar{x}_{.jk} = \left(\sum_{l=1}^{l} x_{ijk}\right) / l \ = \quad ,, \quad ,, \quad ,, \quad j\text{th row}, k\text{th column};$$

$$\bar{x}_{i..} = \left(\sum_{j=1}^{m} \sum_{k=1}^{n} x_{ijk}\right) / mn = \text{mean of } i\text{th group};$$

$$\bar{x}_{.j.} = \left(\sum_{i=1}^{l} \sum_{k=1}^{n} x_{ijk}\right) / ln = \text{mean of } j\text{th row};$$

$$\bar{x}_{..k} = \left(\sum_{i=1}^{l} \sum_{j=1}^{m} x_{ijk}\right) / lm = \text{mean of } k\text{th column}.$$

Table 9.5 will make this notation clear.

The identity upon which the analysis of variance table is based is :

$$\sum_{i=1}^{l} \sum_{j=1}^{m} \sum_{k=1}^{n} (x_{ijk} - \bar{x}_{...})^2 = mn \sum_{i=1}^{l} (\bar{x}_{i..} - \bar{x}_{...})^2$$
$$+ kl \sum_{j=1}^{m} (\bar{x}_{.j.} - \bar{x}_{...})^2 + lm \sum_{k=1}^{n} (\bar{x}_{..k} - \bar{x}_{...})^2$$
$$+ l \sum_{j=1}^{m} \sum_{k=1}^{n} (\bar{x}_{ijk} - \bar{x}_{.j.} - \bar{x}_{..k} + \bar{x}_{...})^2$$
$$+ m \sum_{i=1}^{l} \sum_{k=1}^{n} (\bar{x}_{i.k} - x_{i..} - \bar{x}_{..k} + \bar{x}_{...})^2$$
$$+ n \sum_{i=1}^{l} \sum_{j=1}^{m} (\bar{x}_{ij.} - \bar{x}_{i..} - \bar{x}_{.j.} + \bar{x}_{...})^2$$
$$+ \sum_{i=1}^{l} \sum_{j=1}^{m} \sum_{k=1}^{n} (x_{ijk} - \bar{x}_{.jk} - \bar{x}_{i.k} - \bar{x}_{ij.} + \bar{x}_{i..} + \bar{x}_{.j.} + \bar{x}_{..k} - \bar{x}_{...})^2 \quad (9.5.1)$$

The resulting analysis of variance table is given on page 175.

9.6. The Meaning of "Interaction". In the analysis of variance for three criteria of classification, we have spoken of "interactions" between the factors A, B and C. What do we mean by this term?

Our null hypothesis is that no one of the factors A, B, C separately influences the variate-values. But it is conceivable that any two of these factors acting together may do so. When, therefore, we have three or more criteria of classification, it is necessary to test the estimates of σ^2 based on the "interaction" terms before testing the variations due to the individual factors separately. If none of these "interactions",

TABLE 9.5. *Sample for Three Criteria of Classification*

Groups (Factor A) $i = 1$ to l		Columns (Factor C) $k = 1$ to n: 1	. . .	k	. . .	n	Means~
1	Rows (factor B) $j = 1$ to m: 1	x_{111}	. . .	x_{11k}	. . .	x_{11n}	$\bar{x}_{11.}$
	.	.	. . .	.	. . .	.	.
	j	x_{1j1}	. . .	x_{1jk}	. . .	x_{1jn}	$\bar{x}_{1j.}$
	.	.	. . .	.	. . .	.	.
	m	x_{1m1}	. . .	x_{1mk}	. . .	x_{1mn}	$x_{1m\cdot}$
	MEANS	$\bar{x}_{1\cdot 1}$	. . .	$\bar{x}_{1\cdot k}$	. . .	$\bar{x}_{1\cdot n}$	$\bar{x}_{1\cdot\cdot}$
i	Rows (factor B) $j = 1$ to m: 1	x_{i11}	. . .	x_{i1k}	. . .	x_{i1n}	$\bar{x}_{i1\cdot}$
	.	.	. . .	.	. . .	.	.
	j	x_{ij1}	. . .	x_{ijk}	. . .	x_{ijn}	$\bar{x}_{ij\cdot}$
	.	.	. . .	.	. . .	.	.
	m	x_{im1}	. . .	x_{imk}	. . .	x_{imn}	$\bar{x}_{im\cdot}$
	MEANS	$\bar{x}_{i\cdot 1}$	. . .	$\bar{x}_{i\cdot k}$	. . .	$\bar{x}_{i\cdot n}$	$\bar{x}_{i\cdot\cdot}$
l	Rows (factor B) $j = 1$ to m: 1	x_{l11}	. . .	x_{l1k}	. . .	x_{l1n}	$\bar{x}_{l1\cdot}$
	.	.	. . .	.	. . .	.	.
	j	x_{lj1}	. . .	x_{ljk}	. . .	x_{ljn}	$\bar{x}_{lj\cdot}$
	.	.	. . .	.	. . .	.	.
	m	x_{lm1}	. . .	x_{lmk}	. . .	x_{lmn}	$\bar{x}_{lm\cdot}$
	MEANS	$\bar{x}_{l\cdot 1}$	. . .	$\bar{x}_{l\cdot k}$	. . .	$\bar{x}_{l\cdot n}$	$\bar{x}_{l\cdot\cdot}$
	Means of Rows: 1	$\bar{x}_{\cdot 11}$	. . .	$\bar{x}_{\cdot 1k}$	. . .	$\bar{x}_{\cdot 1n}$	$\bar{x}_{\cdot 1\cdot}$
	.	.	. . .	.	. . .	.	.
	j	$x_{\cdot j1}$	. . .	$\bar{x}_{\cdot jk}$	. . .	$\bar{x}_{\cdot jn}$	$\bar{x}_{\cdot j\cdot}$
	.	.	. . .	.	. . .	.	.
	m	$\bar{x}_{\cdot m1}$	. . .	$\bar{x}_{\cdot mk}$	. . .	$\bar{x}_{\cdot mn}$	$\bar{x}_{\cdot m\cdot}$
	MEANS OF COLUMNS	$\bar{x}_{\cdot\cdot 1}$	. . .	$\bar{x}_{\cdot\cdot k}$	. . .	$\bar{x}_{\cdot\cdot n}$	$\bar{x}_{\cdot\cdot\cdot}$

when tested against the residual estimate of σ^2, is significant, we may pool the corresponding sums of squares, form a revised estimate of σ^2, based on more degrees of freedom, and then proceed to test the estimates due to the individual factors; if, however, one, or more, of the estimates due to interactions is

Analysis of Variance for Three Criteria of Classification

Source of variation.	Sum of squares.	Degrees of freedom.	Estimate of variance.
Between groups	$mn \sum_{i=1}^{l} (\bar{x}_{i..} - \bar{x}_{...})^2$	$l - 1$	$\frac{mn}{l-1} \sum_{i=1}^{l} (\bar{x}_{i..} - \bar{x}_{...})^2$
Between rows	$kl \sum_{j=1}^{m} (\bar{x}_{.j.} - \bar{x}_{...})^2$	$m - 1$	$\frac{kl}{m-1} \sum_{j=1}^{m} (\bar{x}_{.j.} - \bar{x}_{...})^2$
Between columns	$lm \sum_{k=1}^{n} (\bar{x}_{..k} - \bar{x}_{...})^2$	$n - 1$	$\frac{lm}{n-1} \sum_{k=1}^{n} (\bar{x}_{..k} - \bar{x}_{...})^2$
Interaction between groups and rows (A × B)	$n \sum_{i=1}^{l} \sum_{j=1}^{m} (\bar{x}_{ij.} - \bar{x}_{i..} - \bar{x}_{.j.} + \bar{x}_{...})^2$	$(l - 1)(m - 1)$	$\frac{n}{(l-1)(m-1)} \sum_{i=1}^{l} \sum_{j=1}^{m} (\bar{x}_{ij.} - \bar{x}_{i..} - \bar{x}_{.j.} + \bar{x}_{...})^2$
Interaction between rows and columns (B × C)	$m \sum_{i=1}^{l} \sum_{k=1}^{n} (\bar{x}_{i.k} - \bar{x}_{i..} - \bar{x}_{..k} + \bar{x}_{...})^2$	$(l - 1)(n - 1)$	$\frac{m}{(l-1)(n-1)} \sum_{i=1}^{l} \sum_{k=1}^{n} (\bar{x}_{i.k} - \bar{x}_{i..} - \bar{x}_{..k} + \bar{x}_{...})^2$
Interaction between columns and groups (C × A)	$l \sum_{j=1}^{m} \sum_{k=1}^{n} (\bar{x}_{.jk} - \bar{x}_{.j.} - \bar{x}_{..k} + \bar{x}_{...})^2$	$(m - 1)(n - 1)$	$\frac{l}{(m-1)(n-1)} \sum_{j=1}^{m} \sum_{k=1}^{n} (\bar{x}_{.jk} - \bar{x}_{.j.} - \bar{x}_{..k} + \bar{x}_{...})^2$
Residual (A × B × C)	$\sum_{i=1}^{l} \sum_{j=1}^{m} \sum_{k=1}^{n} (x_{ijk} - \bar{x}_{.jk} - \bar{x}_{i.k} - \bar{x}_{ij.} + \bar{x}_{i..} + \bar{x}_{.j.} + \bar{x}_{..k} - \bar{x}_{...})^2$	$(l - 1)(m - 1)(n - 1)$	$\sum_{i=1}^{l} \sum_{j=1}^{m} \sum_{k=1}^{n} (\bar{x}_{ijk} - \bar{x}_{.jk} - \bar{x}_{i.k} - \bar{x}_{ij.} + \bar{x}_{i..} + \bar{x}_{.j.} + \bar{x}_{..k} - \bar{x}_{...})^2 / (l-1)(m-1)(n-1)$
TOTAL	$\sum_{i=1}^{l} \sum_{j=1}^{m} \sum_{k=1}^{n} (x_{ijk} - \bar{x}_{...})^2$	$lmn - 1$	—

found to be significant, we have reason for suspecting the null hypothesis.

Significant interactions, however, do not NECESSARILY *imply real interactions between the factors concerned.*

The working scientist and technologist are only too aware that, from time to time, experiment may give rise to what, at first sight, would appear to be a sensational result, but that closer scrutiny may well reveal that it is due to chance heterogeneity in the data and is no sensation after all. This is just another reason why the closest co-operation between statistician and technologist is always essential, but never more so than when the statistician finds something apparently of " significance ".

9.7. Worked Examples.

1. *Five doctors each test five treatments for a certain disease and observe the number of days each patient takes to recover. The results are as follows (recovery time in days) :*

Doctor.	Treatment.				
	1.	2.	3.	4.	5.
A	10	14	23	18	20
B	11	15	24	17	21
C	9	12	20	16	19
D	8	13	17	17	20
E	12	15	19	15	22

Discuss the difference between : (a) *doctors, and* (b) *treatments.*
(A.I.S.)

Treatment : This is a problem involving two criteria of classification, each criterion grouping the data into five classes. Thus n_i (the number of items in row i) $= n_j$ (the number of items in column i) $= 5$, and $N = 25$.

Transfer to a new origin at 16.

With the suffix i denoting row and the suffix j denoting column, let

$$T = \sum_i \sum_j x_{ij}; \quad T_i = \sum_j x_{ij}; \quad T_j = \sum_i x_{ij};$$

then (cf. 9.3 Treatment (3)) :

$$\sum_i \sum_j (x_{ij} - \bar{x})^2 = \sum_i \sum_j x_{ij}^2 - N\bar{x}^2 = \sum_i \sum_j x_{ij}^2 - T^2/N;$$

$$\sum_i \sum_j (\bar{x}_i - \bar{x})^2 = \sum_i n_i(\bar{x}_i - \bar{x})^2 = \sum_i (T_i^2/n_i) - T^2/N;$$

$$\sum_i \sum_j (\bar{x}_j - \bar{x})^2 = \sum_j n_j(\bar{x}_j - \bar{x})^2 = \sum_j (T_j^2/n_j) - T^2/N$$

We now draw up the following table :

	Treatment. 1.	2.	3.	4.	5.	$T_{i}.$	$T_{i}^{2}.$	$x_{ij}^{2}.$
Doctors A	$-6(36)$	$-2(4)$	$7(49)$	$2(4)$	$4(16)$	5	25	109
Doctors B	$-5(25)$	$-1(1)$	$8(64)$	$1(1)$	$5(25)$	8	64	116
Doctors C	$-7(49)$	$-4(16)$	$4(16)$	$0(0)$	$3(9)$	-4	16	90
Doctors D	$-8(64)$	$-3(9)$	$1(1)$	$1(1)$	$4(16)$	-5	25	91
Doctors E	$-4(16)$	$-1(1)$	$3(9)$	$-1(1)$	$6(36)$	3	9	63
T_j	-30	-11	23	3	22	$T = 7$	$\sum_i T_i^2 = 139$	469
T_j^2	900	121	529	9	484	$\sum_j T_j^2 = 2043$	$\sum_i \sum_j x_{ij}^2$	
x_{ij}^2	190	31	139	7	102	469		

Consequently,

(i) Total sum of squared deviations, $\sum_i \sum_j x_{ij}^2 - T^2/N = 469 - 7^2/25 = 469 - 1{\cdot}96 = 467{\cdot}04$.

(ii) Sum of squares for treatments, $\sum_j (T_j^2/n_j) - T^2/N = 2043/5 - 1{\cdot}96 = 406{\cdot}64$.

(iii) Sum of squares for doctors, $\sum_i (T_i^2/n_i) - T^2/N = 139/5 - 1{\cdot}96 = 25{\cdot}84$.

(iv) Residual sum of squares $= 467{\cdot}04 - 406{\cdot}64 - 25{\cdot}84 = 34{\cdot}56$.

The analysis of variance is, then :

Source of variation.	Sum of squares.	Degrees of freedom.	Estimate of variance.	F.
Between treatments . .	406·64	4	101·66	47·00**
Between doctors	25·84	4	6·46	2·99
Residual . .	34·56	16	2·16	—
TOTAL . .	467·04	24	—	—

Entering Table 8.6 at $\nu_1 = 4$, $\nu_2 = 16$, we find the 5% and 1% points of F to be 3·01 and 4·77 respectively. We conclude, therefore, that *the difference between doctors is hardly significant* (at the 5% level), *while that between treatments is highly so* (highly significant at the 1% level).

2. *P. R. Rider* (An Introduction to Modern Statistical Methods, *John Wiley, New York*) *quotes the following Western Electric Co. data on porosity readings of* 3 *lots of condenser paper. There are* 3 *readings on each of* 9 *rolls from each lot.*

Porosity Readings on Condenser Paper

Lot number.	*Reading number.*	*Roll number.* 1.	2.	3.	4.	5.	6.	7.	8.	9.
I	1	1·5	1·5	2·7	3·0	3·4	2·1	2·0	3·0	5·1
	2	1·7	1·6	1·9	2·4	5·6	4·1	2·5	2·0	5·0
	3	1·6	1·7	2·0	2·6	5·6	4·6	2·8	1·9	4·0
II	1	1·9	2·3	1·8	1·9	2·0	3·0	2·4	1·7	2·6
	2	1·5	2·4	2·9	3·5	1·9	2·6	2·0	1·5	4·3
	3	2·1	2·4	4·7	2·8	2·1	3·5	2·1	2·0	2·4
III	1	2·5	3·2	1·4	7·8	3·2	1·9	2·0	1·1	2·1
	2	2·9	5·5	1·5	5·2	2·5	2·2	2·4	1·4	2·5
	3	3·3	7·1	3·4	5·0	4·0	3·1	3·7	4·1	1·9

We shall carry out the appropriate analysis of variance assuming, for the time being, that we have here *three criteria of classification*—the roll number dividing the data into nine classes, the lot number and the reading number each dividing the data into three classes. This will illustrate the method employed in such a case. Then, less artificially, we shall regard the data as classified by two criteria (roll and lot) with three values of the variate, instead of one, given for each Lot × Roll.

First Treatment: (1) We draw up the table as shown at the top of page 180.

Thus

$$\sum_i \sum_j \sum_k x_{ijk}^2 = (1{\cdot}5^2 + 1{\cdot}5^2 + 2{\cdot}7^2 + \ldots + 3{\cdot}7^2 + 4{\cdot}1^2 + 1{\cdot}9^2) = \underline{812.41}$$

and $T = 231{\cdot}1$, $N = 3 \times 3 \times 9 = 81$ give $T^2/N = \underline{659{\cdot}35}$

The total sum of square deviations from the mean,

$$\sum_i \sum_j \sum_k x_{ijk}^2 - T^2/N = 812{\cdot}41 - 659{\cdot}35 = \underline{153{\cdot}06}.$$

Lot.	Reading.	Roll. 1.	2.	3.	4.	5.	6.	7.	8.	9.	Totals.	
I	1	1·5	1·5	2·7	3·0	3·4	2·1	2·0	3·0	5·1	24·3	
	2	1·7	1·6	1·9	2·4	5·6	4·1	2·5	2·0	5·0	26·8	
	3	1·6	1·7	2·0	2·6	5·6	4·6	2·8	1·9	4·0	26·8	
Totals		4·8	4·8	6·6	8·0	14·6	10·8	7·3	6·9	14·1	77·9	Total (Lot I)
II	1	1·9	2·3	1·8	1·9	2·0	3·0	2·4	1·7	2·6	19·6	
	2	1·5	2·4	2·9	3·5	1·9	2·6	2·0	1·5	4·3	22·6	
	3	2·1	2·4	4·7	2·8	2·1	3·5	2·1	2·0	2·4	24·1	
Totals		5·5	7·1	9·4	8·2	6·0	9·1	6·5	5·2	9·3	66·3	Total (Lot II)
III	1	2·5	3·2	1·4	7·8	3·2	1·9	2·0	1·1	2·1	25·2	
	2	2·9	5·5	1·5	5·2	2·5	2·2	2·4	1·4	2·5	26·1	
	3	3·3	7·1	3·4	5·0	4·0	3·1	2·7	4·1	1·9	35·6	
Totals		8·7	15·8	6·3	18·0	9·7	7·2	8·1	6·6	6·5	86·9	Total (Lot III)
Total (Rolls)		19·0	27·7	22·3	34·2	30·3	27·1	21·9	18·7	29·9	231·1	Grand Total
Total (Readings)	1	24·3 + 19·6 + 25·2									69·1	231·1
	2	26·8 + 22·6 + 26·1									75·5	
	3	26·8 + 24·1 + 35·6									86·5	

(2) We draw up the following LOT × ROLL table:

Lot.	Roll. 1.	2.	3.	4.	5.	6.	7.	8.	9.	Total (Lots).
I	4·8	4·8	6·6	8·0	14·6	10·8	7·3	6·9	14·1	77·9
II	5·5	7·1	9·4	8·2	6·0	9·1	6·5	5·2	9·3	66·3
III	8·7	15·8	6·3	18·0	9·7	7·2	8·1	6·6	6·5	35·6
Total (Rolls)	19·0	27·7	22·3	34·2	30·3	27·1	21·9	18·7	29·9	

The sum of squares for LOT × ROLL classification (i.e., a two criteria classification) is thus $(4{\cdot}8^2 + 4{\cdot}8^2 + 6{\cdot}6^2 + \ldots + 8{\cdot}1^2 + 6{\cdot}6^2 + 6{\cdot}5^2) = \underline{2{,}280{\cdot}37}$, and the sum of the squared deviations from the mean is $2{,}280{\cdot}37/3 - 659{\cdot}35 = \underline{100{\cdot}77}$. *Note that we divide 2,280·37 by 3 because each entry in the body of this* LOT × ROLL *table is the sum of three readings.*

The sum of squared deviations for ROLLS is $(19{\cdot}0^2 + 27{\cdot}7^2 + \ldots + 18{\cdot}7^2 + 29{\cdot}9^2)/9 - 659{\cdot}35 = \underline{26{\cdot}31}$ (why do we here divide by 9?), while the sum of squared deviations for LOTS is $(77{\cdot}9^2 + 66{\cdot}3^2 + 35{\cdot}6^2)/27 - 659{\cdot}35 = \underline{7{\cdot}90}$ (why do we, this time, divide by 27?). Finally, the residual sum of squared deviations, now called *Interaction* (*Lot* × *Roll*) is found by subtracting from the total sum of squared deviations for this classification the sum of that for Rolls and that for Lots, i.e., $100{\cdot}77 - 26{\cdot}31 - 7{\cdot}90 = \underline{66{\cdot}56}$.

(3) The READING × ROLL table is :

Reading.	Roll. 1.	2.	3.	4.	5.	6.	7.	8.	9.	TOTAL (READING).
1	5·9	7·0	5·9	12·7	8·6	7·0	6·4	5·8	9·8	69·1
2	6·1	9·5	6·3	11·1	10·0	8·9	6·9	4·9	11·8	75·5
3	7·0	11·2	10·1	10·4	11·7	11·2	8·6	8·0	8·3	86·5
TOTAL (ROLLS)	19·0	27·7	22·3	34·2	30·3	27·1	21·9	18·7	29·9	

Here the sum of squares, $5{\cdot}9^2 + 7{\cdot}0^2 + 5{\cdot}9^2 + \ldots + 8{\cdot}6^2 + 8{\cdot}0^2 + 8{\cdot}3^2 = 2{,}107{\cdot}73$. The sum of squared deviations from the mean is, then, $2{,}107{\cdot}73/3 - 659{\cdot}35 = 43{\cdot}23$. The sum of squared deviations for READINGS is $(69{\cdot}1^2 + 75{\cdot}5^2 + 86{\cdot}5^2)/27 - 659{\cdot}35 = 5{\cdot}73$. We have the corresponding sum for ROLLS, already : 26·31. *Interaction* (*Rolls* × *Reading*) is, then, $43{\cdot}23 - 5{\cdot}73 - 26{\cdot}31 = 10{\cdot}19$.

(4) The LOT × READING table is :

Lot.	Reading. 1.	2.	3.
I	24·3	26·8	26·8
II	19·6	22·6	24·1
III	25·2	26·1	35·6

The sum of squares in this case is $24{\cdot}3^2 + 26{\cdot}8^2 + \ldots + 26{\cdot}1^2 + 35{\cdot}6^2 = 6{,}086{\cdot}25$. Hence the sum of squared deviations for LOT × READING is $6{,}086{\cdot}25/9 - 659{\cdot}35 = 16{\cdot}90$. We already have the sums of squared deviations for LOTS (= 7·90) and that for READINGS (= 5·73). Consequently, *Interaction* (Lot × Reading) is $16{\cdot}90 - 7{\cdot}90 - 5{\cdot}73 = 3{\cdot}27$.

(5) The analysis of variance table is shown on the top of page 182. We see at once that the Interactions, LOTS × READINGS and READINGS × ROLLS are not significant; nor, for that matter, are they significantly small. However, Interaction ROLLS × LOTS is significant at the 1% level and so is the variation between ROLLS, while that between LOTS is significant at the 5% level.

Since the two Interactions, LOTS × READINGS and READINGS × ROLLS are not significant, we may combine the corresponding sums of squares with that for RESIDUAL to obtain a more accurate estimate of the assumed population variance; this is

$$\frac{3{\cdot}27 + 10{\cdot}19 + 33{\cdot}10}{4 + 16 + 32} = 0{\cdot}89.$$

We find, as the reader will confirm for himself, that the levels of significance are unaltered when this new estimate of σ^2 is used, and

Source of variation.	Sum of squares.	Degrees of freedom.	Estimate of variance.	*F*.
Between rolls . .	26·31	8	3·29	3·14 **
Between lots . .	7·90	2	3·95	3·81 *
Between readings .	5·73	2	2·87	2·76
Interaction (Rolls × Lots) . . .	66·56	16	4·16	4·00 **
Interaction (Lots × Readings) . .	3·27	4	0·82	—
Interaction (Readings × Rolls) . .	10·19	16	0·66	—
Residual . . .	33·10	32	1·04	—
TOTAL . . .	153·06	80	—	—

we conclude that the variation of rolls within lots and that between rolls are highly significant, while that between lots is significant.

Second Treatment : The conclusion we have reached justifies the view we suggested originally that it is less artificial to regard the data as classified by *two* criteria only (ROLL and LOT), with three values of the variate, instead of one, being taken. This being the case, the situation is summarised by the table given in Step II of our first treatment of the problem. The corresponding analysis of variance is:

Source of variation.	Sum of squares.	Degrees of freedom.	Estimate of variance.	*F*.
Between rolls . .	26·31	8	3·29	3·39 **
Between lots . .	7·90	2	3·95	4·07 *
Interaction (Rolls × Lots) . . .	66·56	16	4·16	4·29 **
Residual . . .	52·29	54	0·97	—
TOTAL . . .	153·06	80	—	—

Quite clearly, our null hypothesis, of the homogeneity of the condenser paper with respect to these two factors of classification, lots and rolls, breaks down.

9.8. Latin Squares. When, in the case of three-factor classification, each criterion results in the same number of classes, n, say, some simplification may be effected in our analysis of variance by the use of an arrangement known as a *Latin Square*. Essentially, this device aims at isolating the separate variations due to simultaneously operating causal factors.

Let us suppose that we wish to investigate the yield per acre of *five variates* of a certain crop, when subjected to treatment by *two types of fertiliser, each of five different strengths*. We divide the plot of land used for the experiment into 5^2 sub-plots, considered to be schematically arranged in five parallel rows and five parallel columns. Each of the five columns is treated with one of the five strengths of one of the fertilisers (call it *Fertiliser A*); each of the rows is likewise treated with one of the five strengths of the second fertiliser (*B*). Then the five varieties of the crop under investigation are sown at random in the sub-plots, but in such a way that any one variety occurs but once in any row or column. Denoting the crop-varieties by A, B, C, D, E, we shall have some such arrangement as:

		Fertiliser A				
	Strengths	1	2	3	4	5
Fertiliser B	1	A	B	C	D	E
	2	E	C	A	B	D
	3	B	D	E	C	A
	4	D	E	B	A	C
	5	C	A	D	E	B

Now assume that the following figures (fictitious) for yield per acre are obtained:

A 3·2	B 2·0	C 2·2	D 1·8	E 1·8
E 2·0	C 1·8	A 2·8	B 2·4	D 2·2
B 3·0	D 1·6	E 1·6	C 2·0	A 3·6
D 2·4	E 1·2	B 2·6	A 2·6	C 2·4
C 2·6	A 2·2	D 2·0	E 1·4	B 2·8

Transferring our origin to 2·2 and multiplying each entry by 5, we have:

		Fertiliser A					Totals (B)			Totals (Varieties).		
	Strength	1	2	3	4	5	$\sum_j x_{ij}$	$\sum_j x_{ij}^2$	$\left(\sum_j x_{ij}\right)^2$	A	17	289
Fertiliser B	1	A 5(25)	B −1(1)	C 0(0)	D −2(4)	E −2(4)	0	34	0	B	9	81
	2	E −1(1)	C −2(4)	A 3(9)	B 1(1)	D 0(0)	1	15	1	C	0	0
	3	B 4(16)	D −3(9)	E −3(9)	C −1(1)	A 7(49)	4	84	16	D	−5	25
	4	D 1(1)	E −5(25)	B 2(4)	A 2(4)	C 1(1)	1	35	1	E	−15	225
	5	C 2(4)	A 0(0)	D −1(1)	E −4(16)	B 3(9)	0	30	0	—	6	620
Totals A	$\sum_i x_{ij}$	11	−11	1	−4	9	6	198	18			
	$\sum_i x_{ij}^2$	47	39	23	26	63	198	↙↗				
	$\left(\sum_i x_{ij}\right)^2$	121	121	1	16	81	340					

With $T = 6$ and $N = n^2 = 25$, $T^2/N = 1·44$. The sum total of squares is 198 and so the total sum of squared deviations is 196·56. The sum of squared deviations for Fertiliser A is $340/5 - 1·44 = 66·56$. The sum of squared deviations for Fertiliser B is $18/5 - 1·44 = 2·16$, and the sum of squared deviations for Varieties is $620/5 - 1·44 = 122·56$.

The analysis of variance table is then as shown on page 185.

Both the variation between varieties and that due to the different strengths of Fertiliser A are significant at the 1% level.

By pooling the sum of squares for Fertiliser B and the Residual sum of squares, we may obtain a more accurate estimate of the assumed population variance: $(2·16 + 5·28)/(4 + 12) = 0·465$. This is the estimated variance of the yield of a single sub-plot. The estimated variance of the mean of five such sub-plots is, therefore, $0·465/5 = 0·093$. That of the difference of the means of any two independent samples of 5 sub-plots is $2 \times 0·093 = 0·186$. The Standard

Source of variation.	Sum of squares.	Degrees of freedom.	Estimate of variance.	*F*.
Between varieties .	122·56	4	30·64	69·6 **
Between strengths of Fertiliser A . .	66·56	4	16·64	37·8 **
Between strengths of Fertiliser B . .	2·16	4	0·54	1·2
Residual . . .	5·28	12	0·44	—
TOTAL . . .	196·56	24	—	—

Error of the difference of the means of two such samples is, consequently, $(0{\cdot}186)^{\frac{1}{2}} = 0{\cdot}43$. For 16 degrees of freedom the least difference, *m*, between the means of any two samples of 5 that is significant at the 5% level is given by : $m/0{\cdot}43 = 2{\cdot}12$ or $m = 0{\cdot}9116$.

It will be seen therefore that all the five varieties differ significantly, that only strengths 1 and 5 of Fertiliser A do not differ significantly, while none of the strengths of Fertiliser B differ significantly at the 5% level.

9.9. Making Latin Squares. If a Latin Square has *n* rows and *n* columns it is said to be *a square of order n*. The number of possible squares of order *n* increases very rapidly with *n*. There are, for instance, 576 squares of order 4; 161,280 of order 5; 373,248,000 of order 6; and 61,428,210,278 of order 7. (See R. A. Fisher and F. Yates, *Statistical Tables for Use in Biological, Agricultural and Medical Research*.)

When the letters of the first row and first column are in correct alphabetical order, the square is a *standard square*. Thus

```
A B C
B C A
C A B
```

is a standard square of order three—indeed, it is the only standard square of that order, as the reader will easily realise. The standard squares of order 4 are :

```
A B C D    A B C D    A B C D    A B C D
B A D C    B D A C    B C D A    B A D C
C D B A    C A D B    C D A B    C D A B
D C A B    D C B A    D A B C    D C B A
```

From these standard squares all the remaining, essentially different, non-standard squares may be derived. It is important to understand, however, that what is required when deriving such non-standard squares is a *new pattern* or *lay-out*. Merely interchanging letters does not suffice. For example, the two squares

A	B	C	D	and	D	C	B	A
B	A	D	C		C	D	A	B
C	D	B	A		B	A	C	D
D	C	A	B		A	B	D	C

present the same pattern and are, therefore, no different. If, then, we require to derive a non-standard square from a given standard square, we must permute all columns and all rows except the first. We thereby obtain a total of 12 possible squares of order 3 ($12 = 3! \times 2!$) and 576 of order 4 (in this case each standard square, of which there are four, yields 4 ! different column arrangements and 3 ! different row arrangements : $4 \times 4! \times 3! = 576$).

When all the standard squares of a given order have been set down, we say that the standard squares have been *enumerated*. This has been done for n less than 8, although for $n \geqslant 8$ a considerable number have been listed. To choose a Latin square of given order, then, we select a standard square at random from those enumerated, and permute at random, using, both for selection and permutation, a table of random numbers.

EXERCISES ON CHAPTER NINE

1. The following results were obtained in four independent samplings :

(1)	6	14	12	6	2	5
(2)	10	17	6	19	19	16
(3)	11	11	19	23	8	17
(4)	19	2	29	16	14	20

Carry out an analysis of variance on these data. (L.U.)

2. Four breeds of cattle B_1, B_2, B_3, B_4 were fed on three different rations, R_1, R_2, R_3. Gains in weight in pounds over a given period were recorded.

	B_1	B_2	B_3	B_4
R_1 . .	46·5	62	41	45
R_2 . .	47·5	41·5	22	31·5
R_3 . .	50	40	25·5	28·5

Is there a significant difference : (*a*) between breeds; (*b*) between rations ?

3. *Passenger Traffic Receipts of Main-Line Railways and L.P.T.B.*
(Weekly averages, £000)

	First Quarter.	Second Quarter.	Third Quarter.	Fourth Quarter.
1944 . .	3,376	3,548	4,120	3,836
1945 . .	3,320	4,072	4,898	3,872
1946 . .	3,310	3,884	4,758	3,611
1947 . .	2,991	3,752	4,556	3,703

Carry out an analysis of variance on these data. Is the between-years difference significant?

4. A chemical purification process is carried out in a particular plant with four solvents ($i = 1, 2, 3, 4$) at three different, equidistant temperatures. For every one of the $4 \times 3 = 12$ combinations of solvents with temperatures the process is repeated four times and the resulting 48 test measurements are shown below (a low value indicates a high degree of purity).

Solvent

Temperature	$i = 1$		$i = 2$		$i = 3$		$i = 4$	
$t = 1$	66·9	68·3	71·2	70·3	66·2	64·6	79·1	66·6
	68·6	70·0	71·8	71·8	70·1	69·9	66·2	71·1
$t = 2$	63·4	63·9	70·7	69·0	64·9	62·7	65·9	64·9
	67·2	71·2	69·0	69·3	69·5	66·9	66·2	72·0
$t = 3$	66·4	64·1	67·5	62·7	71·6	70·8	68·9	68·8
	66·2	67·0	64·0	62·4	73·6	70·4	70·5	72·8

Carry out the appropriate analysis of variance. Are there differences between solvents and temperatures, taken as a whole? Is there any interaction between solvents and temperatures? (L.U.)

5. The atmosphere in 4 different districts of a large town was sampled, the samples being taken at 4 different heights. Four different tests for the presence of a certain chemical were made on the samples. The arrangement is shown in the following table with the % by weight of the chemical as determined by the tests. Letters denote the different tests.

Districts

Heights	1	2	3	4
1	A 8	B 5·3	C 4·1	D 5
2	D 6·8	A 4·9	B 4·1	C 3·2
3	B 6·3	C 4·7	D 4·0	A 5
4	C 5·7	D 3·3	A 4·0	B 4·2

Is there evidence of significant variation from district to district and between heights in the percentage of the chemical present in the atmosphere?

Can it be said that there is a decided difference between the sensitivity of the tests?

Solutions

1. Variation between samples significant at 5% point but not at 1% point.
2. No significant difference between breeds or between rations.
3. No significant variation between years but that between quarters is highly significant.
4. Variation between temperatures is not quite significant at 5% point; that between solvents is significant at that point; interaction between solvents and temperatures significant at 1% point.
5. Variation between districts significant at 5% point but not at 1% point; no significant variation between heights or between sensitivity of tests.

CHAPTER TEN

TESTING REGRESSION AND CORRELATION

10.1. The Correlation Coefficient Again. We now return to the problems raised at the beginning of Chapter Seven :

> How do we know that a value of r, the sample correlation coefficient, calculated from a sample of N from a bivariate normal population is really significant? Is there a way of deciding whether such a value of r could have arisen by chance as a result of random sampling from an uncorrelated parent population?

Linked closely with this problem are several others :

> If a sample of N yields a value of $r = r_0$, how can we test whether it can have been drawn from a population known to have a given ρ?
>
> Again, how shall we test whether two values of r obtained from different samples are consistent with the hypothesis of random sampling from a common parent population?
>
> Finally, given a number of independent estimates of a population correlation coefficient, how may we combine them to obtain an improved estimate?

We start to tackle these problems by what may at first appear to be a rather indirect method. For we shall use the technique of analysis of variance (or, more correctly, in this case, *analysis of covariance*) to test the significance of a linear regression coefficient calculated from a sample drawn from a bivariate normal population. But this, as we shall soon see, is equivalent to testing the significance of a value of r, or, what is the same thing, to testing the hypothesis that in the parent population, $\rho = 0$.

10.2. Testing a Regression Coefficient. Let (x_i, y_i), $(i = 1, 2, \ldots N)$, be a sample of N pairs from what we assume to be an uncorrelated bivariate normal population. Taking the sample mean as origin ($\bar{x} = 0 = \bar{y}$), the regression equation of y on x is

$$y = b_{yx}x, \quad \text{where} \quad b_{yx} = s_{xy}/s_x^2 \quad . \quad (10.2.1)$$

Let Y_i be the value of the ordinate at $x = x_i$ on this

regression line. Then the sum of the squared deviations of the y's from the sample mean ($\bar{y} = 0$) is simply $\sum_{i=1}^{N} y_i^2$. But

$$\sum_{i=1}^{N} y_i^2 = \sum_{i=1}^{N} (y_i - Y_i + Y_i)^2$$
$$= \sum_{i=1}^{N} (y_i - Y_i)^2 + 2\sum_{i=1}^{N} (y_i - Y_i)Y_i + \sum_{i=1}^{N} Y_i^2$$

However,

$$\sum_{i=1}^{N} (y_i - Y_i)Y_i = \sum_{i=1}^{N} (y_i - b_{yx}x_i)b_{yx}x_i$$
$$= b_{yx}\left(\sum_{i=1}^{N} x_iy_i - b_{yx}\sum_{i=1}^{N} x_i^2\right) = 0,$$

since $$b_{yx} = s_{xy}/s_x^2 = \sum_{i=1}^{N} x_iy_i / \sum_{i=1}^{N} x_i^2.$$

Hence $$\sum_{i=1}^{N} y_i^2 = \sum_{i=1}^{N} (y_i - Y_i)^2 + \sum_{i=1}^{N} Y_i^2. \quad . \quad (10.2.2)$$

Thus:

> The sum of squared deviations of observed values of y from the sample mean = sum of squared deviations of observed values of y from the regression line of y on x + sum of squared deviations of the corresponding points on the regression line from the sample mean.

or

VARIATION ABOUT MEAN = VARIATION ABOUT REGRESSION LINE + VARIATION OF REGRESSION LINE ABOUT MEAN

Now (10.2.2) may be re-written:

$$\sum_{i=1}^{N} y_i^2 = \sum_{i=1}^{N} (y_i - b_{yx}x_i)^2 + b_{yx}^2\sum_{i=1}^{N} x_i^2$$
$$= \sum_{i=1}^{N} y_i^2 - 2b_{yx}\sum_{i=1}^{N} x_iy_i + b_{yx}^2\sum_{i=1}^{N} x_i^2 + b_{yx}^2\sum_{i=1}^{N} x_i^2$$
$$= Ns_y^2 - 2Ns_{xy}^2/s_x^2 + Ns_{xy}^2/s_x^2 + Ns_{xy}^2/s_x^2$$
$$= Ns_y^2(1 - s_{xy}^2/s_x^2s_y^2) + Ns_y^2\,(s_{xy}^2/s_x^2 \,.\, s_y^2)$$

i.e., $$\sum_{i=1}^{N} y_i^2 = Ns_y^2(1 - r^2) + Ns_y^2r^2 \quad . \quad (10.2.3.)$$

now seen as an obvious algebraic identity.

> *Thus the sample variation of y about the regression line of y on x is measured by $Ns_y^2(1 - r^2)$, while the variation of the regression about the sample mean is measured by $Ns_y^2r^2$.*

To the term $\sum_{i=1}^{N} y_i^2$ there correspond $N - 1$ degrees of freedom, since the y's are subject only to the restriction that their mean is given (in our treatment, $\bar{y} = 0$); corresponding to the sum $\sum_{i=1}^{N} (y_i - Y_i)^2$ there is one additional restraint—that the regression coefficient of y on x shall be b_{yx}. Thus corresponding to $Ns_y^2(1 - r^2)$ we have $N - 2$ degrees of freedom. Consequently $\sum_{i=1}^{N} Y_i^2 = Ns_y^2r^2$ has but one degree of freedom.

Now suppose that the parent population is uncorrelated ($\rho = 0$); then the sample variation of the regression line about the mean and the random variation of the y's about the regression line should yield estimates of the corresponding population parameter not significantly different. If, on the other hand, the regression coefficient *is* significant, i.e., if there is in fact an association between the variates in the population of the kind indicated by the regression equation, the estimate provided by $\sum_{i=1}^{N} Y_i^2/1 \equiv Ns_y^2r^2$ should be significantly greater than that provided by

$$\sum_{i=1}^{N} (y_i - Y_i)^2/(N - 2) \equiv Ns_y^2(1 - r^2)/(N - 2).$$

We may therefore set out an analysis of covariance table as follows:

Source of variation.	Sum of squares.	Degrees of freedom.	Mean square.
Of regression line about mean	$Ns_y^2r^2$	1	$Ns_y^2r^2$
Residual (of variate about regression line)	$Ns_y^2(1 - r^2)$	$N - 2$	$Ns_y^2(1 - r^2)/(N - 2)$
TOTAL	Ns_y^2	$N - 1$	—

If then the sample data does indicate a significant association of the variates in the form suggested by the regression equation, the value of z given by

$$z = \tfrac{1}{2} \log_e \frac{r^2(N - 2)}{1 - r^2} = \log_e r\left[\frac{N - 2}{1 - r^2}\right]^{\frac{1}{2}} \qquad (10.2.4)$$

will be significant at least at the 5% point. Alternatively, the value of

$$F = r^2(N - 2)/(1 - r^2) \quad . \quad . \quad (10.2.4\ (a))$$

can be tested using Table 8.6.

A significant value of either z or F requires the rejection of the null hypothesis that, in the parent population, $\rho = 0$. Thus *when we test the significance of a regression coefficient we are also testing the significance of r, the correlation coefficient.*

If neither z- nor F-tables are available, we may use t-tables, for, as we shall now show, $r[(N - 2)/(1 - r^2)]^{\frac{1}{2}}$ is actually distributed like t with $N - 2$ degrees of freedom.

10.3. Relation between the *t*- and *z*-distributions. We have (8.6.7)

$$dp(z) = \frac{2\nu_1^{\nu_1/2}\nu_2^{\nu_2/2}}{B(\nu_1/2, \nu_2/2)} \cdot \frac{\exp(\nu_1 z)}{(\nu_1 \exp 2z + \nu_2)^{\frac{\nu_1+\nu_2}{2}}} \cdot dz$$

Now put $z = \frac{1}{2}\log_e t^2$, $\nu_1 = 1$ and $\nu_2 = \nu$. Then

$$dp(t) = \frac{2\nu^{\nu/2}}{B(\nu/2, 1)} \cdot \frac{t}{(t^2 + \nu)^{\frac{\nu+1}{2}}} \frac{1}{t}\, dt = \frac{2\nu^{-\frac{1}{2}}}{B(\nu/2, 1)} \cdot \left(1 + \frac{t^2}{\nu}\right)^{-\frac{\nu+1}{2}} dt$$

However, since z ranges from 0 to ∞, while t ranges from $-\infty$ to $+\infty$, we must remove the factor 2, with the result that

$$dp(t) = \frac{1}{\nu^{\frac{1}{2}}B(\nu/2, 1)} \cdot (1 + t^2/\nu)^{-\frac{\nu+1}{2}}\, dt \quad . \quad (\text{see } 8.1.4)$$

In other words the distribution of t, like that of F, is a special case of that of z. Consequently, $r[(N - 2)/(1 - r^2)]^{\frac{1}{2}}$ *is distributed like t with N* $-$ *2 degrees of freedom.*

10.4. Worked Example:

In a sample of N $= 16$ *pairs of values drawn from a bivariate population, the observed correlation coefficient between the variates is 0·5. Is this value significant? Find the minimum value of r for a sample of this size which is significant at the 5% level.*

Treatment:

$$N = 16,\ r = 0{\cdot}5 \qquad \nu_1 = 1,\ \nu_2 = 14.$$

Then $\quad F = 0{\cdot}25 \times 14/(1 - 0{\cdot}25) = 4{\cdot}667$

for 1 and 14 degrees of freedom; or

$$t = 2{\cdot}16 \text{ for 14 degrees of freedom.}$$

The 5% and 1% points of F for $\nu_1 = 1$ and $\nu_2 = 14$ degrees o freedom are 4·60 and 8·86; the value of t significant at the 5% leve is 2·14 (using Tables 8·6 and 8·1 respectively). We conclude, therefore, that the observed value of r, 0·5, is just significant at the 5% level: there is less than 1 chance in 20 but more than 1 chance in 100 that this value should arise by chance in random sampling of an uncorrelated population.

The required minimum value of r is given by

$$r^2 \times 14/(1 - r^2) = 4{\cdot}60$$

or

$$r = \underline{0{\cdot}497}$$

10.5. The Distribution of *r*. So far we have assumed that the population we have been sampling is uncorrelated. We must now consider the problem of testing the significance of an observed value of r when $\rho \neq 0$.

The distribution of r for random samples of N pairs of values from a bivariate normal population in which $\rho \neq 0$ is by no means normal, and in the neighbourhood of $\rho = \pm 1$ it is extremely skew even for large N. It was for this reason that Fisher introduced the important *transformation*

$$z = \tfrac{1}{2} \log_e [(1 + r)/(1 - r)] = \tanh^{-1} r \quad . \qquad (10.5.1)$$

The importance of this transformation lies in the fact that—

> **z is approximately normally distributed with mean $\frac{1}{2} \log_e [1 + \rho)/(1 - \rho)] = \tanh^{-1} \rho$ and variance $1/(N - 3)$ and, as N increases, this distribution tends to normality quite rapidly.**

(*a*) To decide whether a value of r calculated from a sample of N pairs of values from a bivariate normal distribution is consistent with a known value of the population correlation coefficient ρ, we put

$$z = \tfrac{1}{2} \log_e [(1 + r)/(1 - r)] = \tanh^{-1} r;$$
$$Z = \tfrac{1}{2} \log_e [(1 + \rho)/(1 - \rho)] = \tanh^{-1} \rho.$$

Then $(z - Z)/(N - 3)^{-\frac{1}{2}}$ is approximately normally distributed with unit variance. Now the value of such a variate which is exceeded with a probability of 5% is 1·96 (see Table 5.4). Therefore for r to differ significantly from the given value of ρ at the 5% level, we must have

$$(z - Z)(N - 3)^{\frac{1}{2}} > 1{\cdot}96$$

(*b*) Now assume that a sample of N_1 pairs yields a value of $r = r_1$ and a second sample of N_2 pairs a value $r = r_2$. If the sampling is strictly random from the same population or from two equivalent populations, r_1 and r_2 will not differ significantly. Should there be a significant difference, however, we should have reason to suspect either that the sampling had not been strictly random or that the two samples had been drawn from different populations.

Let z_1 be the z-transform of r_1 and z_2 that of r_2. On the hypothesis that the two samples are random samples from the same population (or equivalent populations), we have (p. 141),

$$\text{var}\,(z_1 - z_2) = \text{var}\,z_1 + \text{var}\,z_2 = 1/(N_1 - 3) + 1/(N_2 - 3)$$

Hence the standard error of $z_1 - z_2$ is

$$\sqrt{\frac{1}{N_1 - 3} + \frac{1}{N_2 - 3}}, \text{ and } (z_1 - z_2)\Big/\sqrt{\frac{1}{N_1 - 3} + \frac{1}{N_2 - 3}}$$

will be approximately normally distributed with unit variance. Consequently if

$$|z_1 - z_2|\Big/\sqrt{\frac{1}{N_1 - 3} + \frac{1}{N_2 - 3}} < 1{\cdot}96$$

there is no significant difference between r_1 and r_2 and we have no grounds for rejecting the hypothesis that the samples have been drawn at random from the same population; if, however,

$$|z_1 - z_2|\Big/\sqrt{\frac{1}{N_1 - 3} + \frac{1}{N_2 - 3}} > 1{\cdot}96$$

we have grounds for suspecting that they have been drawn from different populations or that, if they have been drawn from one population, they are not *random* samples.

10.6. Worked Example:

A sample of 19 *pairs drawn at random from a bivariate normal population shows a correlation coefficient of* 0·65. (*a*) *Is this consistent with an assumed population correlation,* $\rho = 0{\cdot}40$? (*b*) *What are the* 95% *confidence limits for* ρ *in the light of the information provided by this sample?* (*c*) *If a second sample of* 23 *pairs shows a correlation,* $r = 0{\cdot}40$, *can this have been drawn from the same parent population?*

Treatment:

$$(a)\quad z = \tfrac{1}{2}\log_e(1{\cdot}65/0{\cdot}35) = 0{\cdot}7753$$
$$Z = \tfrac{1}{2}\log_e(1{\cdot}40/0{\cdot}60) = 0{\cdot}4236$$

$(z - Z)\,(N - 3)^{\frac{1}{2}}$ is normally distributed about zero mean with unit variance. In the present case

$$(z - Z)(N - 3)^{\frac{1}{2}} = 1{\cdot}4068, \text{ which is less than } 1{\cdot}96.$$

Consequently the value $r = 0{\cdot}65$ from a sample of 19 pairs is compatible with an assumed population correlation of 0·40.

(*b*) To find the 95% confidence limits for ρ on the basis of the information provided by the present sample, we put

$$| z - Z | \times 4 \leqslant 1{\cdot}96 \quad \text{or} \quad | z - Z | \leqslant 0{\cdot}49.$$

Consequently

$$0{\cdot}7753 - 0{\cdot}49 \leqslant Z \leqslant 0{\cdot}7753 + 0{\cdot}49$$

giving $0{\cdot}2853 \leqslant Z \leqslant 1{\cdot}2653$ or $\underline{0{\cdot}2775 \leqslant \rho \leqslant 0{\cdot}8524}$

and these are the required 95% confidence limits for ρ.

(*c*) The z-transforms of $r_1 = 0{\cdot}65$ and of $r_2 = 0{\cdot}40$ are respectively $z_1 = 0{\cdot}7753$ and $z_2 = 0{\cdot}4236$.

On the assumption that the samples are from the same normal population (or from equivalent normal populations), the variance of their difference is equal to the sum of their variances. The standard error of $z_1 - z_2$ is then $(1/16 + 1/20)^{\frac{1}{2}} = 0{\cdot}3354$. Thus $(z_1 - z_2)/0{\cdot}3354$ is distributed normally about zero mean with unit variance, and since $(0{\cdot}7753 - 0{\cdot}4236)/0{\cdot}3354 = 1{\cdot}044 < 1{\cdot}96$, we conclude that there is no ground to reject the hypothesis that the two samples have been drawn from the same population (or from equivalent populations).

10.7. Combining Estimates of ρ. Let samples of N_1, N_2, . . . N_k be drawn from a population and let the corresponding values of r be $r_1, r_2, \ldots r_k$. How shall we combine these k estimates of ρ, the population correlation, to obtain a better estimate of that parameter?

Let the z-transforms of r_i, $(i = 1, 2, \ldots k)$ be z_i, $(i = 1, 2, \ldots k)$. Then these k values are values of variates which are approximately normally distributed with variances $(N_i - 3)^{-1}$, $(i = 1, 2, \ldots k)$ about a common mean $Z = \tanh^{-1} \rho$. If we "weight" these k values with weights m_i, $(i = 1, 2, \ldots k)$, the *weighted mean* is

$$\sum_{i=1}^{k} m_i z_i \Big/ \sum_{i=1}^{k} m_i = \sum_{i=1}^{k} M_i z_i \quad \text{where} \quad M_i = m_i \Big/ \sum_{i=1}^{k} m_i.$$

If the variance of z_i is σ_i^2, that of $\sum_{i=1}^{k} M_i z_i$, σ^2, is given by

$$\sigma^2 = \sum_{i=1}^{k} M_i^2 \sigma_i^2 = \sum_{i=1}^{k} m_i^2 \sigma_i^2 \Big/ \Big(\sum_{i=1}^{k} m_i \Big)^2.$$

Now σ^2 is a function of the k quantities m_i. Let us choose these k quantities in such a way that σ^2 is a minimum. The necessary condition that this should be so is that

for all i, $\quad \partial \sigma^2 / \partial m_i = 0$

i.e., for all i,

$$\left(\sum_{i=1}^{k} m_i\right)^2 m_i\sigma_i^2 - \left(\sum_{i=1}^{k} m_i^2\sigma_i^2\right)\left(\sum_{i=1}^{k} m_i\right) = 0$$

i.e., for all i, $\quad m_i\sigma_i^2 = \sum_{i=1}^{k} m_i^2\sigma_i^2 / \sum_{i=1}^{k} m_i$, a constant;

i.e. $\quad m_i \propto 1/\sigma_i^2$, for all i.

The minimum-variance estimate of Z is then

$$\sum_{i=1}^{k} (N_i - 3)z_i / \sum_{i=1}^{k} (N_i - 3)$$

and the required combined estimate of ρ is

$$\rho = \tanh\left[\sum_{i=1}^{k} (N_i - 3)z_i \Big/ \sum_{i=1}^{k} (N_i - 3)\right] \quad . \quad (10.7.1)$$

10.8. Worked Example:

Samples of 20, 30, 40 *and* 50 *are drawn from the same parent population, yielding values of r, the sample correlation coefficient, of* 0·41, 0·60, 0·51, 0·48 *respectively. Use these values of r to obtain a combined estimate of the population correlation coefficient.*

Treatment: We form the following table:

r_i.	z_i.	$N_i - 3$.	$(N_i - 3)z_i$.
0·41	0·436	17	7·412
0·60	0·693	27	18·711
0·51	0·563	37	20·831
0·48	0·523	47	24·581
TOTALS	—	128	71·535

$$\frac{\sum_{i=1}^{4} (N_i - 3)z_i}{\sum_{i=1}^{4} (N_i - 3)} = \frac{71·535}{128} = 0·5589$$

giving $\quad \rho = \tanh 0·5589 = 0·507$

NOTE: (1) To save work tables of the inverse hyperbolic functions should be used to find the z-transforms of r.

(2) The weighted mean of z obtained in the previous section and used here is approximately normally distributed with variance

$1/\sum_{i=1} (N_i - 3)$. The accuracy of our estimate is then that to be expected from a sample of $\left[\sum_{i=1}^{k} (N_i - 3) + 3\right]$ pairs. In the present example this variance is $1/128 = 0{\cdot}0078$, i.e., the standard error of Z is $0{\cdot}0883$. Thus we may expect ρ to lie between $0{\cdot}368$ and $0{\cdot}624$. The value of Z we have obtained may be treated as an individual value calculated from a single sample of 131 pairs.

10.9. Testing a Correlation Ratio. When the regression of y on x in a sample of N pairs of values from a bivariate population is curvilinear, the *correlation ratio of y on x* for the sample, e_{yx}, is defined by (6.14.4)

$$e_{yx}^2 = s_{\bar{y}}^2/s_y^2,$$

where $s_{\bar{y}}^2$ is the variance of the means of the x-arrays and s_y^2 is the sample variance of y. Moreover, $e_{yx}^2 - r^2$ may, provisionally, be taken as a measure of the degree to which the regression departs from linearity (but see below, 10.10).

We now have to devise a method of testing whether a given e_{yx} is significant, i.e., whether such a value of e_{yx} could have arisen by chance in random sampling.

We take Table 6.2.2 to be our correlation table and assume our origin to be taken at the sample mean ($\bar{x} = 0 = \bar{y}$). Then the sum of the squared deviations of the y's from this mean is

$$\sum_i \sum_j f_{ij} y_j^2 = \sum_i \sum_j f_{ij} (y_j - \bar{y}_i + \bar{y}_i)^2,$$

where $\bar{y}_i$ is the mean of the y's in the x_ith array. Expanding the right-hand side,

$$\sum_i \sum_j f_{ij} y_j^2 = \sum_i \sum_j f_{ij}(y_j - \bar{y}_i)^2 + \sum_i \sum_j f_{ij} \bar{y}_i^2 + 2 \sum_i \sum_j f_{ij} \bar{y}_i (y_j - \bar{y}_i)$$

The cross-product vanishes because if $\sum_j f_{ij} = n_i$, the frequency of the y's in the x_ith array,

$$\sum_i \sum_j f_{ij} \bar{y}_i (y_j - \bar{y}_i) = \sum_i (\bar{y}_i \sum_j f_{ij} y_j) - \sum_i (\bar{y}_i^2 \sum_j f_{ij})$$
$$= \sum_i (n_i \bar{y}_i^2 - n_i \bar{y}_i^2) = 0.$$

Consequently

$$\sum_i \sum_j f_{ij} y_j^2 = \sum_i \sum_j f_{ij} (y_j - \bar{y}_i)^2 + \sum_i \sum_j f_{ij} \bar{y}_i^2, \text{ which, by } \mathbf{6.7},$$
$$= N s_y^2 (1 - e_{yx}^2) + N s_y^2 e_{yx}^2 \quad . \quad . \quad (10.9.1)$$

If now there are p x-arrays, the p values of $\bar{y}_i$ are subject to the single restriction $\sum_i \sum_j f_{ij} y_j = \sum_i n_i \bar{y}_i = N\bar{y} (= 0$, with our present origin). Thus the term $N s_y^2 e_{yx}^2$ has $p - 1$ degrees of freedom. Likewise, the Ny_j's are subject to the same restriction and, so, for the term $\sum_i \sum_j f_{ij}y_j^2$ there are $N - 1$ degrees of freedom. Hence the term $Ns_y^2(1 - e_{yx}^2)$ involves $(N - 1) - (p - 1) = N - p$ degrees of freedom.

On the null hypothesis that there is no association between the variates in the population, each array may be regarded as a random sample from the population of y's. $\sum_i \sum_j f_{ij}(y_j - \bar{y}_i)^2$ is the variation sum of squares *within* arrays, while the term $\sum_i \sum_j f_{ij}\bar{y}_i^2$ is the variation sum of squares *between* arrays. On the null hypothesis, then, each of these sums divided by the appropriate number of degrees of freedom should give unbiased estimates of σ_y^2. The corresponding analysis of covariance is, then:

Source of variation.	Sum of squares.	Degrees of freedom.	Estimate of σ_y^2.
Between arrays	$Ns_y^2e_{yx}^2$	$p - 1$	$Ns_y^2e_{yx}^2/(p - 1)$
Within arrays .	$Ns_y^2(1 - e_{yx}^2)$	$N - p$	$Ns_y^2(1 - e_{yx}^2)/(N - p)$
TOTALS . .	Ns_y^2	$N - 1$	—

If, then, the value of

$$F = \frac{e_{yx}^2(N - p)}{(1 - e_{yx}^2)(p - 1)}, \text{ for } \nu_1 = p - 1, \nu_2 = N - p \quad (10.9.2)$$

is found to be significant, we must reject the hypothesis that there is no association of the kind indicated by the regression function in the population. In other words, the value of e_{yx} obtained from the sample data is significant.

10.10. Linear or Non-linear Regression? In 10.2 we assumed that the regression of y on x was linear; in 10.9 we assumed it to be non-linear. We must now complete this set of tests with one which will indicate whether, on the sample data, regression is linear or non-linear, a test which is in fact logically prior to the other two.

To do this we return to equation

$$\sum_i \sum_j f_{ij}y_j^2 = \sum_i \sum_j f_{ij}(y_j - \bar{y}_i)^2 + \sum_i \sum_j f_{ij}\bar{y}_i^2.$$

Let b_{yx} be the coefficient of regression of y on x; then, with our assumption that $\bar{x} = 0 = \bar{y}$, the regression *line* is $y = b_{yx}x$.

Let Y_i be the estimate of y obtained from this equation when $x = x_i$. Then we may write

$$\sum_i \sum_j f_{ij} y_j^2 = \sum_i \sum_j f_{ij}(y_j - \bar{y}_i)^2 + \sum_i \sum_j f_{ij}(\bar{y}_i - Y_i + Y_i)^2$$
$$= \sum_i \sum_j f_{ij}(y_j - \bar{y}_i)^2 + \sum_i \sum_j f_{ij}(\bar{y}_i - Y_i)^2 + \sum_i \sum_j f_{ij} Y_i^2,$$

the cross-product again vanishing (why?)

The first term on the right-hand side of this equation still represents the variation of y *within arrays*; the second term represents the variation of array-means from the regression *line*; and the third term represents the variation of the regression line about the sample mean.

We have already seen that the term

$$\sum_i \sum_j f_{ij}(y_i - \bar{y}_i)^2 \equiv N s_y^2(1 - e_{yx}^2)$$

has $N - p$ degrees of freedom. Furthermore,

$$\sum_i \sum_j f_{ij}(\bar{y}_i - Y_i)^2 + \sum_i \sum_j f_{ij} Y_i^2 = N s_y^2 e_{yx}^2$$

with $p - 1$ degrees of freedom. Now we may write

$$\sum_i \sum_j f_{ij} Y_i^2 = b_{yx}^2 \sum_i \sum_j f_{ij} x_i^2 = b_{yx}^2 \sum_i n_i x_i^2.$$

But $\sum_i n_i x_i^2$ is independent of the regression and, so, the variation it represents depends only on b_{yx} and to it, therefore, corresponds but one degree of freedom. Moreover,

$$b_{yx}^2 \sum_i n_i x_i^2 = (s_{xy}^2/s_x^4) \,.\, N s_x^2 = N r^2 s_y^2.$$

Consequently the term $\sum_i \sum_j f_{ij}(\bar{y}_i - Y_i)^2 = N s_y^2(e_{yx}^2 - r^2)$, with $p - 2$ degrees of freedom.

On the hypothesis that regression is linear, the mean square deviation of array-means from the regression line should not be significantly greater than that of y within arrays. The analysis is shown in the table on page 200.

We may thus test

$$F = \frac{(e_{yx}^2 - r^2)(N - p)}{(1 - e_{yx}^2)(p - 2)}, \text{ for } \nu_1 = p - 2,\ \nu_2 = N - p \qquad (10.10.1)$$

If this value of F is significant, the hypothesis of linear regression must be rejected. It follows that it is not sufficient to regard $e_{yx}^2 - r^2$ by itself as a measure of departure from

Source of variation.	Sum of squares.	Degrees of freedom.	Mean square.
Of array means about regression line	$Ns_y^2(e_{yx}^2 - r^2)$	$p - 2$	$Ns_y^2(e_{yx}^2 - r^2)/(p - 2)$
Of regression line about sample mean	$Nr^2s_y^2$	1	$Nr^2s_y^2$
Within arrays	$Ns_y^2(1 - e_{yx}^2)$	$N - p$	$Ns_y^2(1 - e_{yx}^2)/(N - p)$
TOTALS	Ns_y^2	$N - 1$	—

linearity, for F depends also on e_{yx}^2, N and p. If the value of F is not significant, there is no reason to reject the hypothesis and analysis may proceed accordingly.

10.11. Worked Example:

Test for non-linearity of regression the data of 6·8 *and* 6·15.

Treatment: We have $e_{yx}^2 = 0{\cdot}471$; $e_{yx}^2 - r^2 = 0{\cdot}009$; $N = 1000$ and $p = 9$.

$$F = \frac{0{\cdot}009 \times 991}{0{\cdot}529 \times 7} = 2{\cdot}409 \text{ for } \nu_1 = 7,\ \nu_2 = 991.$$

Using Table 9·6, we find that the 1% and 5% points of F for $\nu_1 = 7$, $\nu_2 = 991$ are 2·66 and 2·02. The value of F is, therefore, significant at the 5% level, but not at the 1% level. There is some ground for believing that the regression is non-linear.

EXERCISES ON CHAPTER TEN

1. Test for significance the value of r found in Exercise 4 to Chapter Six.

2. A sample of 140 pairs is drawn at random from a bivariate normal population. Grouped in 14 arrays, the data yielded $r = 0{\cdot}35$ and $e_{yx} = 0{\cdot}45$. Are these values consistent with the assumption that the regression of y on x is linear?

3. Test the values of e_{yx} and r found in Exercise 8 to Chapter Six. Is there reason to believe that the regression of y on x is non-linear?

4. Random samples of 10, 15 and 20 are drawn from a bivariate normal population, yielding $r = 0{\cdot}3$, $0{\cdot}4$, $0{\cdot}49$ respectively. Form a combined estimate of ρ.

Solutions

2. Yes. 3. No. 4. $\rho = 0{\cdot}43$ (2 d.p.).

CHAPTER ELEVEN

CHI-SQUARE AND ITS USES

11.1. Curve-fitting. What we are actually trying to do when we " fit " a continuous curve to an observed frequency distribution is to find a curve such that the given frequency distribution is that of a random sample from the (hypothetical) population defined by the curve we ultimately choose. Suppose that the observed frequencies of the values x_i of the variate x are n_i, $(i = 1, 2, \ldots k)$, where $\sum_{i=1}^{k} n_i = N$. The value x_i will in fact be the mid-value of a class-interval, $x_i \pm \frac{1}{2}h_i$, say. Let $\phi(x)$ be the probability density of the continuous distribution corresponding to the curve we fit to the data. Then the *theoretical* frequency of x_i in a sample of N will be

$$N \int_{x_i - \frac{1}{2}h_i}^{x_i + \frac{1}{2}h_i} \phi(x)dx = Np_i,$$

say. The question we now ask is: How well does this theoretical curve fit the observed data?

On the hypothesis that the fitted curve does in fact represent the (hypothetical) population from which the set of observed values of x is a random sample, the divergence of observed from theoretical frequencies must result from random sampling fluctuations only. If, however, this total divergence is greater than that which, to some specified degree of probability, is likely to result from random sampling, we shall be forced to conclude that, at this level of significance, the fitted curve does not adequately represent the population of which the observed x's have been regarded as a sample. Crudely, the " fit " is not good.

11.2. The Chi-Square Distribution. Of a sample of N values of a variate x, let x take the value x_1 on n_1 occasions out of the N, the value x_2 on n_2 occasions, and, finally, the value x_k on n_k occasions, so that $\sum_{i=1}^{k} n_i = N$. If now the probability of x taking the value x_i, $(i = 1, 2, \ldots k)$ be p_i, $(i = 1, 2, \ldots k)$, the probability of x taking the value x_1 on n_1 occasions, the value x_2 on n_2 occasions and so on, regardless of order, will be (2.10)

$$P = \frac{N!}{\prod_{i=1}^{k} n_i!} \cdot \prod_{i=1}^{k} p_i^{n_i} \quad . \quad . \quad . \quad (11.2.1)$$

For sufficiently large values of n_i, we may use Stirling's approximation to $n\,!$, viz.,

$$n\,! \simeq (2\pi)^{\frac{1}{2}} n^{(n+\frac{1}{2})} \,.\, \exp(-n)$$

then

$$P \simeq \frac{(2\pi)^{\frac{1}{2}} N^{N+\frac{1}{2}} \exp(-N)}{\prod_{i=1}^{k} [(2\pi)^{\frac{1}{2}} n_i^{n_i+\frac{1}{2}} \exp(-n_i)]} \cdot \prod_{i=1}^{k} p_i^{n_i}$$

$$= \frac{N^{N+\frac{1}{2}} \exp(-N)}{(2\pi)^{\frac{k-1}{2}} \exp\left(-\sum_{i=1}^{k} n_i\right)} \cdot \prod_{i=1}^{k} [p_i^{n_i} / n_i^{n_i+\frac{1}{2}}]$$

But $\sum_{i=1}^{k} n_i = N$, and, therefore

$$P \simeq \frac{N^{\left[\sum_{i=1}^{k}(n_i+\frac{1}{2})\right]-\frac{k-1}{2}}}{(2\pi)^{\frac{k-1}{2}} \prod_{i=1}^{k} p_i^{\frac{1}{2}}} \cdot \prod_{i=1}^{k} [p_i/n_i]^{n_i+\frac{1}{2}}$$

or
$$P \simeq \frac{1}{(2\pi N)^{\frac{k-1}{2}} \prod_{i=1}^{k} p_i^{\frac{1}{2}}} \cdot \prod_{i=1}^{k} [Np_i/n_i]^{n_i+\frac{1}{2}} \quad . \quad (11.2.2)$$

Now the expression $(2\pi N)^{(k-1)/2} \prod_{i=1}^{k} p_i^{\frac{1}{2}}$ is independent of the n_i's, and, for a given N and a given set of theoretical probabilities, p_i, is constant. Therefore, putting $1/C$ for this expression, we have, *for sufficiently large* n_i,

$$\log_e P \simeq \log_e C + \sum_{i=1}^{k} (n_i + \tfrac{1}{2}) \log_e (Np_i/n_i).$$

Write

$$X_i = (n_i - Np_i)/(Np_i)^{\frac{1}{2}}, \quad \text{i.e.,} \quad n_i = Np_i + X_i(Np_i)^{\frac{1}{2}}.$$

Then, since

$$\sum_{i=1}^{k} n_i = N = \sum_{i=1}^{k} Np_i, \ \sum_{i=1}^{k} X_i(Np_i)^{\frac{1}{2}} = 0$$

indicating that *only* $k - 1$ *of the* X_i*'s are independent.* It follows that

$$\log_e P \simeq \log_e C + \sum_{i=1}^{k} [Np_i + X_i (Np_i)^{\frac{1}{2}} + \tfrac{1}{2}] \times$$
$$\times \log_e [Np_i/(Np_i + X_i(Np_i)^{\frac{1}{2}})]$$

$$\simeq \log_e C - \sum_{i=1}^{k} [Np_i + X_i(Np_i)^{\frac{1}{2}} + \tfrac{1}{2}] \log_e [1 + X_i(Np_i)^{-\frac{1}{2}}]$$

If none of the p_i's are of the order N^{-1}, we have, on expanding the logarithm in a power series (see Abbott, *Teach Yourself Calculus*, p. 332) and using the fact that $\sum_{i=1}^{k} X_i(Np_i)^{\frac{1}{2}} = 0$,

$$\log_e P \simeq \log_e C - \tfrac{1}{2} \sum_{i=1}^{k} X_i^2 - \tfrac{1}{2} \sum_{i=1}^{k} X_i(Np_i)^{-\frac{1}{2}}$$

or, since N is large and terms in $N^{-\frac{1}{2}}$ and higher powers of $N^{-\frac{1}{2}}$ may be neglected,

$$\log_e P \simeq \log_e C - \tfrac{1}{2} \sum_{i=1}^{k} X_i^2$$

or

$$P \simeq C \exp \left(- \tfrac{1}{2} \sum_{i=1}^{k} X_i^2\right). \quad . \quad (11.2.3)$$

Now the n_i's are integers and since $n_i = Np_i + X_i(Np_i)^{\frac{1}{2}}$, to a change of unity in n_i, the corresponding change in X_i, ΔX_i, will be given by $\Delta X_i = (Np_i)^{-\frac{1}{2}}$. Remembering that only $k - 1$ of the X_i's are independent, we have

$$P \simeq \frac{1}{(2\pi N)^{(k-1)/2} \prod_{i=1}^{k} p_i^{\frac{1}{2}}} \exp \left(- \tfrac{1}{2} \sum_{i=1}^{k} X_i^2\right)$$

$$\simeq \frac{1}{(2\pi)^{(k-1)/2} \prod_{i=1}^{k-1} (Np_i)^{\frac{1}{2}} \cdot p_k^{\frac{1}{2}}} \exp \left(- \tfrac{1}{2} \sum_{i=1}^{k} X_i^2\right)$$

$$\simeq \frac{1}{(2\pi)^{(k-1)/2} p_k^{\frac{1}{2}}} \exp \left(- \tfrac{1}{2} \sum_{i=1}^{k} X_i^2\right) \Delta X_1 \Delta X_2 \ . \ . \ . \ \Delta X_{k-1}$$

or, as N tends to infinity, the probability of n_1x_1's, n_2x_2's, etc., P, is given approximately by the probability differential of a continuous distribution defined by

$$P \simeq dp = B \exp\left(-\tfrac{1}{2}\sum_{i=1}^{k} X_i^2\right) dX_1 dX_2 \ldots dX_{k-1} \quad (11.2.4)$$

Let us now consider the variate X_i in more detail. We begin by recalling that $\sum_{i=1}^{k} n_i = N$; if then we allow N, the sample size, to vary, we have on the assumption that the frequencies are independent,

$$\sum_{i=1}^{k} \sigma_{n_i}^2 = \sigma_N^2 \quad . \quad . \quad . \quad . \quad (11.2.5)$$

or

$$\text{var } N = \sum_{i=1}^{k} \text{var } n_i \quad . \quad (11.2.5(a))$$

Again, if we treat the event of x taking the particular value x_i as a success in N trials, the frequency of success will be distributed binomially with mean Np_i and variance $Np_i(1 - p_i)$. Now put $z_i = n_i - Np_i$. When N is treated as constant, var $(z_i) = Np_i(1 - p_i)$. If, however, we write $n_i = z_i + Np_i$ and allow N to vary, var (n_i) = var (z_i) $+ p_i^2$ var (N), or var $(n_i) = Np_i(1 - p_i) + p_i^2$ var (N). Summing over the i's, we have

$$\text{var }(N) = \sum_{i=1}^{k} \text{var }(n_i) = N\sum_{i=1}^{k} p_i(1 - p_i) + \text{var }(N) \, . \sum_{i=1}^{k} p_i^2$$

or, since $\sum_{i=1}^{k} p_i = 1$, $\qquad$ var $(N) = N$.

Therefore,

$$\text{var }(n_i) = Np_i(1 - p_i) + Np_i^2 = Np_i \quad (11.2.6)$$

When, then, N is sufficiently large, the variates $X_i \equiv (n_i - Np_i)/(Np_i)^{\frac{1}{2}}$ are approximately normally distributed about zero mean with unit variance. It remains, therefore, to find the distribution of the sum of the squares of k standardised normal variates, subject to the restriction that only $k - 1$ of them are independent.

Let $P \equiv (X_1, X_2, \ldots X_k)$ be a point in a k-dimensional Euclidean space and put

$$\sum_{i=1}^{k} X_i^2 = \chi^2$$

subject to the restriction $\sum_{i=1}^{k} X_i(Np_i)^{\frac{1}{2}} = 0$. An element of volume in the X-space now corresponds (see 7.11) to the element of volume between the two hyperspheres $\sum_{i=1}^{k} X_i^2 = \chi^2$ and $\sum_{i=1}^{k} X_i^2 = (\chi + d\chi)^2$ subject to $\sum_{i=1}^{k} X_i(Np_i)^{\frac{1}{2}} = 0$. Using arguments parallel to those used in 7.11, we find that the probability that of the N values of the variate x, n_i are x_i, $(i = 1, 2, \ldots k)$, is approximately equal to the probability that $\chi \equiv \left(\sum_{i=1}^{k} X_i^2\right)^{\frac{1}{2}}$ lies between χ and $\chi + d\chi$ viz.,

$$dp = A \exp(-\tfrac{1}{2}\chi^2)\chi^{k-2}d\chi \quad . \quad . \quad (11.2.7)$$

where, since the probability of χ taking some value between 0 and ∞ is unity,

$$1 = A\int_0^\infty \exp(-\tfrac{1}{2}\chi^2)\chi^{k-2}d\chi$$

giving

$$1/A = 2^{(k-3)/2}\Gamma[(k-1)/2] \quad . \quad . \quad (11.2.8)$$

This defines a *continuous* distribution, which although actually that of χ is sometimes erroneously called the χ^2-distribution.

Since of the kX_i's only $k - 1$ are independent, we may say that χ has $k - 1$ degrees of freedom. Putting, conventionally, $\nu = k - 1$, we have

$$dp = \frac{1}{2^{\frac{\nu-2}{2}}\Gamma(\nu/2)}\chi^{\nu-1}\exp(-\tfrac{1}{2}\chi^2)d\chi \quad (11.2.9)$$

It can be shown, however, that if instead of one equation of constraint, there are p such linear equations and the number of degrees of freedom for χ is, consequently, $k - p$, (11.2.9) still holds. When $\nu = 1$,

$$dp = (2/\pi)^{\frac{1}{2}}\exp(-\tfrac{1}{2}\chi^2)d\chi,$$

which is the normal distribution with probability density doubled—due to the fact that $\chi \geqslant 0$, whereas in the normal distribution the variate takes negative and positive values.

The χ^2-distribution proper is obtained by writing (11.2.9) in the form

$$dp = \frac{1}{2^{\nu/2}\Gamma(\nu/2)}\exp(-\tfrac{1}{2}\chi^2)(\chi^2)^{\nu/2-1}d(\chi^2) \quad (11.2.10)$$

If now we write $\chi^2 = S$,

$$dp = \frac{1}{2^{\nu/2}\,\Gamma(\nu/2)} \exp\left(-\tfrac{1}{2}S\right) S^{\nu/2-1} dS \quad (12.2.10(a))$$

Then the probability that χ^2 will not exceed a given value $\chi_0{}^2$ is

$$P(\chi^2 \leqslant \chi_0{}^2) = \frac{1}{2^{\nu/2}\,\Gamma(\nu/2)} \int_0^{S=\chi_0{}^2} \exp\left(-\tfrac{1}{2}S\right) S^{\nu/2-1} dS$$

The right-hand side is, in fact, an Incomplete Γ-function, and the above equation may be written in Karl Pearson's notation

$$P(\chi^2 \leqslant \chi_0{}^2) = I\left(\frac{\chi_0{}^2}{\sqrt{\nu/2+1}}, \nu/2\right) . \quad (11.2.11)$$

Tables of this function are given in *Tables of the Incomplete Γ-function*, edited by Pearson and published by the Biometrika

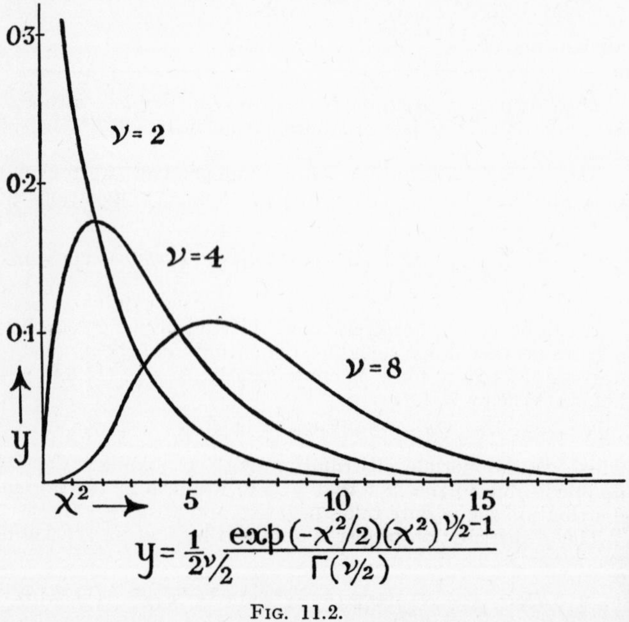

FIG. 11.2.

Office, University College, London. With them we can evaluate $P(\chi^2 \leqslant \chi_0^2)$ for $\nu \leqslant 30$.

For many practical purposes, however, we may use two formulas which given an approximate value of χ^2 exceeded with a probability of 0·05. The approximate 0·05 point of χ^2 for $\nu \leqslant 10$ is

$$1{\cdot}55(\nu + 2),$$

while that for $35 \geqslant \nu > 10$ is

$$1{\cdot}25(\nu + 5).$$

Tables of χ^2 for various values of $\nu \leqslant 30$ are readily available. They include those in :

(1) *Statistical Tables for use in Biological, Agricultural and Medical Research,* by Sir R. A. Fisher and F. Yates;
(2) *Statistical Methods for Research Workers,* by Sir R. A. Fisher; and
(3) *Cambridge Elementary Statistical Tables,* by D. V. Lindley and J. C. P. Miller.

Our Table 11.2 is reproduced, by permission of the author and publisher, from (2).

TABLE 11.2. *Values of χ^2 with Probability P of Being Exceeded in Random Sampling*

ν \ P.	0·99	0·95	0·05	0·01	ν \ P.	0·99	0·95	0·05	0·01
1	0·0002	0·004	3·81	6·64	16	5·81	7·96	26·30	32·00
2	0·020	0·103	5·90	9·21	17	6·41	8·67	27·59	33·41
3	0·115	0·35	7·82	11·34	18	7·02	9·39	28·87	34·80
4	0·30	0·71	9·49	13·28	19	7·63	10·12	30·14	36·19
5	0·55	1·14	11·07	15·09	20	8·26	10·85	31·41	37·57
6	0·87	1·64	12·59	16·81	21	8·90	11·59	32·67	38·93
7	1·24	2·17	14·07	18·48	22	9·54	12·34	33·92	40·29
8	1·65	2·73	15·51	20·09	23	10·20	13·09	35·17	41·64
9	2·09	3·32	16·92	21·67	24	10·86	13·85	36·42	42·98
10	2·56	3·94	18·31	23·21	25	11·52	14·61	37·65	44·31
11	3·05	4·58	19·68	24·72	26	12·20	15·38	38·88	45·64
12	3·57	5·23	21·03	26·22	27	12·88	16·15	40·11	46·96
13	4·11	5·89	22·36	27·69	28	13·56	16·93	41·34	48·28
14	4·66	6·57	23·68	29·14	29	14·26	17·71	42·56	49·59
15	5·23	7·26	25·00	30·58	30	14·95	18·49	43·77	50·89

NOTE: (1) The value of χ^2 obtained from a sample may be *significantly small.* Fig. 11.2 will make this clear. When the value of P obtained from the table is greater than 0·95, the probability of a smaller value of χ^2 is less than 5% and this value must, therefore, be regarded as significantly small. The "fit" is too good to be regarded without suspicion! (see also WARNING in 11.4).

(2) When $\nu > 30$, Fisher has shown that $\sqrt{2\chi^2}$ is approximately normally distributed about mean $\sqrt{2\nu - 1}$ with unit variance. Thus $\sqrt{2\chi^2} - \sqrt{2\nu - 1}$ may be considered as a standardised normal variate for values of $\nu > 30$.

11.3. More Properties of Chi-Squares. The moment-generating function of the χ^2-distribution is

$$M(t) \equiv \mathcal{E}(e^{\chi^2 t}) = \mathcal{E}(e^{St})$$

$$= \frac{1}{2^{\nu/2}\Gamma(\nu/2)}\int_0^\infty \exp(-\tfrac{1}{2}S)S^{\nu/2-1}\exp(St)dS$$

$$= \frac{1}{2^{\nu/2}\Gamma(\nu/2)}\int_0^\infty S^{\nu/2-1}\exp[-\tfrac{1}{2}S(1-2t)]dS$$

Putting $\quad \tfrac{1}{2}S(1-2t) = v,\ dS = \dfrac{2}{1-2t}dv$

$$M(t) = \frac{(1-2t)^{-\nu/2}}{\Gamma(\nu/2)}\int_0^\infty \exp(-v)v^{\nu/2-1}dv$$

$$= \frac{(1-2t)^{-\nu/2}}{\Gamma(\nu/2)}\cdot\Gamma(\nu/2)$$

i.e.,
$$\boldsymbol{M(t) = (1-2t)^{-\nu/2}} \quad . \quad . \quad . \quad (11.3.1)$$

Expanding $[1-2t]^{-\nu/2}$, we have

$$M(t) = 1 + \nu t + \nu(\nu+2)\frac{t^2}{2!} + \ldots$$

Hence $\mu_1' = \nu$; $\mu_2' = \nu(\nu+2)$ and, consequently, $\mu_2 = \mu_2' - \mu_1'^2 = 2\nu$.

The mean of the χ^2-distribution for ν degrees of freedom is, therefore, ν and the variance 2ν.

The mean-moment-generating function in standardised units is, then,

$$M_m(t) = \exp\left(-\frac{\nu t}{\sqrt{2\nu}}\right)\left[1-\frac{2t}{\sqrt{2\nu}}\right]^{-\nu/2} \quad . \quad (11.3.2)$$

Hence

$$\log_e M_m(t) = -\frac{\nu t}{\sqrt{2\nu}} - \frac{\nu}{2}\log_e\left[1-\frac{2t}{\sqrt{2\nu}}\right]$$

$$= -\frac{\nu t}{\sqrt{2\nu}} + \frac{\nu}{2}\left[\frac{2t}{\sqrt{2\nu}} + \frac{1}{2}\cdot\frac{4t^2}{2\nu} + \ldots \text{ higher powers of } \nu^{-1}\right]$$

$$= \frac{t^2}{2} + \text{higher powers of } \nu^{-1}$$

Thus
$$M_m(t) \to \exp(\tfrac{1}{2}t^2) \text{ as } \nu \to \infty \quad . \quad . \quad (11.3.3)$$

and, comparing with (5.4.2), we see that the distribution tends to normality about mean ν with unit variance.

The *mode* of the χ^2-distribution is given by

$$\frac{d}{dS}[S^{\nu/2-1}\exp(-\tfrac{1}{2}S)] = 0$$

i.e., $(\nu/2 - 1)S^{\nu/2-2}\exp(-\tfrac{1}{2}S) - \tfrac{1}{2}S^{\nu/2-1}\exp(-\tfrac{1}{2}S) = 0$

or
$$S = \chi^2 = \nu - 2. \quad . \quad . \quad . \quad (11.3.4)$$

Using Karl Pearson's measure of skewness, (mean-mode)/standard deviation, the skewness of χ^2 is given by

$$\frac{\nu - (\nu - 2)}{\sqrt{2\nu}} = \sqrt{\frac{2}{\nu}} \quad . \quad . \quad . \quad (11.3.5)$$

Now consider $p\chi^2$-variates, $\chi_1^2, \chi_2^2, \ldots \chi_p^2$ with $\nu_1, \nu_2, \ldots \nu_p$ degrees of freedom respectively. If $S_i = \chi_i^2$ $(i = 1, 2, 3, \ldots p)$, the moment-generating-function of S_i with respect to the origin is $[1 - 2t]^{-\nu/2}$.

But the moment generating function of $\sum_{i=1}^{p} S_i$ is, by definition

$$\mathcal{E}\left[\exp\left(\sum_{i=1}^{p} S_i t\right)\right] = \mathcal{E}\left(\prod_{i=1}^{p}\exp S_i t\right)$$
$$= \prod_{i=1}^{p}\mathcal{E}(\exp S_i t)$$

since the S's are independent.

Consequently, the m.g.f. of

$$\sum_{i=1}^{p} S_i = \prod_{i=1}^{p}(1 - 2t)^{-\nu_i/2}$$

$$= (1 - 2t)^{-\frac{1}{2}\sum_{i=1}^{p}\nu_i} = (1 - 2t)^{-\nu/2}, \text{ where } \nu = \sum_{i=1}^{p}\nu_i$$

Hence we have the important theorem :

If the independent positive variates x_i, $(i = 1, 2, \ldots p)$, are each distributed like χ^2 with ν_i degrees of freedom, $(i = 1, 2, \ldots p)$, then $\sum_{i=1}^{p} x_i$ is distributed like χ^2 with $\nu = \sum_{i=1}^{p}\nu_i$ degrees of freedom.

It follows at once that if the sum of two independent positive variates x_1 and x_2 is distributed like χ^2 with ν degrees of

I

freedom, and if x_1 is distributed like χ^2 with ν_1 degrees of freedom, x_2 is distributed like χ^2 with $\nu_2 = \nu - \nu_1$ degrees of freedom.

Some consequences of this additive property are :

(1) Suppose we conduct a set of n similar experiments to test a hypothesis. Let the values of χ^2 corresponding to these experiments be χ_i^2 $(i = 1, 2, \ldots n)$ for ν_i $(i = 1, 2, \ldots n)$ degrees of freedom. If then we write $\chi^2 = \Sigma \chi_i^2$, this value of χ^2 will in fact be the value obtained from pooling the data of the n experiments and will correspond to $\nu = \Sigma\nu_i$ degrees of freedom. For example—

Three experiments designed to test a certain hypothesis yielded

$$\chi_1^2 = 9{\cdot}00 \text{ for } \nu_i = 5; \quad \chi_2^2 = 13{\cdot}2 \text{ for } \nu_2 = 10; \quad \chi_3^2 = 19{\cdot}1 \text{ for } \nu_3 = 15.$$

None of these on its own is significant at the 10% point, as the reader may verify. Their sum $\chi^2 = 41{\cdot}3$ for $\nu = 30$ d.f. *is*, however, significant at the 10% point. Thus we see that *the data of the three experiments, when pooled, give us less reason for confidence in our hypothesis than do those of any one of the experiments taken singly.*

(2) Next assume that a number of tests of significance (three, say) have yielded probabilities p_1, p_2, p_3. We know nothing more about the tests than this, yet—in view of the experience of (1)—we require to obtain some over-all probability corresponding to the pooled data.

Now any probability may be translated into a value of χ^2 for an arbitrarily chosen ν. But when $\nu = 2$, $\log_e p = -\frac{1}{2}\chi^2$. This is very convenient, for if χ_1^2, χ_2^2, χ_3^2 are the values of χ^2 for $\nu = 2$ corresponding to p_1, p_2, p_3 respectively, the pooled value of χ^2 is $-2(\log_e p_1 + \log_e p_2 + \log_e p_3)$ for $\nu = 2 + 2 + 2 = 6$ d.f. and the required pooled probability is obtained. For example :

$$\begin{aligned} p_1 &= 0{\cdot}150 & \log_e p_1 &= -\ 1{\cdot}897120 \\ p_2 &= 0{\cdot}250 & \log_e p_2 &= -\ 1{\cdot}386294 \\ p_3 &= 0{\cdot}350 & \log_e p_3 &= -\ 1{\cdot}049812 \\ & & & \overline{-\ 4{\cdot}333226} \\ & & & \times -2 \\ & & & \overline{8{\cdot}666452} \end{aligned}$$

The 5% point of χ^2 for $\nu = 6$ is 12·592
„ 10% „ „ $\nu = 6$ „ 10·645

We see then that the pooled probability is slightly less than 0·10. To find this more accurately, we notice that the pooled value of χ^2 exceeds the 10% point by 0·021, while the 5% point exceeds the 10% by 1·947.

Now [1] $\log_{10} 0{\cdot}10 = -1$ and $\log_{10} 0{\cdot}05 = \bar{2}{\cdot}69897 = -1{\cdot}30103$. The difference between these is 0·30103. Therefore the pooled value of χ^2 corresponds to

$$-1 - \frac{0{\cdot}021}{1{\cdot}947} \times 0{\cdot}30103 = -1{\cdot}0325 = \bar{2}{\cdot}9675.$$

The antilog of $\bar{2}{\cdot}9675$ is 0·0944. Interpolating thus, then, we find the required pooled probability to be 0·094, to three decimal places.

11.4. Some Examples of the Application of χ^2:

(*A*) *Theoretical Probabilities Given*

Twelve dice were thrown 26,306 *times and a* 5 *or a* 6 *was counted as a success. The number of successes in each throw was noted, with the following results* (*Weldon's data*) :

Number of successes.	*Frequency*	*Number of successes.*	*Frequency.*
0	185	6	3,067
1	1,149	7	1,331
2	3,265	8	403
3	5,475	9	105
4	6,114	10	18
5	5,194		
		Total	26,306

Is there evidence that the dice are biased ?

Treatment : We set up the hypothesis that the dice are unbiased. This means that the probability of throwing a 5 or a 6, a success, is $\frac{2}{6} = \frac{1}{3}$ and the probability of a failure, $\frac{2}{3}$. The theoretical frequency generating function on this hypothesis is then 26,306 $(\frac{2}{3} + \frac{1}{3}t)^{12}$.

[1] Either natural logarithms (base e) or common logarithms (base 10) may be used, since $\log_e x = \log_e 10 \times \log_{10} x$.

The estimated frequencies are then found to be (correct to the nearest integer):

Number of successes	0	1	2	3	4	5	6
Observed frequency (o) .	185	1,149	3,265	5,425	6,114	5,194	3,067
Theoretical frequency (ϵ)	203	1,217	3,345	5,576	6,273	5,018	2,927

Number of successes	7	8	9	10	Totals
Observed frequency (o) .	1,331	403	105	18	26,306
Theoretical frequency (ϵ)	1,254	392	87	14	26,306

Then
$$\chi^2 \simeq \Sigma \frac{(o - \epsilon)^2}{\epsilon} = \underline{38{\cdot}2}.$$

There are 11 classes and one restriction, namely, the size of the sample total, has been imposed. The number of degrees of freedom is thus 10.

The 1% level of χ^2 for $\nu = 10$ is 23·31. The value of χ^2 obtained is then highly significant and the hypothesis that the dice are unbiased is, therefore, rejected.

(*B*) *Theoretical Probabilities not Given*

The following table gives the distribution of the length, measured in cm., of 294 eggs of the Common Tern collected in one small coastal area:

Length (central values).	*Frequency.*	*Length (central values).*	*Frequency.*
3·5	1	4·2	54
3·6	1	4·3	34
3·7	6	4·4	12
3·8	20	4·5	6
3·9	35	4·6	1
4·0	53	4·7	2
4·1	69		

Test whether these results are consistent with the hypothesis that egg-length is normally distributed. (L.U.)

Treatment: We have first to fit a normal curve. This entails calculating the sample mean and sample variance. The sample mean is an unbiased estimate of the population mean. The sample variance may be taken to be an unbiased estimate of the population variance, since $N = 294$ is large.

We find by the usual methods that

$$\bar{x} = 4{\cdot}094\,;\quad s = 0{\cdot}184.$$

Estimated frequencies are obtained by the method of 5·6 and we find

Length	3·5	3·6	3·7	3·8	3·9	4·0	4·1
		8					
Observed frequency (o)	1	1	6	20	35	53	69
Estimated frequency (ϵ)	0·4	2·0	6·7	17·9	37·0	55·3	62·6
		9·1					

Length	4·2	4·3	4·4	4·5	4·6	4·7	Total
					9		
Observed frequency (o)	54	34	12	6	1	2	294
Estimated frequency (ϵ)	54·1	33·8	16·3	6·1	1·4	0·4	294
					7·9		

$$\chi^2 \simeq \Sigma \frac{(o - \epsilon)^2}{\epsilon} = \Sigma \frac{o^2}{\epsilon} - 2\Sigma o + \Sigma \epsilon;\ \text{but } N = \Sigma o = \Sigma \epsilon,$$

$$\therefore\ \chi^2 \simeq \Sigma \frac{o^2}{\epsilon} - N$$

NOTE: (1) This form is preferable where the estimated frequencies are not integers and, consequently, $o - \epsilon$ is not integral, since it removes the labour of squaring non-integers.

(2) *Because we derived the distribution of χ^2 on the assumption that Stirling's approximation for $n!$ held, i.e., that the class frequencies were sufficiently large, we group together into one class the first* 3 *classes with theoretical frequencies* <10 *and into another class the last* 3 *classes with frequencies* < 10. *This effectively reduces the number of classes to* 9. There is some divergence of opinion as to what constituted a

"low frequency" in this connection. Fisher (*Statistical Methods for Research Workers*) has used the criterion < 5; Aitken (*Statistical Mathematics*) prefers < 10; while Kendall (*Advanced Theory of Statistics*) favours < 20. The reader would do well to compromise with a somewhat elastic figure around 10.

$$\chi^2 \simeq \frac{8^2}{9\cdot1} + \frac{20^2}{17\cdot9} + \frac{35^2}{37\cdot0} + \frac{53^2}{55\cdot3} + \frac{69^2}{62\cdot6} + \frac{54^2}{54\cdot1} + \frac{34^2}{33\cdot8} + \frac{12^2}{16\cdot3} + \frac{9^2}{7\cdot9} - 294$$

$$= 296\cdot5 - 294 = 2\cdot5$$

We must now calculate the corresponding degrees of freedom. There are effectively 9 classes. One restriction results from the fact that the total observed and total estimated frequencies are made to agree. Also, from the sample data, we have estimated both the mean and variance of the theoretical parent population. We have then 3 constraints and, consequently there are $9 - 3 = 6$ degrees of freedom. Entering the table at $\nu = 6$, we find that the chance of such a value of χ^2 being obtained at $\nu = 6$ lies between $P = 0\cdot95$ and $P = 0\cdot50$ at approximately $P = 0\cdot82$. We conclude, therefore, that the fit is good but not unnaturally good, and, consequently, there is good reason to believe that egg-length is normally distributed.

WARNING: It may happen that the fit is *unnaturally good*. Suppose the value of χ^2 obtained was such that its probability of occurrence was $0\cdot999$. Fisher has pointed out that in this case if the hypothesis were true, such a value would occur only once in a thousand trials. He adds:

> "Generally such cases are demonstrably due to the use of inaccurate formulæ, but occasionally small values of χ^2 beyond the expected range do occur. . . . In these cases the hypothesis considered is as definitely disproved as if P had been $0\cdot001$" (*Statistical Methods for Research Workers*, 11th Edition, p. 81).

11.5. Independence, Homogeneity, Contingency Tables. When we use the χ^2-distribution to test goodness of fit we are testing for agreement between expectation and observation. Tests of independence and homogeneity also come under this general heading.

Suppose we have a sample of individuals which we can classify in two, or more, different ways. Very often we want to know whether these classifications are *independent*. For instance, we may wish to determine whether deficiency in a certain vitamin is a factor contributory to the development of a certain disease. We take a sample of individuals and classify them in two ways: into those deficient in the vitamin and those not. If there is no link-up between the disease and the vitamin deficiency (i.e., if the classifications are independent), then we calculate the expected number of individuals in each of the four sub-groups resulting from the classification : those deficient in the vitamin and diseased; those deficient in the vitamin and not diseased; those diseased but not deficient in the vitamin, and those neither diseased nor deficient in the vitamin. We thus obtain four observed frequencies and four expected frequencies. If the divergence between observation and expectation is greater than is probable (to some specified degree of probability) as a result of random sampling fluctuations alone, we shall have to reject the hypothesis and conclude that there is a link-up between vitamin-deficiency and the disease.

It is usual to set out the sample data in a *contingency table* (a table in which the frequencies are grouped according to some non-metrical criterion or criteria). In the present case, where we have two factors of classification, resulting in the division of the sample into two different ways, we have a 2×2 *contingency table*. Now suppose classification 1 divides the sample of N individuals into two classes, A and not-A, and classification 2 divides the sample into two classes, B and not-B. Let the observed frequency in the sub-class " A and B " be a; that in " not-A and B " be b; that in " not-B and A " be c; and that in " not-A and not-B " be d; we may display this in the 2×2 contingency table

	A.	Not-A.	Totals.
B . .	a	b	$a + b$
Not-B .	c	d	$c + d$
TOTALS .	$a + c$	$b + d$	$a + b + c + d = N$

On the assumption that the classifications are independent, we have, on the evidence of the sample data, and working from margin totals,

the probability of being an A $= (a + c)/N$;
" " " " a not-A $= (b + d)/N$;
" " " " a B $= (a + b)/N$;
" " " " a not-B $= (c + d)/N$.

Then the probability of being " A and B " will be $\dfrac{(a + c)}{N}$

$\times \frac{(a+b)}{N}$ and the expected frequency for this sub-class in a sample of N will be $\frac{(a+c)(a+b)}{N}$. Likewise, the probability of being " B and not-A " is $\frac{(a+b)(b+d)}{N}$, and the corresponding expected frequency $\frac{(a+b)(b+d)}{N}$. In this way we can set up a table of corresponding expected frequencies :

	A.	Not-A.
B . . .	$\frac{(a+c)(a+b)}{N}$	$\frac{(b+d)(a+b)}{N}$
Not-B . .	$\frac{(a+c)(c+d)}{N}$	$\frac{(b+d)(c+d)}{N}$

Providing the frequencies are not too small, we may then use the χ^2-distribution to test for agreement between observation and expectation, as we did in the goodness-of-fit tests, and this will, in fact, be testing our hypothesis of independence. χ^2, in this case, will be given by

$$\chi^2 \simeq \frac{\left[a - \frac{(a+c)(a+b)}{(a+b+c+d)}\right]^2}{\frac{(a+c)(a+b)}{(a+b+c+d)}} + \frac{\left[b - \frac{(b+d)(a+b)}{(a+b+c+d)}\right]^2}{\frac{(b+d)(a+b)}{(a+b+c+d)}}$$
$$+ \frac{\left[c - \frac{(a+c)(c+d)}{(a+b+c+d)}\right]^2}{\frac{(a+c)(c+d)}{(a+b+c+d)}} + \frac{\left[d - \frac{(b+d)(c+d)}{(a+b+c+d)}\right]^2}{\frac{(b+d)(c+d)}{(a+b+c+d)}}$$
$$\simeq \frac{(ad-bc)^2}{N}\left[\frac{1}{(a+c)(a+b)} + \frac{1}{(b+d)(a+b)} + \frac{1}{(a+c)(c+d)} + \frac{1}{(b+d)(c+d)}\right]$$
$$\simeq \frac{(ad-bc)^2}{N} \cdot \frac{N^2}{(a+b)(a+c)(c+d)(b+d)}$$

or

$$\chi^2 \simeq \frac{(ad-bc)^2(a+b+c+d)}{(a+b)(a+c)(c+d)(b+d)} \quad . \quad (11.5.1)$$

It remains to determine the appropriate number of degrees of freedom for this value of χ^2. We recall that the expected values are calculated from the marginal totals of the sample. Directly then we calculate one value, say that for " A and B ", the others are fixed and may be written in by subtraction from the marginal totals. Thus the observed values can differ from the expected values by only 1 degree of freedom. Consequently

for a 2×2 *contingency table, the number of degrees of freedom for* χ^2 *is one.*

Worked Example : *A certain type of surgical operation can be performed either with a local anæsthetic or with a general anæsthetic. Results are given below :*

	Alive.	*Dead.*
Local . .	511	24
General . .	173	21

Test for any difference in the mortality rates associated with the different types of anæsthetic. (R.S.S.)

Treatment : Our hypothesis is that there is no difference in the mortality rates associated with the two types of anæsthetic. The contingency table is :

	Alive.	Dead.	Totals.
Local . .	511	24	535
General . .	173	21	194
TOTALS . .	684	45	729

Using the marginal totals, the expected values are (correct to the nearest integer) :

	Alive.	Dead.	Totals.
Local . .	$\frac{684 \times 535}{729} = 502$	33	535
General . .	182	12	194
TOTAL . .	684	45	729

Accordingly, $\chi^2 \simeq 9{\cdot}85$ for $\nu = 1$ d.f. The probability of this value of χ^2 is $0{\cdot}0017$ approximately. The value of χ^2 obtained is, therefore, highly significant, and we conclude that there *is* a difference between the mortality rates associated with the two types of anæsthetics.

Suppose we were to regard the frequencies in the general 2×2 contingency table to represent two samples distributed according to some factor of classification (being A or not-A) into 2 classes, thus :

	A.	Not-A.	Totals.
Sample I .	a	b	$a + b$
Sample II .	c	d	$c + d$
TOTALS . .	$a + c$	$b + d$	$a + b + c + d (= N)$

We now ask : " On the evidence provided by the data, can these samples be regarded as drawn from the same population ? " Assuming that they are from the same population, the probability that an individual falls into the class A, say, will be the same for both samples. Again basing our estimates on the marginal totals, this probability will be $(a + c)/N$ and the estimated or expected frequency on this hypothesis of the A's in the first sample will be $(a + c) \times (a + b)/N$. In this way we calculate the expected frequencies in both classes for the two samples, and, if the divergence between expectation and observation is greater to some specified degree of probability than the hypothesis of homogeneity demands, it will be revealed by a test which is mathematically identical with that for independence.

11.6. Homegeneity Test for 2 × *k* Table. *The individuals in two very large populations can be classed into one or other of* k *categories. A random sample (small compared to the size of the population) is drawn from each population, and the following frequencies are observed in the categories :*

Category.	1 2 . . . t . . . k	Total.
Sample 1 . .	n_{11} n_{12} . . . n_{1t} . . . n_{1k}	N_1
Sample 2 . .	n_{21} n_{22} . . . n_{2t} . . . n_{2k}	N_2

Devise a suitable form of the χ^2-criterion for testing the hypothesis that the probability that an individual falls into the tth *category* ($t = 1, 2, \ldots k$) *is the same in the two populations. Derive the appropriate number of degrees of freedom for* χ^2. (L.U.)

This is a homogeneity problem, for the question could well be reformulated to ask whether the two samples could have come from the same population.

On the assumption that the probability that an individual falls into the tth class is the same for the two populations, we use the marginal totals, $n_{1t} + n_{2t}$, ($t = 1, 2, \ldots k$), to estimate these probabilities. Thus our estimate of the probability of an individual falling into the tth class, on this assumption, is $(n_{1t} + n_{2t})/(N_1 + N_2)$. The expected frequency, on this assumption, in the tth class of the 1st Sample is therefore $N_1(n_{1t} + n_{2t})/(N_1 + N_2)$ and that for the same class of the 2nd Sample is $N_2(n_{1t} + n_{2t})/(N_1 + N_2)$. Consequently,

$$\chi^2 \doteq \sum_{t=1}^{k} \left\{\left[n_{1t} - \frac{N_1}{N_1 + N_2}(n_{1t} + n_{2t})\right]^2 \Big/ \frac{N_1(n_{1t} + n_{2t})}{N_1 + N_2} + \left[n_{2t} - \frac{N_2}{N_1 + N_2}(n_{1t} + n_{2t})\right]^2 \Big/ \frac{N_2(n_{1t} + n_{2t})}{N_1 + N_2}\right\}$$

$$\doteq \sum_{t=1}^{k} \left\{\frac{[N_2 n_{1t} - N_1 n_{2t}]^2}{N_1(N_1 + N_2)(n_{1t} + n_{2t})} + \frac{[N_1 n_{2t} - N_2 n_{1t}]^2}{N_2(N_1 + N_2)(n_{1t} + n_{2t})}\right\}$$

or

$$\chi^2 \doteq \sum_{t=1}^{k} \frac{(N_2 n_{1t} - N_1 n_{2t})^2}{N_1 N_2 (n_{1t} + n_{2t})} = N_1 N_2 \sum_{t=1}^{k} \frac{(n_{1t}/N_1 - n_{2t}/N_2)^2}{(n_{1t} + n_{2t})} \quad (11.6.1)$$

How many degrees of freedom must be associated with this value of χ^2? To construct the table of expected frequencies, we must know the grand total, one of the sample totals and $k - 1$ of the class totals. There are, therefore, $1 + 1 + k - 1 = k + 1$ equations of constraint, and, since there are $2k$ theoretical frequencies to be calculated, $\nu = 2k - (k + 1) = k - 1$ degrees of freedom.

11.7. $h \times k$ Table. In the case of a $h \times k$ table, we follow exactly the same principles, whether we are testing for independence or homogeneity. To calculate the appropriate number of degrees of freedom, we note that there are $h \times k$ theoretical frequencies to be calculated. Given the grand total, we require $h - 1$ and $k - 1$ of the marginal totals to be given also. There are thus $h + k - 1$ equations of constraint, and consequently $\nu = kh - (h + k - 1) = (h - 1)(k - 1)$ degrees of freedom.

Worked Example : *A Ministry of Labour Memorandum on Carbon Monoxide Poisoning* (1945) *gives the following data on accidents due to gassing by carbon monoxide* :

	1941.	1942.	1943.	*Totals.*
At blast furnaces . .	24	20	19	63
At gas producers . .	28	34	41	103
At gas ovens and works .	26	26	10	62
In distribution and use of gas	80	108	123	311
Miscellaneous sources .	68	51	32	151
	226	239	225	690

Is there significant association between the site of the accident and the year ?

Treatment : On the assumption that there is no association between the origin of an accident and the year, the probability of an accident in any given class will be constant for that class.

The probability of an accident at a blast furnace is estimated from the data to be $(24 + 20 + 19)/(690) = 63/690$. Hence the expected frequency of accidents for this source in a yearly total of 226 will be $63 \times 226/690 = 20{\cdot}64$.

Proceeding in this way, we set up the following table :

	1941.		1942.		1943.	
	o.	ε.	o.	ε.	o.	ε.
Blast furnaces .	24	20·64	20	21·82	19	20·54
Gas producers .	28	33·74	34	35·68	41	33·59
Gas-works and coke ovens .	26	20·31	26	21·48	10	20·22
Gas use and distribution .	80	101·86	108	107·72	123	101·41
Miscellaneous .	68	49·46	51	52·30	32	49·27

We find that $\chi^2 \simeq 34{\cdot}22$ for $\nu = (5 - 1)(3 - 1) = 8$ d.f. and the table shows that this is a highly significant value. We, therefore, reject our hypothesis of no association between source of accident and year, i.e., the probability of an accident at a given source is not constant through the years considered.

11.8. Correction for Continuity. The χ^2-distribution is derived from the multinomial distribution on the assumption that the expected frequencies in the cells are sufficiently large to justify the use of Stirling's approximation to n! When, in some cells or classes, these frequencies have fallen below 10, we have adjusted matters by pooling the classes with such low frequencies. If c such cells are pooled, the number of degrees of freedom for χ^2 is reduced by $c - 1$. If, however, we have a 2×2 table with low expected frequencies, no pooling is possible since $\nu = 1$ for a 2×2 table. We have, therefore, to tackle the problem from some other angle. In fact, we may either modify the table and then apply the χ^2-test or we may abandon approximate methods and calculate from first principles the exact probability of any given set of frequencies in the cells for the given marginal totals. In the present section we shall consider the method by which we "correct" the observed frequencies to compensate somewhat for the fact that, whereas the distribution of observed frequencies is necessarily discrete, that of the χ^2-distribution is essentially continuous. In the course of treatment of the example in the next section we shall develop and illustrate the "exact" method.

Suppose we toss an unbiased coin ten times. The expected number of heads is $\frac{1}{2} \times 10 = 5$ and the probability of obtaining just r heads is the coefficient of t^r in the expansion of $(\frac{1}{2}t + \frac{1}{2})^{10}$. We have:

The probability of 10 heads, $p(10H) = (\frac{1}{2})^{10} = 0{\cdot}00099$. This is also the probability of 0 heads (or 10 tails). Therefore the probability of either 10H or 0H is $2 \times 0{\cdot}00099 = 0{\cdot}00198$.

Using the χ^2-distribution, the value of χ^2 for 10 heads or 0 heads is

$$\chi^2 \simeq \frac{(10 - 5)^2}{5} + \frac{(0 - 5)^2}{5} = 10$$

and this value is attained or exceeded for $\nu = 1$ with a probability of $0{\cdot}00157$. Half this, $0{\cdot}000785$, gives the χ^2-estimate of the probability of just 10 heads.

The probability of 9 heads is $10 \times 0{\cdot}00099 = 0{\cdot}0099$ and hence the probability of 9 or more heads in 10 tosses is $0{\cdot}00099 + 0{\cdot}0099 = 0{\cdot}01089$, while the probability of 9 or more heads and 1 or less tails is $2 \times 0{\cdot}01089 = 0{\cdot}02178$.

The corresponding value of $\chi^2 \simeq \dfrac{(9 - 5)^2}{5} + \dfrac{(1 - 5)^2}{5} = 6{\cdot}4$

and, for $\nu = 1$, the probability of this value being attained or exceeded is $0{\cdot}1141$. Half this value, $0{\cdot}05705$, gives us the χ^2-estimate of the probability of obtaining 9 or more heads.

We can see that the χ^2-estimates are already beginning to diverge quite considerably from the "exact" values. The problem is: can we improve matters by finding out why this should be?

We recall that when $\nu = 1$, the χ^2-distribution reduces to the positive half of a normal distribution. The area of the tail of this distribution to the right of the ordinate corresponding to a given deviation, r, of observed from expected frequency, gives therefore a normal-distribution approximation to the probability of a deviation attaining or exceeding this given deviation, *irrespective of sign*. However, in the case we are considering, the symmetrical binomial histogram is composed of frequency cells based on unit class intervals, the *central values* of the intervals being the various values of r; the sum of the areas

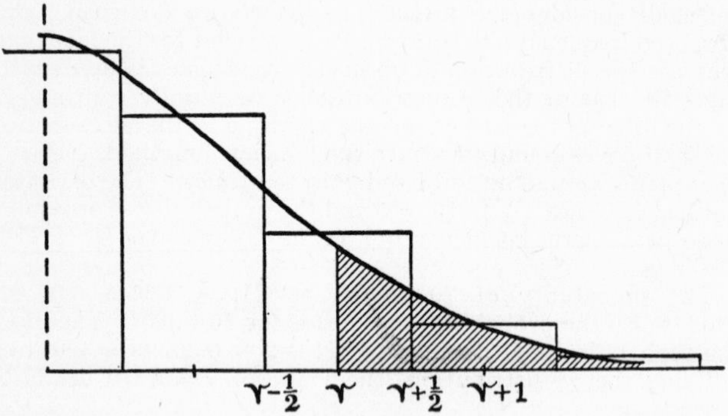

FIG. 11.8.

of the cells corresponding to the values r, $r + 1$, $r + 2$, etc., gives the exact probability of a deviation $\geqslant + r$. When, however, the frequencies in the tail are small, we are taking, for the continuous curve, the area to the right of r, but for the histogram the area to the right of $r - \frac{1}{2}$ (see Fig. 11.8). *Clearly a closer approximation would be obtained if we calculated χ^2 for values not of r, the deviation of observed from expected frequency, but for values of $|r - \frac{1}{2}|$, i.e., if we "correct" the observed frequencies by making them $\frac{1}{2}$ nearer expectation, we shall obtain a "better" value of χ^2.*

This is *Yates' correction for continuity* for small expected frequencies. Its justification is based on the assumption that the theoretical frequency distribution is a symetrical binomial distribution ($p = q = \frac{1}{2}$). If this is not so, the theoretical distribution is skew, and no simple adjustment has been discovered as yet to offset this. However, if p is near $\frac{1}{2}$, the correction should still be made when the expected frequencies are small, for the resulting value of χ^2 yields a probability definitely closer to the "exact" value than that we obtain when the correction is not made. This is brought out in the following example.

11.9. Worked Example.

In experiments on the immunisation of cattle from tuberculosis, the following results were obtained:

	Died of T.B. or very seriously affected.	*Unaffected or slightly affected.*	*Totals.*
Inoculated with vaccine .	6	13	19
Not inoculated or inoculated with control media	8	3	11
Totals . . .	14	16	30

Show that for this table, on the hypothesis that inoculation and susceptibility to tuberculosis are independent, $\chi^2 = 4{\cdot}75$, $P = 0{\cdot}029$; *with a correction for continuity, the corresponding probability is* 0·072; *and that by the exact method,* $P = 0{\cdot}071$.

(*Data from* Report on the Sphalinger Experiments in Northern Ireland, 1931–1934. *H.M.S.O.*, 1934, *quoted in Kendall,* Advanced Theory of Statistics, I).

Treatment: (1) On the hypothesis of independence—i.e., that the probability of death is independent of inoculation—the probability of death is $\frac{14}{30}$. Therefore the expected frequencies are:

$\dfrac{14 \times 19}{30} = 8{\cdot}87$	$10{\cdot}13$
$5{\cdot}13$	$5{\cdot}87$

Each observed frequency deviates from the corresponding expected frequency by $\pm 2{\cdot}87$. Hence

$$\chi^2 \simeq (2{\cdot}87)^2 \left[\frac{1}{5{\cdot}13} + \frac{1}{5{\cdot}87} + \frac{1}{8{\cdot}87} + \frac{1}{10{\cdot}13}\right]$$
$$\simeq 8{\cdot}237 \times 0{\cdot}577 = \underline{4{\cdot}75}$$

and for $\nu = 1$ the probability of χ^2 attaining or exceeding this value is <u>0·029.</u> This figure, it must be emphasised, is the probability of a proportion of deaths to unaffected cases of 6 : 13 or lower in a sample of 19 inoculated animals *and* of a proportion of 8 : 3 or higher in a sample of 11 animals not inoculated, on the hypothesis of independence, i.e., on the assumption that the expected proportion for either sample is 14 : 16.

(2) The observed frequency with the continuity correction applied are :

6·5	12·5
7·5	3·5

and, consequently $\chi^2 \simeq (2{\cdot}37)^2 \times 0{\cdot}577 = \underline{3{\cdot}24}$, yielding, for $\nu = 1$, $\underline{P = 0{\cdot}072}$.

(3) We must now discuss the method of finding the exact probability of any particular array of cell frequencies for a 2 × 2 table. Consider the table

a	b	$(a + b)$
c	d	$(c + d)$
$(a + c)$	$(b + d)$	$(a + b + c + d) = N$, say.

First, we consider the number of ways in which such a table can be set up with the margin totals given from a sample of N. From N items we can select $a + c$ items in $\binom{N}{a+c}$ ways, when $b + d$ items remain, while from N items we may select $a + b$ items in $\binom{N}{a+b}$ ways, with $c + d$ items remaining. Therefore, the total number of ways of setting up such a table with the marginal totals as above is

$$\binom{N}{a+c}\binom{N}{a+b} = \frac{(N!)^2}{(a+c)!\,(b+d)!\,(a+b)!\,(c+d)!} = n_1, \text{ say.}$$

Secondly, we ask in how many ways we can complete the 4 cells in the body of the table with N items. Clearly this is the number of ways in which we can divide the N items into groups of a items of one kind, b items of a second kind, c items of a third kind and d items of a fourth kind, where $N = a + b + c + d$. But (2.10) we know this to be

$$\frac{N!}{a!\,b!\,c!\,d!} = n_2, \text{ say.}$$

Consequently the probability of any particular arrangement, $P(a, b, c, d)$, will be given by

$$P(a, b, c, d) = \frac{n_2}{n_1} = \frac{(a+b)!\,(c+d)!\,(a+c)!\,(b+d)!}{N!\,a!\,b!\,c!\,d!} \quad . \quad (11.9.1)$$

How shall we use this result to solve our present problem?

We are interested here, we emphasise, in the probability of obtaining a proportion of deaths to unaffected cases of 6 : 13 or lower in a sample of 19 inoculated animals and of obtaining a proportion of deaths to unaffected cases of 8 : 3 or higher in a sample of 11 animals not inoculated. In other words, we are interested in the probability of each of the following arrays :

$$\begin{vmatrix} 6 & 13 \\ 8 & 3 \end{vmatrix}, \begin{vmatrix} 5 & 14 \\ 9 & 2 \end{vmatrix}, \begin{vmatrix} 4 & 15 \\ 10 & 1 \end{vmatrix}, \begin{vmatrix} 3 & 16 \\ 11 & 0 \end{vmatrix}$$

But it will be seen immediately that the probability of obtaining a 6 : 13 ratio among inoculated animals is also precisely that of obtaining a ratio of 8 : 3 among animals not inoculated. Hence the *required probability will be twice that of the sum of the probabilities of these* 4 *arrays.*

The probability of $\begin{vmatrix} 3 & 16 \\ 11 & 0 \end{vmatrix}$ is, (by 11.9.1),

$$\frac{19!\,16!\,14!\,11!}{30!\,16!\,11!\,3!\,0!} = \frac{19!\,14!}{30!\,3!}.$$

We may evaluate this by means of a table of log factorials (e.g., *Chambers' Shorter Six-Figure Mathematical Tables.* We have

$$\begin{array}{ll} \log 19! = 17{\cdot}085095 & \log 30! = 32{\cdot}423660 \\ \log 14! = 10{\cdot}940408 & \log\ 3! = \ \ 0{\cdot}778151 \\ \hline \qquad\quad 28{\cdot}025503 & \qquad\quad 33{\cdot}201811 \end{array}$$

$28{\cdot}025503 - 33{\cdot}201811 = \bar{6}{\cdot}823692$ and the antilog of this is

$$P(3, 16, 11, 0) = \underline{0{\cdot}00000666}$$

$$P(4, 15, 10, 1) = \frac{19!\,16!\,14!\,11!}{30!\,15!\,10!\,4!\,1!} = \frac{16{\cdot}11}{4{\cdot}1} P(3, 16, 11, 0)$$
$$= 44 \times 0{\cdot}00000666 = \underline{0{\cdot}00029304}$$

Similarly,

$$P(5, 14, 9, 2) = \frac{15{\cdot}10}{5{\cdot}2} P(4, 15, 10, 1)$$
$$= 15 \times 0{\cdot}00029304 = \underline{0{\cdot}00439560}$$

Finally,

$$P(6, 13, 8, 3) = \frac{14{\cdot}9}{6{\cdot}3} = P(5, 14, 9, 2)$$
$$= 7 \times 0{\cdot}00439560 = \underline{0{\cdot}03076920}$$

The required probability then is $2 \times 0{\cdot}03546450 = \underline{0{\cdot}07092900}$.

11.10. χ^2-determination of the Confidence Limits of the Variance of a Normal Population. We conclude with an example of the way the χ^2-distribution may be used to give exact results when the observed data are not frequencies.

Let us draw a small sample of $N (< 30)$ from a normal population. If $NS^2 = \sum_{i=1}^{N} (x_i - \bar{x})^2$ and σ^2 is the population variance, $NS^2/\sigma^2 = \sum_{i=1}^{N} (x_i - \bar{x})^2/\sigma^2$ and is thus distributed like χ^2 with $N - 1$ degrees of freedom (the one constraint being $\sum_{i=1}^{N} x_i = N\bar{x}$). Our problem is this :

Given N and S^2, to find the 95% confidence limits for σ^2.

Since NS^2/σ^2 is distributed like χ^2, the value of NS^2/σ^2 that will be exceeded with a probability of 0·05 will be the 0·05 point of the χ^2-distribution for $\nu = N - 1$. Let ${\chi_{0\cdot05}}^2$ be this value. Then the *lower* 95% confidence limit required, on the basis of the sample information, will be $NS^2/{\chi_{0\cdot05}}^2$. Likewise the *upper* 95% confidence limit will be $NS^2/{\chi_{0\cdot95}}^2$, where ${\chi_{0\cdot95}}^2$ is the 0·95 point of the χ^2-distribution for $\nu = N - 1$.

Worked Example : *A sample of* 8 *from a normal population yields an unbiased estimate of the population variance of* 4·4. *Find the* 95% *confidence limits for* σ.

Treatment: We have $4\cdot4 = 8S^2/(8 - 1)$ or $8S^2 = 30\cdot8$. The 0·95 and 0·05 points of the χ^2-distribution for $\nu = 7$ are 2·17 and 14·07 respectively. Therefore the lower and upper 95% confidence limits for σ^2 are, respectively,

$$30\cdot8/14\cdot07 = \underline{2\cdot19} \text{ and } 30\cdot8/2\cdot17 = \underline{13\cdot73}.$$

The corresponding limits for σ are $(2\cdot19)^{\frac{1}{2}} = \underline{1\cdot48}$ and $(13\cdot73)^{\frac{1}{2}} = \underline{3\cdot69}$.

EXERCISES ON CHAPTER ELEVEN

1. The Registrars-General give the following estimates of children under five at mid-1947 :

	England and Wales.	Scotland.	Total.
Males . . .	1,813,000	228,000	2,041,000
Females . . .	1,723,000	221,000	1,944,000
TOTAL . . .	3,536,000	449,000	3,985,000

On the assumption that there is no difference between the proportion of males to females in the two regions, calculate the probability that a child under five will be a girl. Hence find the expected number of girls under five in Scotland and say whether the proportion is significantly high. (L.U.)

2. The following data give N, the number of days on which rainfall exceeded R in. at a certain station over a period of a year :

R .	0·00	0·04	0·10	0·20	0·50	1·00
N .	296	246	187	119	30	3

Test by means of χ^2 whether the data are consistent with the law $\log_{10} N = 2{\cdot}47 - 1{\cdot}98R$. Is the " fit " too good? (R.S.S.)

3. The following information was obtained in a sample of 50 small general shops :

	Shops in		Total
	Urban Districts.	Rural Districts.	
Owned by man .	17	18	35
,, women .	3	12	15
TOTAL . . .	20	30	50

Can it be said that there are relatively more women owners of small general shops in rural than in urban districts? (L.U.)

4. A certain hypothesis is tested by three similar experiments. These gave $\chi^2 = 11{\cdot}9$ for $\nu = 6$, $\chi^2 = 14{\cdot}2$ for $\nu = 8$ and $\chi^2 = 18{\cdot}3$ for $\nu = 11$. Show that the three experiments together provide more justification for rejecting the hypothesis than any one experiment alone.

5. Apply the χ^2 test of goodness of fit to the two theoretical distributions obtained in 4.7., p. 72.

Solutions

1. 219,000. Yes. 2. Far too good, $\chi^2 < 0{\cdot}02$ for $\nu = 5$.
3. No.

APPENDIX:

CONTINUOUS BIVARIATE DISTRIBUTIONS

Suppose that we have a sample of N value-pairs (x_i, y_j) from some continuous bivariate parent population. Across the scatter diagram draw the lines

$$x = x + \tfrac{1}{2}\Delta x,\ x = x - \tfrac{1}{2}\Delta x,\ y = y + \tfrac{1}{2}\Delta y$$

and

$$y = y - \tfrac{1}{2}\Delta y$$

(Fig. A.1). Consider the rectangle $ABCD$ of area $\Delta x \Delta y$ about

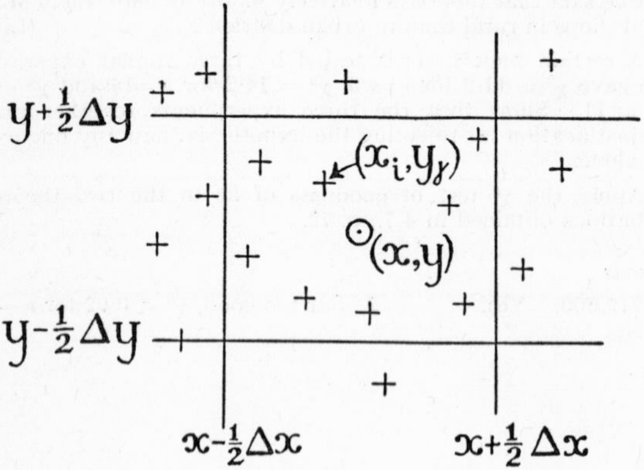

FIG. A.1.

the point (x, y). Within this rectangle will fall all those points representing value pairs (x_i, y_j) for which

$$x - \tfrac{1}{2}\Delta x < x_i < x + \tfrac{1}{2}\Delta x$$

and

$$y - \tfrac{1}{2}\Delta y < y_j < y + \tfrac{1}{2}\Delta y$$

Let the number of these points be ΔN. The proportion of points inside the rectangle to the total number N in the diagram is then $\Delta N/N = \Delta p$, say. Δp, the relative frequency of the value-pairs falling within the rectangle $ABCD$, will clearly

< 1. The average, or mean, relative frequency per unit area within this rectangle is $\Delta p/\Delta A$, where $\Delta A = \Delta x \,.\, \Delta y$. If we now increase N, the sample size, indefinitely and, simultaneously, reduce Δx and Δy, we may write

$$\underset{\substack{\Delta x \to 0 \\ \Delta y \to 0}}{\text{Limit}} \; \Delta p/\Delta A = dp/dA,$$

which is now the *relative-frequency density at* (x, y) of the continuous parent population. In this parent population, however, the values of the variates are distributed according to some law, which may be expressed by saying that the relative-frequency density at (x, y) is a certain function of x and y, $\phi(x, y)$, say. Thus

$$dp/dA = \phi(x, y) \text{ or, in differentials,}$$
$$dp = \phi(x, y)dA = \phi(x, y)dxdy \quad . \quad . \quad \text{(A.1)}$$

Here dp is the relative-frequency with which the variate x assumes a value between $x \pm \frac{1}{2}dx$, while, simultaneously, the variate y assumes a value between $y \pm \frac{1}{2}dy$. But, since the relative frequency of an event E converges stochastically, as the number of occurrences of its context-event tends to infinity, to the probability of E's occurrence in a single occurrence of its context-event, we may say :

> dp is the probability that the variate x will assume a value between $x \pm \frac{1}{2}dx$, while, simultaneously, the variate y assumes a value between $y \pm \frac{1}{2}dy$. Then $\phi(x, y)$ is the *joint probability function of* x, y or the *joint probability density of* x, y.

Now let the range of possible values of x be $a \geqslant x \geqslant b$ and that of y, $c \geqslant y \geqslant d$; then, since both x and y must each assume some value

$$\int_{x=b}^{x=a} \int_{y=d}^{y=c} \phi(x, y)dxdy = 1$$

or, if for values outside $a \geqslant x \geqslant b$, $c \geqslant y \geqslant d$, we define $\phi(x, y)$ to be zero, we may write

$$\int_{-\infty}^{+\infty} \int_{-\infty}^{+\infty} \phi(x, y)dxdy = 1 \quad . \quad . \quad \text{(A.2)}$$

It follows that the probability that $X_1 \geqslant x \geqslant X_2$ and $Y_1 \geqslant y \geqslant Y_2$ is

$$P(X_1 \geqslant x \geqslant X_2,\ Y_1 \geqslant y \geqslant Y_2) = \int_{X_2}^{X_1} \int_{Y_2}^{Y_1} \phi(x, y)dxdy \qquad \text{(A.3)}$$

If x and y are statistically independent, i.e., if the probability, $dp_1 = \phi_1(x)dx$, of x taking a value between $x \pm \frac{1}{2}dx$ is independent of the value taken by y, and if the probability, $dp_2 = \phi_2(y)dy$, of y taking a value between $y \pm \frac{1}{2}dy$ is independent of the value taken by x, by the law of multiplication of probabilities we have

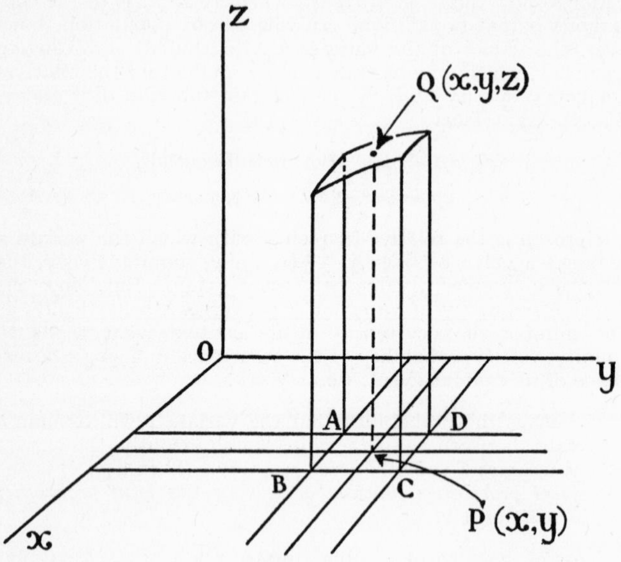

FIG. A.2.

$$\phi(x, y) = \phi_1(x) \cdot \phi_2(y) \quad . \quad . \quad . \quad \text{(A.4)}$$

and all double integrals resolve into the product of two single integrals. For instance (A.3) becomes

$$P(X_1 \geqslant x \geqslant X_2,\ Y_1 \geqslant y \geqslant Y_2) = \int_{X_2}^{X_1} \phi_1(x)dx \,.\int_{Y_2}^{Y_1} \phi_2(y)dy$$

Clearly variates for which (A.4) holds are *uncorrelated.*

In Fig. A.2 let the rectangle $ABCD$ in the xOy plane be formed by the lines $x = x \pm \frac{1}{2}dx$, $y = y \pm \frac{1}{2}dy$. At every point P, (x, y), in this plane for which $\phi(x, y)$ is defined, erect a perpendicular, z, of length $\phi(x, y)$. Then as x and y vary over the xOy plane, Q generates a surface $z = \phi(x, y)$, the *probability-* or *correlation-surface.* dp, the probability that x lies within $x \pm \frac{1}{2}dx$ and y within $y \pm \frac{1}{2}dy$, is then represented by the volume of the right prism on $ABCD$ as base below the correlation-surface.

Moments. Let the ΔN values of (x, y) lying within the rectangle $\Delta x \Delta y$ of the scatter diagram of our sample of N value-pairs from a continuous bivariate population be considered as " grouped " in this class-rectangle. Their *product moment of order* r, s about $x = 0$, $y = 0$, m_{rs}' is given by

$$m_{rs}' = \frac{\Delta N}{N} x^r y^s = \frac{\Delta p}{\Delta A} x^r y^s \Delta A$$

For the corresponding class rectangle of the continuous parent population, we have, accordingly,

$$\mu_{rs}' = \frac{dp}{dA} x^r y^s dA = \phi(x, y) x^r y^s dx dy ;$$

therefore, for the entire parent distribution,

$$\mu_{rs}' = \int_{-\infty}^{+\infty} \int_{-\infty}^{+\infty} \phi(x, y) x^r y^s dx dy \quad . \quad \text{(A.5)}$$

In particular:

$$\left.\begin{aligned}
\bar{x} \equiv \mu_{10}' &= \int_{-\infty}^{+\infty} \int_{-\infty}^{+\infty} x\phi(x, y) dx dy ; \\
\bar{y} \equiv \mu_{01}' &= \int_{-\infty}^{+\infty} \int_{-\infty}^{+\infty} y\phi(x, y) dx dy ; \\
\mu_{20}' &= \int_{-\infty}^{+\infty} \int_{-\infty}^{+\infty} x^2\phi(x, y) dx dy ; \\
\mu_{02}' &= \int_{-\infty}^{+\infty} \int_{-\infty}^{+\infty} y^2\phi(x, y) dx dy ; \\
\mu_{11}' &= \int_{-\infty}^{+\infty} \int_{-\infty}^{+\infty} xy\phi(x, y) dx dy
\end{aligned}\right\} \quad \text{(A.6)}$$

The corresponding moments about the mean $(\bar{x}, \bar{y})$ of the distribution are:

$$\left.\begin{aligned} \sigma_x^2 \equiv \mu_{20} &= \int_{-\infty}^{+\infty}\int_{-\infty}^{+\infty} (x - \bar{x})^2\phi(x, y)dxdy; \\ \sigma_y^2 \equiv \mu_{02} &= \int_{-\infty}^{+\infty}\int_{-\infty}^{+\infty} (y - \bar{y})\phi(x, y)dxdy; \\ \text{cov}(x, y) \equiv \sigma_{xy} &= \int_{-\infty}^{+\infty}\int_{-\infty}^{+\infty} (x - \bar{x})(y - \bar{y})\phi(x, y)dxdy \end{aligned}\right\} \quad \text{(A.7)}$$

Also, since $\int_{-\infty}^{+\infty}\int_{-\infty}^{+\infty} \phi(x, y)dxdy = 1$ (A.2), we have:

$$\sigma_x^2 \equiv \mu_{20} = \int_{-\infty}^{+\infty}\int_{-\infty}^{+\infty} (x^2 - 2\bar{x}x + \bar{x}^2)\phi(x, y)dxdy$$

$$= \int_{-\infty}^{+\infty}\int_{-\infty}^{+\infty} x^2\phi(x, y)dxdy - 2\bar{x}\int_{-\infty}^{+\infty}\int_{-\infty}^{+\infty} x\phi(x, y)dxdy + \bar{x}^2$$

or $\qquad \sigma_x^2 \equiv \mu_{20} = \mu_{20}' - \bar{x}^2$

and likewise $\qquad \sigma_y^2 \equiv \mu_{02} = \mu_{02}' - \bar{y}^2 \qquad \ldots \quad$ (A.8)

Finally,

$$\sigma_{xy} \equiv \mu_{11} = \int_{-\infty}^{+\infty}\int_{-\infty}^{+\infty} (xy - x\bar{y} - \bar{x}y + \bar{x}\bar{y})\phi(x, y)dxdy$$

$$= \int_{-\infty}^{+\infty}\int_{-\infty}^{+\infty} xy\phi(x, y)dxdy - \bar{y}\int_{-\infty}^{+\infty}\int_{-\infty}^{+\infty} x\phi(x, y)dxdy$$

$$- \bar{x}\int_{-\infty}^{+\infty}\int_{-\infty}^{+\infty} y\phi(x, y)dxdy + \bar{x}\bar{y}$$

$$= \mu_{11}' - \bar{y}\bar{x} - \bar{x}\bar{y} + \bar{x}\bar{y}$$

i.e., $\qquad \sigma_{xy} \equiv \mu_{11} = \mu_{11}' - \bar{x}\bar{y} \qquad \ldots \quad$ (A.9)

The *moment-generating function*, $M(t_1, t_2)$ of a bivariate continuous distribution is defined to be

$$M(t_1, t_2) \equiv \mathcal{E}(e^{xt_1 + yt_2})$$
$$= \int_{-\infty}^{+\infty} \int_{-\infty}^{+\infty} \exp(xt_1 + yt_2)\phi(x, y)dxdy \quad \text{(A.10)}$$

As the reader should verify, the moment of order r, s about $x = 0$, $y = 0$ is given by the coefficient of $t_1{}^r t_2{}^s/r!\,s!$ in the expansion of $M(t_1, t_2)$.

Regression and Correlation. Since the probability, dp, that x lies between $x \pm \frac{1}{2}dx$, when y lies between $y \pm \frac{1}{2}dy$ is $dp = \phi(x, y)dxdy$, the probability that x lies between $x \pm \frac{1}{2}dx$ when y takes *any* value in its range is

$$\int_{-\infty}^{+\infty} (\phi(x, y)dx)dy = dx \int_{-\infty}^{+\infty} \phi(x, y)dy$$

Now $\int_{-\infty}^{+\infty} \phi(x, y)dy$ is a function of x, $\phi_1(x)$, say, and is the relative frequency of the y's in the x-array. Likewise $\int_{-\infty}^{+\infty} \phi(x, y)dx \equiv \phi_2(y)$, is the probability that y lies between $y \pm \frac{1}{2}dy$ for any value of x, i.e., the relative frequency of the x's in the y-array.

The mean of the y's in the x-array, $\bar{y}_x$, is, then, given by

$$\phi_1(x) \,.\, \bar{y}_x = \int_{-\infty}^{+\infty} y\phi(x, y)\,dy$$

or

$$\bar{y}_x = \int_{-\infty}^{+\infty} \frac{y\phi(x, y)}{\phi_1(x)}\,dy$$

Likewise,

$$\bar{x}_y = \int_{-\infty}^{+\infty} \frac{x\phi(x, y)}{\phi_2(y)}\,dx \quad . \quad . \quad . \quad \text{(A.11)}$$

Exercise: *Show that the variance of the y's in the x-array,* $(\sigma_y{}^2)_x$, *is*

$$\int_{-\infty}^{+\infty} \frac{(y - \bar{y}_x)^2\phi(x, y)}{\phi_1(x)}\,dy$$

Now the right-hand side of (A.11) is a function of x, and, therefore,

The equation of the curve of means of the x-arrays, i.e., the curve of regression of y on x is

$$y = \int_{-\infty}^{+\infty} \frac{y\phi(x, y)}{\phi_1(x)} dy \quad . \quad . \quad . \quad \text{(A.12)}$$

while the *regression equation of x on y is*

$$x = \int_{-\infty}^{+\infty} \frac{x\phi(x, y)}{\phi_2(y)} dx \quad . \quad . \quad . \quad \text{(A.13)}$$

If the regression of y on x is linear, we must have

$$y = \int_{-\infty}^{+\infty} \frac{y\phi(x, y)}{\phi_1(x)} dy = Ax + B \quad \text{(A.14)}$$

Multiply this equation by $\phi_1(x)$ and integrate over the whole x-range; we have

$$\int_{-\infty}^{+\infty}\int_{-\infty}^{+\infty} y\phi(x, y)dxdy = A\int_{-\infty}^{+\infty} x\phi_1(x)dx + B\int_{-\infty}^{+\infty} \phi_1(x)dx$$

$$= A\int_{-\infty}^{+\infty}\int_{-\infty}^{+\infty} x\phi(x, y)dxdy + B\int_{-\infty}^{+\infty}\int_{-\infty}^{+\infty} \phi(x, y)dxdy$$

i.e.,

$$\mu_{01}' = A\mu_{10}' + B \quad . \quad . \quad . \quad \text{(A.15)}$$

Now multiply (A.14) by $x\phi_1(x)$ and integrate, obtaining

$$\int_{-\infty}^{+\infty}\int_{-\infty}^{+\infty} xy\phi(x, y)dxdy = A\int_{-\infty}^{+\infty}\int_{-\infty}^{+\infty} x^2\phi(x, y)dxdy$$

$$+ B\int_{-\infty}^{+\infty}\int_{-\infty}^{+\infty} x\phi(x, y)dxdy$$

i.e.,

$$\mu_{11}' = A\mu_{20}' + B\mu_{10}' \quad . \quad . \quad . \quad \text{(A.16)}$$

Solving (A.15) and (A.16) for A and B, we have

$$A = \frac{\mu_{11}' - \mu_{10}'\mu_{01}'}{\mu_{20}' - (\mu_{10}')^2} = \frac{\mu_{11}}{\mu_{20}} = \frac{\sigma_{xy}}{\sigma_x^2}$$

$$B = \frac{\mu_{01}'\mu_{20}' - \mu_{10}'\mu_{11}'}{\mu_{20}' - (\mu_{10}')^2} = \frac{\mu_{01}'(\mu_{20} + \mu_{10}'^2) - \mu_{10}'(\mu_{11} + \mu_{10}'\mu_{01}')}{\mu_{20}}$$

$$= \frac{\mu_{01}'\mu_{20} - \mu_{10}'\mu_{11}}{\mu_{20}} = \bar{y} - \bar{x}\frac{\sigma_{xy}}{\sigma_x^2}$$

Consequently, (A.14) becomes

$$y - \bar{y} = \frac{\sigma_{xy}}{\sigma_x^2}(x - \bar{x}) \text{ or } \frac{y - \bar{y}}{\sigma_y} = \frac{\sigma_{xy}}{\sigma_x\sigma_y}\left(\frac{x - \bar{x}}{\sigma_x}\right) \quad . \quad \text{(A.17)}$$

and the correlation coefficient between x and y, ρ, is

$$\rho = \frac{\sigma_{xy}}{\sigma_x\sigma_y} = \frac{\mu_{11}}{\sigma_x\sigma_y} \quad . \quad . \quad . \quad . \quad \text{(A.18)}$$

It should be noted, however, that if we define ρ by (A.18), this does not necessitate that the regression be linear.

Finally, consider the standard error of estimate of y from (A.17) : since

$$\sigma_{xy}/\sigma_x^2 = (\sigma_{xy}/\sigma_x\sigma_y)\ \sigma_y/\sigma_x = \rho\sigma_y/\sigma_x,$$

$$S_y^2 = \int_{-\infty}^{+\infty}\int_{-\infty}^{+\infty} [y - \bar{y} - \rho\frac{\sigma_y}{\sigma_x}(x - \bar{x})]^2\phi(x, y)dxdy$$

$$= \int_{-\infty}^{+\infty}\int_{-\infty}^{+\infty} [(y - \bar{y})^2 - 2\rho\frac{\sigma_y}{\sigma_x}(y - \bar{y})(x - \bar{x})$$

$$+ \rho^2\frac{\sigma_y^2}{\sigma_x^2}(x - \bar{x})^2]\phi(x, y)dxdy$$

$$= \sigma_y^2 - 2\rho\frac{\sigma_y}{\sigma_x} \cdot \sigma_{xy} + \rho^2\frac{\sigma_y^2}{\sigma_x^2} \cdot \sigma_x^2$$

i.e., $S_y^2 = \sigma_y^2(1 - \rho^2)$ . . . . (A.19)

The Bivariate Normal Distribution. Consider the bivariate distribution whose probability density is

$$\left.\begin{aligned} &\phi(x, y) = C \exp(-Z) \\ \text{where}\quad &C = 1/2\pi\sigma_x\sigma_y(1 - \rho^2)^{\frac{1}{2}} \\ \text{and}\quad &Z = \{x^2/\sigma_x^2 - 2\rho xy/\sigma_x\sigma_y + y^2/\sigma_y^2\}/2(1 - \rho^2) \end{aligned}\right\} \text{(A.20)}$$

The distribution so defined is called the *Bivariate Normal distribution.* For the moment we shall regard σ_x, σ_y and ρ as undefined constants.

We begin by finding what are usually called the *marginal distributions*, viz., the probability function of x for any value or all values of y, and the probability function of y for any or all x. The probability that x lies between $x \pm \frac{1}{2}dx$, whatever the value assumed by y, is given by

$$\phi_1(x)dx = dx\int_{-\infty}^{+\infty}\phi(x, y)dy$$

i.e., $$\phi_1(x) = C\int_{-\infty}^{+\infty} \exp\{-\frac{1}{2(1-\rho^2)}[(\rho^2x^2/\sigma_x^2 - 2\rho xy/\sigma_x\sigma_y + y^2/\sigma_y^2) + (1-\rho^2)x^2/\sigma_x^2]\}dy$$

$$= C\exp\{-x^2/2\sigma_x^2\} \times \times \int_{-\infty}^{+\infty} \exp\{-\frac{1}{2(1-\rho^2)}(y/\sigma_y - \rho x/\sigma_x)^2\}dy$$

Put $Y = y/\sigma_y - \rho x/\sigma_x$.

Then $dy = \sigma_y dY$ and as $y \to \pm\infty$, $Y \to \pm\infty$.

Hence,

$$\phi_1(x) = C\sigma_y \exp(-x^2/2\sigma_x^2)\int_{-\infty}^{+\infty} \exp\left[-\frac{y^2}{2(1-\rho^2)}\right]dy.$$

But (see footnote to 5.4 (*e*), page 82)

$$\int_{-\infty}^{+\infty} \exp[-Y^2/2(1-\rho^2)]dY = [2\pi(1-\rho^2)]^{\frac{1}{2}}.$$

Therefore

$$\phi_1(x) = \frac{1}{\sigma_x\sqrt{2\pi}}\exp(-x^2/2\sigma_x^2)\,. \quad . \quad \text{(A.21)}$$

and, likewise,

$$\phi_2(y) = \frac{1}{\sigma_y\sqrt{2\pi}}\exp(-y^2/2\sigma_y^2)$$

Thus, *marginally*, both x and y are normally distributed with zero mean and variances σ_x^2 and σ_y^2 respectively. Moreover, if we put $\rho = 0$ in (A.20)

$$\phi(x, y) = \frac{1}{\sigma_x\sqrt{2\pi}}\exp(-x^2/2\sigma_x^2)\,.\,\frac{1}{\sigma_y\sqrt{2\pi}}\exp(-y^2/2\sigma_y^2)$$
$$= \phi_1(x)\,.\,\phi_2(y)$$

and thus we obtain a clue to the significance of ρ: when $\rho = 0$ the variates are uncorrelated. May not ρ then be the correlation coefficient of x and y? That is indeed so and that var (x) and var (y) are respectively σ_x^2 and σ_y^2 may be seen by considering the moment-generating function of the distribution. We have

$$M(t_1, t_2) = C\int_{-\infty}^{+\infty}\int_{-\infty}^{+\infty} \exp\left[xt_1 + yt_2 - \frac{1}{2(1-\rho^2)}\{x^2/\sigma_x^2 - 2\rho xy/\sigma_x\sigma_y + y^2/\sigma_y^2\}\right]dxdy \quad \text{(A.22)}$$

The reader will verify that, if we make the substitutions

$$X = x - \sigma_x(\sigma_x t_1 + \rho\sigma_y t_2)$$
$$Y = y - \sigma_y(\sigma_y t_2 + \rho\sigma_x t_1),$$

(A.22) becomes

$$M(t_1, t_2) = \exp\left(\tfrac{1}{2}(\sigma_x^2 t_1^2 + 2\rho\sigma_x\sigma_y t_1 t_2 + \sigma_y^2 t_2^2)\right) \times$$
$$\times \frac{1}{2\pi\sigma_x\sigma_y(1-\rho^2)^{\frac{1}{2}}}\int_{-\infty}^{+\infty}\int_{-\infty}^{+\infty} \exp\,[(X^2/\sigma_x^2 - 2\rho XY/\sigma_x\sigma_y + Y^2/\sigma_y^2)/2(1-\rho^2)]dXdY$$

But the second factor in the right-hand expression is equal to unity; therefore

$$M(t_1, t_2) = \exp\,[\tfrac{1}{2}(\sigma_x^2 t_1^2 + 2\rho\sigma_x\sigma_y t_1 t_2 + \sigma_y^2 t_2^2)] \quad \text{(A.23)}$$

But the exponential contains only squares of t_1 and t_2 and the product $t_1 t_2$ and, so, the coefficients of t_1 and t_2 in its expansion are zero, i.e., $\bar{x} = 0 = \bar{y}$, and $M(t_1, t_2)$ *is the mean-moment generating function.* Consequently

$$\mu_{20} = \sigma_x^2;\ \mu_{11} = \rho\sigma_x\sigma_y \quad \text{or} \quad \rho = \frac{\mu_{11}}{\sigma_x\sigma_y};\ \mu_{02} = \sigma_y^2$$

Thus, although up to now we have not considered σ_x, σ_y, and ρ to be other than undefined constants, they are in fact the standard deviations of x and y and the correlation coefficient of x and y respectively.

Exercise: *Show that*: (i) $\mu_{rs} = 0$, *when* $r + s$ *is odd*; (ii) $\mu_{40} = 3\sigma_x^4$; $\mu_{31} = 3\rho\sigma_x^3\sigma_y$; $\mu_{22} = (1 + 2\rho^2)(\sigma_x^2\sigma_y^2)$; $\mu_{13} = 3\rho\sigma_x\sigma_y^3$; $\mu_{04} = 3\sigma_y^4$.

Some other properties: (A.20) may be written

$$\phi(x, y) = \frac{1}{2\pi\sigma_x\sigma_y(1-\rho^2)^{\frac{1}{2}}}\exp\,[-(y^2/\sigma_y^2 - 2\rho yx/\sigma_y\sigma_x + \rho^2x^2/\sigma_x^2)/(2(1-\rho^2))]\,.\exp\,(-x^2/2\sigma_x^2)$$
$$= \frac{1}{\sigma_x\sqrt{2\pi}}\exp\,(-x^2/2\sigma_x^2)\,.\,\frac{1}{\sigma_y(1-\rho^2)^{\frac{1}{2}}\sqrt{2\pi}} \times$$
$$\times \exp\left\{-\left[\left(y - \rho\frac{\sigma_y}{\sigma_x}x\right)^2\Big/\{2\sigma_y^2(1-\rho^2)\}\right]\right\}$$

But by (A.19) $S_y^2 = \sigma_y^2(1-\rho^2)$, and, therefore,

$$\phi(x, y) =$$
$$\frac{1}{\sigma_x\sqrt{2\pi}}\exp\,(-x^2/2\sigma_x^2)\,.\,\frac{1}{S_y\sqrt{2\pi}}\exp\left[-\left(y - \rho\frac{\sigma_y}{\sigma_x}x\right)^2\Big/2S_y^2\right]$$

We see, then, that, if x is held constant, i.e., in any given x-array, the y's are distributed normally with mean $\bar{y} = \rho\sigma_y x/\sigma_x$ and variance S_y^2.

Thus the regression of y on x is linear, the regression equation being

$$y = \frac{\rho\sigma_y}{\sigma_x} . x \quad . \quad . \quad . \quad . \quad \text{(A.24)}$$

and the variance in each array, being S_y^2, is constant. Consequently, regression for the bivariate normal distribution is *homoscedastic* (see 6.14).

SOME MATHEMATICAL SYMBOLS AND THEIR MEANINGS

$\exp x = e^x$, exponential function, where $e = 2{\cdot}71828\ldots$ is base of natural logarithms.

$\log x = \log_e x$, natural logarithm.

Δx = small increment of x.

$\underset{x \to a}{\mathrm{Lt}} f(x)$ or

$\underset{x \to a}{\mathrm{Limit}} f(x)$ = the limit of $f(x)$ as x tends to a.

$\to$ = tend to (limit).

∞ = infinity.

$n!$ = factorial n, $n(n-1)(n-2)$ . . . (3.2.1)

$\binom{r}{s} = r!/s!\,(r-s)!$

$\sum_{i=1}^{n} x_i = x_1 + x_2 + \ldots + x_n$; sum of . . .

$$\sum_{i=1}^{m}\sum_{j=1}^{n} x_{ij} = x_{11} + x_{12} + \ldots + x_{1n}$$
$$+ x_{21} + x_{22} + \ldots + x_{2n}$$
$$+ \ldots +$$
$$+ x_{m1} + x_{m2} + \ldots + x_{mn}$$

$\prod_{i=1}^{n} x_i = x_1 . x_2 . x_3 \ldots x_{n-1} . x_n$; product of . . .

$\simeq$ = approximately equal to.

$>$; $<$ = greater than; less than.

$\geqslant$; $\leqslant$ = greater than or equal to; less than or equal to.

Population parameters are, in general, denoted by Greek letters; estimates of these parameters from a sample are denoted by the corresponding Roman letter.

SUGGESTIONS FOR FURTHER READING

B. C. Brookes and W. F. L. Dick, *Introduction to Statistical Method* (Heinemann).
K. A. Brownlee, *Industrial Experimentation* (H.M.S.O.).
F. N. David, *A Statistical Primer* (Griffin).
B. V. Gnedenko and A. Ya. Khinchin, *An Elementary Introduction to the Theory of Probability* (Freeman).
P. G. Moore, *Principles of Statistical Techniques* (Cambridge University Press).
M. J. M. Moroney, *Facts from Figures* (Penguin Books).
F. Mosteller, R. E. K. Rourke, G. B. Thomas Jr., *Probability and Statistics* (Addison–Wesley)
C. G. Paradine and B. H. P. Rivett, *Statistical Methods for Technologists* (English Universities Press).
M. H. Quenouille, *Introductory Statistics* (Pergamon).
L. H. C. Tippett, *Statistics* (Oxford University Press).
S. S. Wilks, *Elementary Statistical Analysis* (Princeton University Press).
G. Yule and M. G. Kendall, *Introduction to the Theory of Statistics* (Griffin).

More Advanced

A. C. Aitken, *Statistical Mathematics* (Oliver and Boyd).
F. N. David, *Probability Theory for Statistical Methods* (Cambridge University Press).
W. Feller, *An Introduction to Probability Theory and its Application* (Wiley).
R. A. Fisher, *Statistical Methods for Research Workers* (Oliver and Boyd).
I. J. Good, *Probability and the Weighing of Evidence* (Griffin).
P. G. Hoel, *Introduction to Mathematical Statistics* (Wiley).
M. G. Kendall, *The Advanced Theory of Statistics* (Griffin).
and A. Stuart, *The Advanced Theory of Statistics* (Vol. I of new three-volume edition) (Griffin).
M. G. Kendall, *Exercises in Theoretical Statistics* (Griffin).
A. M. Mood, *Introduction to the Theory of Statistics* (McGraw-Hill).
Answers to Problems in Introduction (McGraw-Hill).
M. H. Quenouille, *The Design and Analysis of Experiment* (Griffin).

C. E. Weatherburn, *A First Course in Mathematical Statistics* (Cambridge University Press).

Also

M. G. Kendall and W. R. Buckland, *A Dictionary of Statistical Terms* (Oliver and Boyd).